6/28/78

Contemporary Science—Book 2

MILTON LESSER
Formerly Chairman
Department of Biological Sciences
Abraham Lincoln High School
New York City

CONSTANTINE CONSTANT
Teacher of Earth Science
Forest Hills High School
New York City

JULES J. WEISLER
Assistant Principal
Supervision of Science
Robert A. Van Wyck Junior High School 217
New York City

General Editor
SAUL L. GEFFNER
Formerly Chairman
Department of Physical Sciences
Forest Hills High School
New York City

CONTEMPORARY SCIENCE
BOOK 2

Dedicated to serving
AMSCO
our nation's youth

When ordering this book, please specify:
either **R 191 P** or CONTEMPORARY SCIENCE—BOOK 2

AMSCO SCHOOL PUBLICATIONS, INC.
315 Hudson Street
New York, N.Y. 10013

The publisher is indebted to the American Museum of Natural History for permission to reprint the photographs appearing on page 92. Cover photograph by Alan Pitcairn from Grant Heilman.

ISBN 0-87720-006-8

Printed in the United States of America

PREFACE

Contemporary Science—Books 1, 2, and 3—presents a modern, comprehensive general science course. Content from the areas of life science, physical science, and earth science, carefully integrated, emphasizes fundamental principles and current problems. Among these problems are the environment, conservation, and energy. Depending on local needs, the three books may be used for a three-year science sequence, or individual books may be used for single-year courses.

Organization of the Series

Each book in the series has the same structure of units and chapters. A general overview of content opens each unit. Then, each chapter in the unit sets forth learning objectives for the student. A laboratory experience follows these objectives and stresses the role of experimentation in the development of scientific ideas. The laboratory experience opens the door, and leads to an introduction to the essential facts, principles, and concepts within the chapter. Every chapter closes with a summary; a glimpse of what is to come in the next chapter; and review questions to test recall and reasoning.

Scientific models are employed, where pertinent, to enable students to relate abstract ideas to more easily understood situations.

Outstanding Features of These Books

1. *Laboratory Experiences.* Every chapter introduces a laboratory exercise that is closely integrated with one or more major ideas in the chapter. These exercises are well within the range of comprehension and manipulative ability of most students above the elementary grades. Much of the laboratory work can be carried out either at home or in classrooms, and requires simple equipment. If the teacher so desires, the laboratory experiences can readily be converted to classroom demonstrations. In addition to simple, clear instructions, each laboratory exercise includes questions that direct observation and evoke the independent formulation of conclusions. These same conclusions become focal points in the development of the text content, and ap-

pear in the text where pertinent. Where feasible, a portion of the laboratory exercise is open-ended—the student is encouraged to investigate further.

2. *Language Level.* The language level is kept as simple as possible. Although many terms are introduced, they are carefully defined.

Some technical terms recur from book to book. The first time such a term is encountered in a book, the term is defined (or redefined or reexplained, if necessary). Thus, each book is independent of the others and may be used without reference to the others.

3. *Illustrations.* All three books are profusely illustrated with drawings, photographs, and cartoons. All illustrations assist the learning and retention of scientific principles. Each illustration is keyed to the text to make the illustration readily available to the reader.

4. *Questions.* The end-of-chapter questions are numerous and varied. They include short-answer types such as multiple-choice, modified true-false, and matching, as well as thought questions requiring longer answers. Where applicable, simple numerical problems are also given, but only after sample exercises and solutions have been discussed.

5. *Appendix.* A useful appendix appears in each book. The appendix contains metric conversion tables and a periodic table of the elements modified to suit the intermediate level. Books 2 and 3 also provide an explanation of significant figures and rules for their use. This section can be particularly valuable for the ambitious, abler student.

6. *Answer Keys.* Answers to the end-of-chapter questions are contained in an answer key, available to teachers. Included in this key are lists of materials and equipment for the laboratory experiences as well as notes regarding experimental techniques and teaching emphases. Answers to the questions posed in the laboratory experience sections are also included.

7. *Multiple Uses.* The books lend themselves to a variety of uses, depending on the local situation.

a. *As Basic Texts.* Selected content in life science, physical science, and earth science is presented in each book in adequate depth for the needs of students at the intermediate level. Thus, the books can be used in any spiral, integrated type of general science sequence. Alternatively, since each book can stand alone, these books may be used in any order. In either case, they provide a solid foundation for later study in each major science.

b. *As Alternate Texts.* The content of these books relates readily to other modern general science texts. Consequently, the content may be used to provide the student with an alternate approach or a second view. Such a procedure may help the underachiever and at the same time stimulate the more able pupils.

c. *As a Sourcebook for Experiments.* Although it is recommended that a laboratory experience introduce each topic, the laboratory work can be fitted in wherever it suits the teacher's unit plan. In addition to the opening laboratory experience associated with each chapter, other experiments are described as integral parts of the text. These experiments provide the teacher with an extensive source of ideas and materials for illustrating principles.
d. *For Pretesting.* The inclusive end-of-chapter questions are suitable as a pretest for a chapter. The results of such testing will indicate how much of the chapter should be taught and with what emphasis the chapter should be taught.
e. *For Adapting to Individual Needs.* Since students in general can independently carry out most of the work set forth in this book, the teacher can assign specific sections to ambitious students, to students who have been absent, or to students who need more repetition and drill before they can consolidate their learning. To the small number of students for whom the study of general science is terminal, these books contain sufficient material to provide a broad, unified understanding and appreciation of the earth, its inhabitants, its composition and features, the forces that act on it, and its place in the universe.
f. *For Evaluation.* The learning objectives set the instructional goals of each chapter. Students can also use the questions at the end of each chapter as self-testing devices. The coverage of the questions is sufficiently broad to enable the teacher to use them to measure student progress, chapter by chapter. The questions can also serve as homework for students or for drill work in class.

The topics and laboratory experiences presented in *Contemporary Science—Book 2* have been selected to match the comprehension and maturity levels usual for the school grade. Accordingly, the major topics from the areas of life science, physical science, and earth science include: our environment, our planet's environment, energy on our planet, and how living things adjust to the environment.

Wherever possible, the metric system of measurement is used. Weather data, however, is expressed in customary units, since the National Weather Service continues to use customary units for weather data.

The section on the solar system contains information provided by *Pioneers 10* and *11* and *Vikings I* and *II*. Discussed in appropriate sections are the current energy crisis, fuel cells, solar heating, radio and television transmission and reception, and damage to the ozone layer.

CONTENTS

Contemporary Science—Book 2

UNIT I
Our Environment—The Atmosphere

Overview

Humans, like other organisms of our world, depend upon the environment for their life needs. Before the great developments in science and invention and the huge population increases of modern times, humans and other organisms lived in harmony with the environment. They used food, water, air, and wood. At the same time, they produced wastes. The wastes presented no problem because they were relatively small in quantity and, therefore, were soon decomposed and used again by other organisms. In other words, the wastes were naturally recycled. As a result, the early environment remained stable—that is, relatively unchanged.

As humans developed more complex societies, they used more and more energy. They learned how to extract metals, coal, and oil from the earth. They began to use up the materials which were stored in the earth and to change them into other forms.

In this way, they began to control their home environment, to produce many conveniences, and to live more comfortably. At the same time, they began to change the rest of the environment—to make it unstable.

As civilization progressed and the human population increased, waste materials began to pile up on land. Some were dumped into oceans, rivers, and lakes. Others were added to the air. All of these wastes plague us now with the problem of *pollution*—the spoiling of our environment by harmful substances, or *pollutants*.

Can we escape pollution by moving every living thing from the earth to the moon? Obviously, we cannot. We cannot run away from what we have done and are doing to our environment. Rather, we must do what we can now to repair the damage already done to the environment and to prevent further damage to it. As you continue to learn about the nature of matter, energy, and living things in our world, you will better understand and appreciate the advances humans have made. At the same time, you will gain a better understanding of what we must do in the future, if we are to have a world fit to live in.

In this unit, we will become familiar with the part of the environment known as the *atmosphere*. The atmosphere consists of the air near the surface of the earth and the air extending above us that merges with outer space. By realizing that air surrounds every part of your body not in contact with the ground, you may appreciate better how important a part of your environment the atmosphere really is.

When America was young, the air was "clean," or natural. The early inhabitants polluted the air so little that any pollutants in it were rapidly recycled and the air remained clean. Unpolluted air not only enables our bodies to function (operate) normally, but it is also essential to the plants and animals that provide us with food and other necessities.

As the population of America has grown, what has happened to the clean air? Studies of the air in this century reveal some startling facts. In 1940, human activities added over 160 million tons of pollutants to the air. In 1950, the pollutants totaled about 190 million tons; in 1960, about 225 million tons; in 1970, about 270 million tons. If we continue adding pollutants to the air at this rate, what can we expect in 1980? in 2000?

Of the 270 million tons of pollutants discharged into the air in 1970, about 55% was contributed by automobiles and other means of transportation. Heating of buildings and manufacturing processes contributed about 30% and all other sources together, about 15%.

Can air pollution be controlled? The experiences of cities such as Los Angeles and New York in reducing air pollution indicate that the answer is yes. As you become more familiar with the composition of the atmosphere and its relationship to energy and to living things, you will better understand how air pollution affects us and what may be done to control it.

Using the Customary and Metric Systems of Measurement

Units of measurement for length, volume, weight, and temperature in our customary system differ from those in the metric system. The unit of time is the same in both systems. In this book, we will use units of the metric system wherever possible. For convenient conversion tables, see pages 406–407 in the Appendix.

CHAPTER 1
WHAT IS THE COMPOSITION OF OUR ATMOSPHERE?

When you have completed this chapter, you should be able to:

1. *Discuss* the origin of the earth's present atmosphere.
2. *Relate* the gases in the atmosphere to the activities of plants and to the activities of humans and other animals.
3. *List,* with approximate percentages, the gases present in pure air.
4. *Describe* the properties of each major gas in the atmosphere.
5. *Identify* the major air pollutants and their sources.
6. *Compare* the major regions of the atmosphere.

In the laboratory experience that follows, you will investigate the composition and properties of some gases in the atmosphere.

Laboratory Experience

HOW CAN WE SEPARATE SOME OF THE GASES IN THE ATMOSPHERE?

You will receive several closed bottles labeled oxygen and several labeled carbon dioxide. These are two of the several gases present in air.

A. Place a sheet of white paper behind a bottle of carbon dioxide.
   1. Describe the color of carbon dioxide.

B. Fill a medicine dropper with limewater. Remove the stopper from the bottle of carbon dioxide and quickly add about 10 drops of the limewater to the bottle. Put the stopper back in the bottle and shake it.
   2. What change takes place in the bottle?

C. Loosen the stopper of another bottle of carbon dioxide. Ignite a wooden splint, remove the stopper, and insert the burning splint into the bottle of carbon dioxide. Keep the flame small, and do not allow it to touch the sides of the bottle.

3. Describe what happens to the burning splint.

D. Add about 10 drops of limewater to an empty bottle, that is, a bottle containing ordinary air. Stopper the bottle and shake it.

4. What happens to the limewater?

Note: The change of fresh limewater, which is a clear, colorless liquid, to a milky color is used as a test for the presence of carbon dioxide.

5. What does this tell you about the composition of ordinary air?

E. Remove the stopper from the same bottle of air and insert a lighted splint for a few seconds. Remove the splint. Stopper the bottle and shake it.

6. What happens to the limewater?
7. What can you conclude from your observations?

F. Place a sheet of white paper behind a bottle of oxygen.

8. Describe the color of oxygen.

G. Loosen but do not remove the stopper of the bottle of oxygen. Light a wooden splint. Let the splint burn for several seconds, then blow the flame out.

While the splint is still glowing, quickly remove the stopper from the bottle and carefully thrust the glowing splint into the bottle. Repeat this procedure several times.

9. Describe what happens to the glowing splint.

H. Insert a glowing splint into a bottle of air.

10. What happens to the glowing splint?
11. What does this experiment tell you about the composition of ordinary air?
12. Contrast the effect of carbon dioxide and oxygen on a burning splint.

I. Wet the inside of a test tube with water. Pour iron filings inside the test tube. Holding your thumb over the mouth of the test tube, shake the test tube until its inner surface is coated with some of the filings. (Instead of iron filings, you can insert a wad of wet, untreated steel wool inside the test tube.) Place the test tube in a jar or beaker of water, as shown in Fig. 1–1. Mark the level of the water inside the tube.

13. What is the length of the test tube? (See pages 410–412 for use of significant figures.)
14. What does the test tube contain besides the iron filings?

J. Set the test tube aside for 24 hours.

15. Describe the contents of the test tube after 24 hours have passed.

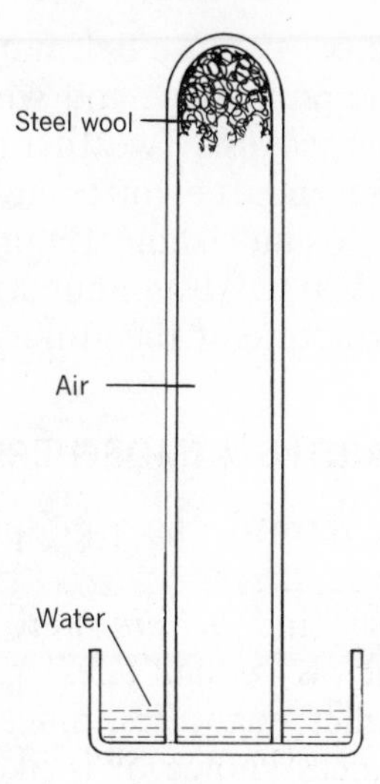

Fig. 1–1.

16. Mark the level of water inside the test tube now. What is the height of water inside the test tube?
17. Approximately how much change has taken place in the level of water inside the test tube?
18. Account for the change in water levels.
19. What percent does this change in the level of water represent? (Divide the value obtained in the answer to question 17 by the value obtained in the answer to question 13. Multiply the quotient by 100.)
20. Does the test tube contain the same quantity of air that it did originally? Explain.

Introduction

The part of the environment that completely envelops each of us is the atmosphere. The atmosphere is the layer of air that completely surrounds the *hydrosphere* (water layer) and the *lithosphere* (rock layer) of our planet. All three layers are composed of numerous atoms and molecules of a variety of elements and compounds. *Elements* are substances that cannot be broken down by ordinary means to any simpler substances. Hydrogen and oxygen are examples of elements. *Compounds* are substances composed of two or more elements chemically united. Water and carbon dioxide are examples of compounds.

Prehistoric humans were probably more interested in the atmosphere than in the other two "spheres" because lightning, thunder, and storms frightened them and because rain, snow, and winds strongly influenced their daily lives. Today, *meteorologists* (weather scientists) have learned much about the atmosphere and the forces at work within it. Their discoveries have enabled us to understand the atmosphere that was so mysterious to our ancestors. We will begin our study of these discoveries with the composition and structure of the atmosphere.

DEVELOPMENT OF THE EARTH'S ATMOSPHERE

When the earth was first formed, the atmosphere was very different from what it is today.

Scientists believe *hydrogen* and *helium* were very abundant in the atmosphere when the earth was young. These gases are still present in our atmosphere, but in smaller quantities. Since hydrogen and helium gases are the lightest substances known, it is likely that much of these gases quickly escaped into space.

As the earth cooled into solid matter, hot lava and volcanic eruptions released additional gases into the atmosphere, mainly the compounds *ammonia, methane, water vapor,* and *carbon dioxide.* The rays of the sun decomposed (broke down) some of these compounds into elemental gases, such as *nitrogen, oxygen,* and hydrogen. Much of the hydrogen escaped into space. Since nitrogen is too heavy to escape the earth's gravity, it gradually accumulated in the atmosphere.

Addition of Oxygen to the Atmosphere

Some oxygen probably existed in the earth's original atmosphere but in very small quantities. It was not until green plants developed on earth (well over a half billion years ago) that oxygen became an important ingredient of the atmosphere.

In the presence of sunlight, green plants can extract carbon dioxide from the atmosphere. They use this carbon dioxide in manufacturing food by the process called *photosynthesis.* The plants then release oxygen into the atmosphere as a waste product (Fig. 1–2). As the number of green plants gradually increased, more and more oxygen was added to the atmosphere. At the same time, of course, more and more carbon dioxide was removed from the atmosphere.

Removal of Carbon Dioxide From the Atmosphere

Photosynthesis removes carbon dioxide from the atmosphere. In addition, some of the carbon dioxide that was present in the original atmosphere dissolved in the ocean. Some of this carbon dioxide combined

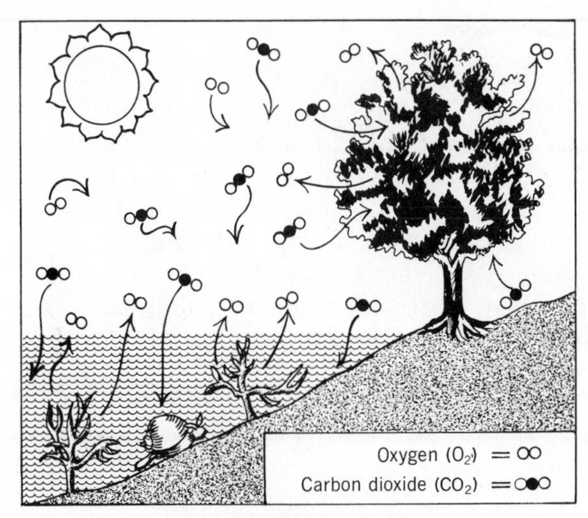

Fig. 1–2. Photosynthesis.

with calcium compounds in the water to form *carbonate* compounds. Small plants and animals in the ocean used these carbonate compounds to build the shells and other hard parts of their bodies. Thus, as a result of the activity of green plants and the dissolving of carbon dioxide in the ocean, the amount of carbon dioxide in the atmosphere gradually decreased.

PRESENT COMPOSITION OF THE ATMOSPHERE

Scientists believe that the proportion of gases in today's atmosphere has remained constant for the last half-billion years, ever since green plants first appeared in abundance on earth. The major reason for this belief is that plants and animals keep the proportion of oxygen and carbon dioxide in the atmosphere in balance as part of the *carbon dioxide-oxygen cycle.* In this cycle, green plants carrying on photosynthesis remove carbon dioxide from the atmosphere. They use the carbon dioxide in making their food and liberate oxygen as a waste product. All other living things, including humans, take in oxygen during respiration and oxidize their food. As a result of oxidation, they liberate carbon dioxide as a waste product. At night, green plants, like animals, use oxygen and liberate carbon dioxide during oxidation. During the day, however, the plants liberate more oxygen than they need. Nitrogen, which makes up a large part of the atmosphere today, goes through a similar cycle that keeps the nitrogen in the atmosphere at a constant level.

Oxygen in the Atmosphere

In our laboratory experience, we wedged a pad of wet untreated steel wool (or iron filings) into the bottom of a test tube. We allowed the test tube to remain undisturbed for a day and then examined the water level inside the tube. This experiment shows us that, when oxygen is removed from air, the amount of gas remaining in the tube is about four-fifths of what it was originally. Oxygen, therefore, occupies about one-fifth of the volume of the atmosphere.

The gas remaining in the tube now is mainly the element nitrogen. Table 1–1 shows the composition of a sample of pure, dry air.

Table 1–1. Composition of Pure, Dry Air

Gas	*Approximate Percentage (by volume)*
Nitrogen (N_2)	78.08
Oxygen (O_2)	20.95
Argon (Ar)	0.94
Carbon dioxide (CO_2)	0.03 or 0.04
Neon (Ne)	
Helium (He)	
Krypton (Kr)	
Xenon (Xe)	0.003
Hydrogen (H_2)	
Nitrous oxide (N_2O)	
Methane (CH_4)	
Other gases	

Water Vapor in the Atmosphere

Water in gaseous form, known as water vapor, is present in the atmosphere. The amount of water vapor varies, however, in different parts of the world at different times. The percent of water vapor may vary from about $\frac{1}{2}$% to as much as 4% of the total volume of air.

Humidity is another name for the amount of water vapor in the atmosphere. On very humid days, the water-vapor content may be close to 4%; on extremely dry days, the water-vapor content may be 1% or less.

When water vapor enters the atmosphere, it displaces (takes the place of) other gases. This reduces the percentages of the other gases in the atmosphere. On a very humid day, for example, the oxygen content of the atmosphere may be about 18% instead of the more usual 21% on a dry day.

Dust in the Atmosphere

Normally, the atmosphere also contains different kinds of dust particles. These particles include sand, clay, soil, salt, and volcanic ash. Dust particles are an especially important part of the atmosphere because water vapor collects on the particles and, under the proper conditions, water droplets will form around each particle. The water droplets usually form clouds, which may bring rain or snow.

Dust is also partly responsible for the blue color of the daytime sky. The sky appears blue during the daylight hours because dust particles and air molecules (gases) separate some blue from the other colors (wavelengths) in sunlight (Fig. 1–3). This effect is called *light scattering*. When the sun is directly overhead, sunlight takes the shortest possible route through the atmosphere. The amount of dust and gases through which it passes causes a little blue to be scattered. When you look at the sky, your eyes receive these scattered blue wavelengths, and you see the color blue.

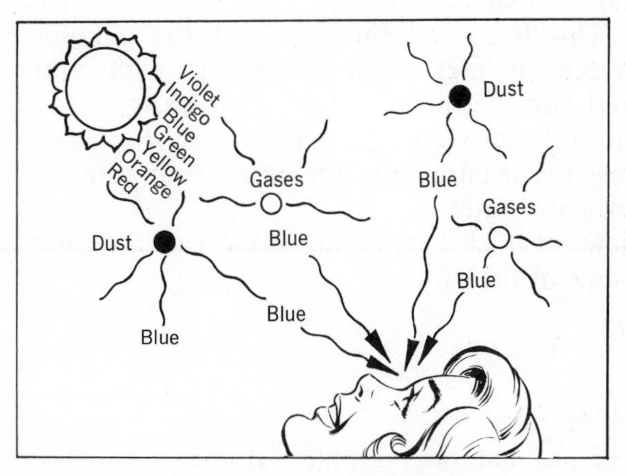

Fig. 1–3. Why the sky is blue.

At sunrise or sunset, on the other hand, sunlight travels to the observer at an angle, thus taking a much longer path through the atmosphere and passing through a much larger quantity of dust and gases. As a result, much more blue is scattered. In effect, the blue wavelengths are now lost to the observer. Instead, red comes through more easily, and the sunrise or sunset appears to be red.

To an astronaut in a rocket, the sky appears black. Beyond the atmosphere, virtually no dust is present, and no light scattering occurs.

The relation of dust particles in the atmosphere to fog and smog is discussed in Chapter 5, page 88.

PROPERTIES OF GASES IN THE ATMOSPHERE

The properties of many of the gases in the atmosphere are important to humans. The oxygen in the atmosphere enables wood, coal, and many other substances to burn; that is, oxygen supports combustion. In the laboratory, when you dropped a glowing splint into a bottle of oxygen and saw it burst into flame, you observed this important property of oxygen. Liquefied oxygen (oxygen cooled to the point where it condenses into a liquid) is used in rocket engines. This liquid oxygen causes the rocket fuel to burn with great violence, which is why the rocket engine has the force to lift the rocket into outer space.

Carbon dioxide, on the other hand, does not support combustion, as you saw in your laboratory experience. In fact, carbon dioxide is used to put out fires, especially gasoline and oil fires. The carbon dioxide smothers the fire by cutting off the air supply needed for the combustion of gasoline or oil.

If the same experiment were conducted using a bottle of pure nitrogen gas, we would see that nitrogen, like carbon dioxide, does not support combustion. This is a good thing, too. If the atmosphere consisted mainly of oxygen gas, fires would always burn with great violence and humans would also "burn up" faster. Vast areas of the world would have gone up in flames years ago. It is because the atmosphere consists of 78% nitrogen that burning in the atmosphere proceeds fairly slowly and with reasonable safety.

Listed below are brief descriptions of most of the gases in the atmosphere and some of their uses.

Nitrogen

Nitrogen, an element, does not burn; it does not support combustion. It is an important ingredient in fertilizers and in the manufacture of explosives such as TNT, nitroglycerine, and guncotton. Nitrogen is also used in the production of dyes, chemicals, and plastics.

Nitrogen bubbles in the blood are responsible for the *bends,* a disease of deep-sea divers and others who must breathe air under pressure. Normally (at sea level), we inhale both oxygen and nitrogen. Part of the oxygen is used up in respiration. The nitrogen is not used. At great depths (below sea level), the increased pressure forces nitrogen gas to dissolve in the blood. When a diver comes back to the surface too quickly, the rapid decrease in pressure around the body permits the dissolved nitrogen to bubble out of the blood. This causes pain in the large joints and other serious conditions that could result in death.

Oxygen

Oxygen, an element, is extremely active chemically; that is, it combines readily with other substances. Oxygen does not burn, but it does support combustion. Oxygen is a source of energy for animals and is a waste product given off by plants. Oxygen combines with iron to form rustlike compounds. It makes up nearly half the weight of the rocks and minerals in the crust of the earth. It is an important ingredient in household chemicals such as hydrogen peroxide, laundry bleaches, and ordinary water. Oxygen is also used in oxyacetylene torches and in rocket engines.

Carbon Dioxide

Carbon dioxide, a compound, does not burn and does not support combustion. It is a product of the combustion of wood, coal, and many liquid fuels. Carbon dioxide is used by plants in manufacturing their food; it is given off by animals (including humans) as a waste product. It blocks the escape of heat from the atmosphere into outer space.

Carbon dioxide combines with water to form carbonic acid; it makes up the bubbles seen in soft drinks such as ginger ale; it is used in fire extinguishers to extinguish oil, gasoline, and electrical fires. Carbon dioxide is called *dry ice* when it is in the solid form. Because the temperature of dry ice is $-79°C$, it can be used as a refrigerant.

Water Vapor

Water vapor is the gaseous form of ordinary water, a compound. It neither burns nor supports combustion. Since a given quantity of water vapor is lighter than an equal quantity of either nitrogen or oxygen, the weight of air decreases as the quantity of water vapor in the air increases. Water vapor prevents the escape of heat from the atmosphere into outer space. It is the basic ingredient of clouds, fog, haze, rain, snow, and hail.

Argon

Argon is chemically inactive. It is an *inert* element. That is, it does not generally combine with other elements. Argon is used to fill electric light bulbs, making the bulbs last longer.

Neon

Neon, like argon, is an inert element. Neon gas glows red when electricity passes through it. It is used in electrical advertising signs.

Helium

Helium is the second lightest element. It is chemically inactive; it does not burn; it does not support combustion. Helium is used to give buoyancy (lift) to balloons, blimps, and dirigibles. It is used by deep-sea divers in place of nitrogen in their breathing equipment because helium does not cause the bends. Old and valuable documents are preserved by being stored in a helium atmosphere.

Hydrogen

Hydrogen is the lightest element. It burns in air. Hydrogen was once used to give buoyancy to balloons, blimps, and dirigibles. Because mixtures of hydrogen and oxygen, when ignited, are explosive, hydrogen has since been replaced by helium in lighter-than-air craft. Hydrogen is an important ingredient in hydrogen peroxide, acids, animal and vegetable oils, fuels, and water.

POLLUTION OF THE ATMOSPHERE

Except for small variations over particular parts of the earth, the composition of the atmosphere should remain the same far into the future. This statement does not take into account any changes humans may bring about as they continue to add pollutants to the atmosphere. The enormous quantities of coal, oil, and gasoline that have been burned in the past 100 years have added to the atmosphere large quantities of carbon dioxide, some poisonous gases, and solid particles. Since carbon dioxide keeps heat from escaping into space, some scientists believe that some harmful changes in the world's climate may yet take place.

Gas Pollutants in the Atmosphere

The burning of fuels such as coal, fuel oil, and gasoline often releases numerous poisonous gases. Among these are *carbon monoxide* and *sulfur dioxide.*

Carbon monoxide, a compound, is a colorless, odorless gas. It is formed when fuels containing carbon are burned in a limited supply of oxygen. Ordinarily, when carbon burns in air, carbon dioxide is formed. Although the carbon dioxide produced by burning is usually harmless, carbon monoxide is deadly. When carbon monoxide is inhaled, even in small quantities, it blocks the ability of the blood to carry oxygen to the cells, resulting in death by suffocation.

Sulfur dioxide, a compound, is a colorless gas that has a very irritating odor. Sulfur dioxide is formed when fuels containing sulfur are burned. Examples of such fuels are soft coal and heavy fuel oil.

When sulfur dioxide gas comes in contact with water, an acid is formed. Thus, when sulfur dioxide is present in air, the acid forms in the breathing passages and eyes, which are moist. The acid causes the eyes to smart and tear and brings on fits of coughing and sneezing. Inhaling sulfur dioxide is dangerous for people who have certain lung conditions.

Solid Pollutants in the Atmosphere

Smoke from any source contains many tiny solid particles. The particles may consist of unburned carbon (soot), ash, and, if the smoke comes from a chemical factory, a variety of other substances. When smoke particles are inhaled, they irritate the breathing passages and lungs and damage them. Continued inhalation of smoke may cause some types of cancer.

STRUCTURE OF THE ATMOSPHERE

The atmosphere extends thousands of kilometers above the earth.

Close to the surface of the earth, the gases in the atmosphere are constantly being mixed together by winds and air currents. As a result, the lower regions of the atmosphere have about the same composition over the entire earth.

Most of the gases in the atmosphere—about 90% by weight—are within 32 kilometers of the earth's surface. The remainder of the gases extend thousands of kilometers upward. However, even 150 kilometers above the earth, the particles of gas are so far apart that a spacecraft traveling through this region is in an almost perfect vacuum.

There are great differences in the temperature and composition of the atmosphere at different altitudes. For convenience in describing these differences, the atmosphere is usually divided into four different regions, or layers. These four regions are called the *troposphere*, the *stratosphere*, the *ionosphere*, and the *exosphere* (Fig. 1–4, page 14).

Troposphere

Over the North and South Poles, the troposphere extends from the ground to an altitude of approximately 9 kilometers. Over the equator, the troposphere extends to an altitude of about 16 kilometers. Most of the changes in the atmosphere, which we call the *weather*, are due to the movements of large masses of air in the troposphere. These movements of air are described in Chapter 4. The troposphere also contains almost all of the dust and moisture found in the atmosphere.

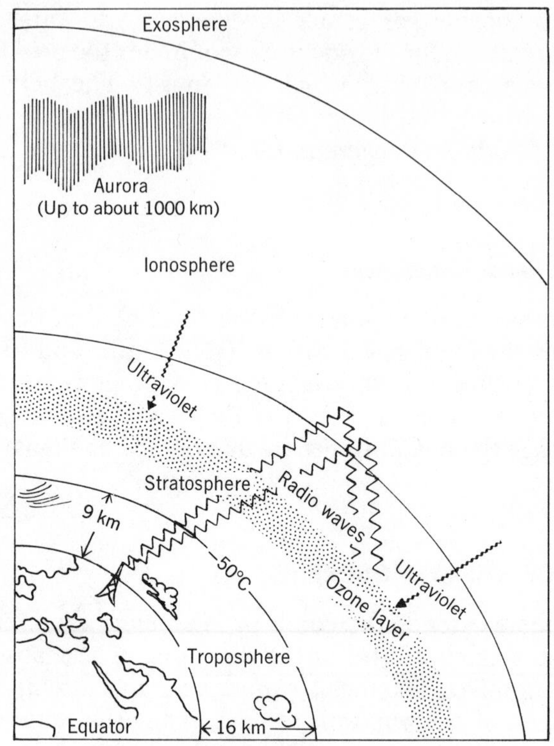

Fig. 1–4. Regions of the atmosphere.

Ordinarily, temperatures in the troposphere decrease with increasing altitude. In still, dry air, the temperature usually decreases at the rate of about 1°C for every increase of 100 meters in altitude. The troposphere ends when the temperature ceases to decrease with increasing altitude. At this altitude, the troposphere blends into the next higher region of the atmosphere, the stratosphere.

Over the continental United States, the temperatures at the region between the troposphere and the stratosphere are usually around −50°C. The lowest temperatures in this region, from about −60°C to −75°C, are found over equatorial regions.

Stratosphere

The stratosphere is a region in the atmosphere that has almost no weather; that is, there are no storms, no rain, and no snow. The stratosphere is almost completely free of moisture and dust. Only a rare type of cloud, consisting of a thin layer of dust or ice, may be seen at times. Otherwise, the air in the stratosphere is similar in composition to the air in the troposphere.

Within the stratosphere is a layer of gases that contains a form of oxygen called *ozone*. This layer is called the *ozone layer*. The ozone layer protects all the living things on earth, including humans, because it absorbs most of the harmful *ultraviolet* rays given off by the sun.

The next higher region of the atmosphere above the stratosphere is the ionosphere.

Ionosphere

The ionosphere consists of several layers of electrically charged, or *ionized*, gases. Radiations from the sun strike the gases in the ionosphere with high energy. This causes the gaseous atoms to lose electrons and, thereby, to acquire a positive electrical charge.

The ionized gases form several layers that range from about 50 kilometers to about 1000 kilometers above the earth. These layers of ionized gases are important in long-distance radio communication. The ionized layers reflect back to the earth radio signals that would otherwise disappear into space.

At times of increased *sunspot activity* (Chapter 7, page 128), the gases in the ionosphere are disturbed. Since the sunspots and disturbances in the ionosphere occur together, they are believed to be related. These disturbances interfere with long-distance radio communications on earth.

Another effect produced within the ionosphere at the same time as spots appear on the sun is the strange and beautiful *aurora borealis,* or *northern lights.* (In the Southern Hemisphere, the effect is called the *aurora australis,* or *southern lights.*) The auroras appear as shimmering bands, folds, and streamers of red, green, blue, and violet light. The auroras are thought to be produced by the impact of the sun's high-energy particles on the gases in the ionosphere.

Exosphere

The outermost layer of the atmosphere, the exosphere, is an almost perfect vacuum. At the upper levels of the exosphere, rapidly moving particles of hydrogen and other gases can escape the influence of the earth's gravity and travel into space.

Looking Back

The atmosphere of our environment consists of numerous gases and particles which are essential for life. The addition of pollutants to the atmosphere threatens life.

Looking Ahead

Although a sample of air weighs very little, the combined weight of all the air in the atmosphere exerts a tremendous force on the earth's surface. We will study the effects of this force in Chapter 2.

Multiple-Choice Questions

Write the letter preceding the word or expression that best completes the statement or answers the question.

1. Oxygen became an important part of the atmosphere after the emergence of
   a. green plants b. dinosaurs c. volcanoes d. fossils
2. A gas that has increased in quantity in the atmosphere as a result of the increased combustion of fuels is
   a. nitrogen b. oxygen c. carbon dioxide d. helium
3. The volume of nitrogen in the atmosphere at sea level is about
   a. 4% b. 21% c. 78% d. 96%
4. Of the following, the *least* abundant gas in the atmosphere is
   a. oxygen b. neon c. carbon dioxide d. argon
5. On a very humid day, the water vapor content of the atmosphere, by volume, may be as high as
   a. $\frac{1}{2}$% b. 0.04% c. 4% d. 96%
6. On a normal day, the gas in the atmosphere that makes up about 20% of the total volume of air is
   a. hydrogen b. carbon dioxide c. nitrogen d. oxygen
7. The second lightest of all the elements is
   a. neon b. oxygen c. hydrogen d. helium
8. The part of the atmosphere that lies closest to the surface of the earth is called the
   a. exosphere b. ozonosphere c. ionosphere d. troposphere
9. On a hot summer day, when the temperature at sea level is 35°C, the temperature 3000 meters above sea level is about
   a. 0°C b. 5°C c. 30°C d. 45°C
10. Temperatures between the troposphere and the stratosphere are usually about
    a. −273°C b. −100°C c. −50°C d. −10°C
11. The part of the atmosphere that protects the earth from harmful ultraviolet rays is called the
    a. equatorial bulge c. ozone layer
    b. ionic layer d. protective layer
12. The layer of the atmosphere that deflects radio waves back to earth is called the
    a. ionosphere c. aurora borealis
    b. radiation zone d. ozone layer

13. Which of the following would most probably cause the aurora borealis?
    a. gases escaping from the earth
    b. particles deflected off the moon
    c. particles given off by the sun
    d. rays given off by the earth's magnetic field
14. The ionosphere is believed to end at an altitude of about
    a. 10 kilometers
    b. 100 kilometers
    c. 1000 kilometers
    d. 10,000 kilometers
15. An air pollutant that affects the eyes and lungs is
    a. carbon monoxide
    b. carbon dioxide
    c. sulfur
    d. sulfur dioxide

Modified True-False Questions

In some of the following statements, the italicized term makes the statement incorrect. For each incorrect statement, write the term that must be substituted for the italicized term to make the statement correct. For each correct statement, write the word "true."

1. Both green plants and seawater can remove *carbon dioxide* from the atmosphere.
2. On very humid days, the amount of water vapor in the atmosphere may be as much as *ninety-six percent* of the total volume of air.
3. The bubbles seen in soda water consist of *carbon dioxide* gas.
4. Neon gas glows with *a yellow* color when electricity passes through it.
5. Priceless documents are stored in containers of *hydrogen* gas to keep them from deteriorating.
6. Almost all of the dust and moisture in the atmosphere is located in the *stratosphere*.
7. The ionosphere consists of electrically charged *gases*.
8. In the *stratosphere*, some particles of gas escape into space.

Thought Questions

1. Explain how the emergence of green plants on earth millions of years ago caused the composition of the atmosphere to change.
2. List the four major regions of the atmosphere. Briefly describe the special characteristics of each of these regions.
3. Name at least three sources of air pollution, and suggest how to eliminate them.

CHAPTER 2
WHAT ARE THE CAUSES AND EFFECTS OF ATMOSPHERIC PRESSURE?

When you have completed this chapter, you should be able to:

1. *Relate* the weight of air to air pressure.
2. *Describe* some devices, other than barometers, that depend on air pressure for their operation.
3. *Compare* the operation of two types of barometers.
4. *Account* for the effects of altitude, temperature, and humidity on air pressure.
5. *Discuss* the world pressure belts.

In the laboratory experience that follows, you will determine the weight of a given volume of air.

Laboratory Experience

HOW MUCH DOES AIR WEIGH?

A. Obtain an empty 500-cubic-centimeter (or larger) plastic bottle that has a tight-fitting stopper or cap. Carefully weigh the sealed bottle on a platform balance, as shown in Fig. 2–1.
   1. What substance is inside the bottle?
   2. What is the weight of the bottle?

B. Remove the bottle from the balance. Remove the stopper or cap, place the bottle on a table, and flatten it as much as you can with-

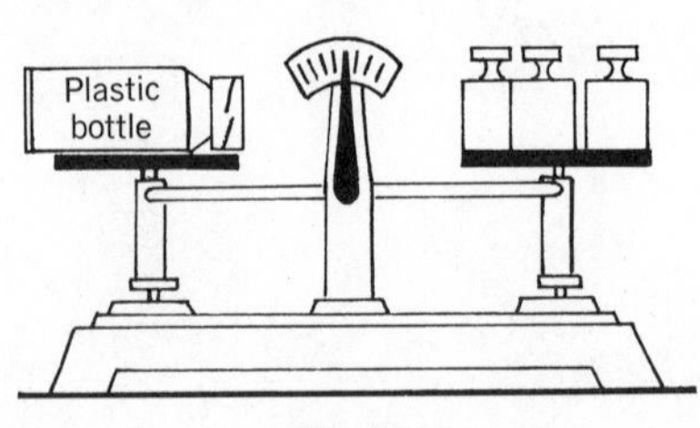

Fig. 2–1.

out breaking the bottle. Seal the bottle again. Carefully weigh the flattened, sealed bottle again.

3. In what way did you change the contents of the bottle?
4. What is the weight of the bottle now?
5. Explain any difference in weight.
6. Suppose you were to repeat this experiment several times. Would any weight differences be the same? Explain.

C. Obtain a 4-liter tin can. Remove the cap. Carefully weigh the container on the platform balance as shown in Fig. 2–2.

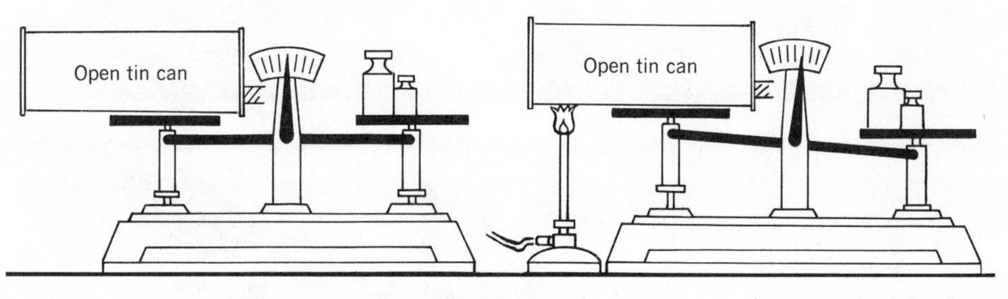

Fig. 2–2.

7. What is the weight of the container?

D. Heat one end of the container with a Bunsen burner or an alcohol burner for about 2 minutes. Use a pair of pliers or a padded glove to handle the container.

CAUTION: Do not touch the hot container with your hands.

---

8. What is the weight of the container now?
9. Is there any difference in weight between the heated and unheated container? If so, how do you explain the difference in weight?

E. Allow the container to cool while it rests on the balance. As the container cools, note the position of the pointer on the balance.

10. Does the movement of the indicator mean that the container is increasing or decreasing in weight? Explain.

Introduction

In our environment, we live at the bottom of a deep ocean of air. This air, which extends thousands of kilometers above us, presses down on our bodies, exerting a force of many tons. This force affects our lives, but we are not crushed to death by it. The pressure inside our bodies exerts a force that exactly balances the force exerted by the air pressure outside our bodies.

Sometimes we feel uncomfortable when the air pressure changes too quickly. For example, when you ride to the top of a mountain in an automobile, you sometimes feel a strange sensation inside your ears (Fig. 2–3). This sensation results from the air pressure on the outside of your eardrums changing more rapidly than the air pressure on the inside of your ears. The difference in air pressure causes your eardrums to bulge outward slightly. It is the bulging that is the source of the unpleasant feeling. By opening your mouth and yawning, by swallowing, or by chewing gum, you can equalize the air pressure on both sides of your eardrums.

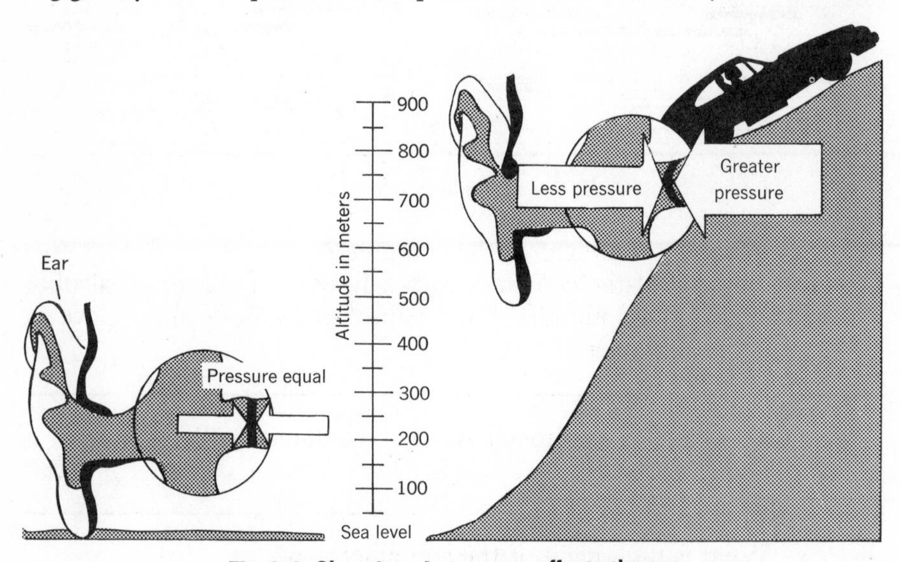

Fig. 2–3. Changing air pressure affects the ear.

The air pressure is different in different places and at different times. These differences are too slight to be noticed by the ordinary person. However, there is an important relationship between these slight changes in air pressure and changes in the weather. To understand this relationship, we must learn more about air, or atmospheric, pressure—its origin, its measurement, and the factors that cause it to change.

CAUSE OF AIR PRESSURE

We commonly say that a drinking glass is empty when it contains no water. Of course, the glass is not really empty—the water has been replaced by air. Air and water are examples of *fluids*—substances that flow. Air and water (or any other fluid) have many similar properties. Both air and water occupy space and have weight. Under ordinary conditions, both expand when they are warmed, and both contract when they are chilled.

Weight of Air

You saw in your laboratory experience that air has weight. Careful measurements indicate that at sea level one liter (or 1000 cubic centimeters) of air weighs about 1.3 grams. The air in a classroom 9 meters long by 6 meters wide by 3 meters high occupies a volume of 162,000 liters (or 162 cubic meters). If one liter of air weighs about 1.3 grams, the air in the classroom weighs over 200 kilograms.

If you can imagine an experiment in which the air in the classroom is reshaped into a column of air 30 centimeters square, the column would be 180 kilometers high. If this column of air were then placed on a scale, the scale would read over 200 kilograms (Fig. 2–4, page 22). Thus, the bottommost layer of air would have over 200 kilograms of air pressing down on it. Since air can be compressed, a larger number of air molecules would be squeezed into the bottommost cubic meter of air than would be contained in any cubic meter of air above it. On the other hand, the topmost cubic meter of air would contain fewer air molecules than any cubic meter of air below it.

What is true about our imaginary column of air is also true of the atmosphere. A column of air in the atmosphere is densest (that is, contains a maximum number of molecules) close to the ground. In fact, about one-half the weight of the atmosphere is concentrated below an altitude of 5.5 kilometers. About 99.9% of the weight of the atmosphere is concentrated within 50 kilometers of the earth's surface.

If a vertical column of the atmosphere 1 centimeter square and extending to the top of the atmosphere could be weighed, the column would weigh about 1 kilogram. That is, all the molecules of air in the column would press down against the scale with a combined force of about 1 kilogram per square centimeter (Fig. 2–5, page 22). Another way of saying the same thing is that atmospheric pressure, or air pressure, at sea level is 1 kilogram per square centimeter.

Direction of Air Pressure

The total force with which the air presses down on the surface of a 20-centimeter by 25-centimeter sheet of paper (which is an area of 500 square centimeters) is 500 kilograms:

$$500 \text{ square centimeters} \times 1 \frac{\text{kilogram}}{\text{square centimeter}} = 500 \text{ kilograms}$$

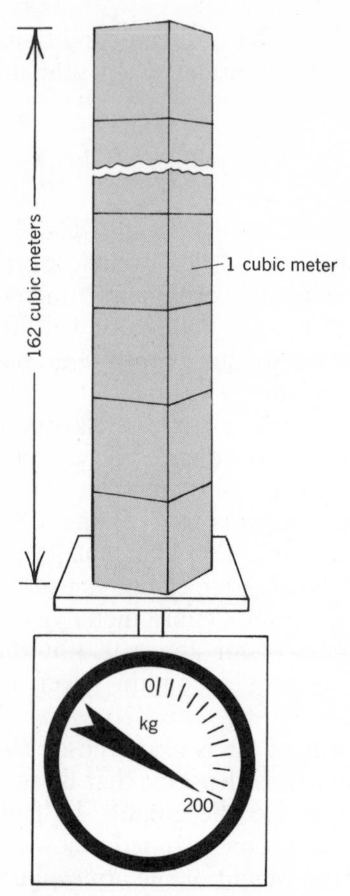

Fig. 2–4. The air in a classroom weighs over 200 kilograms.

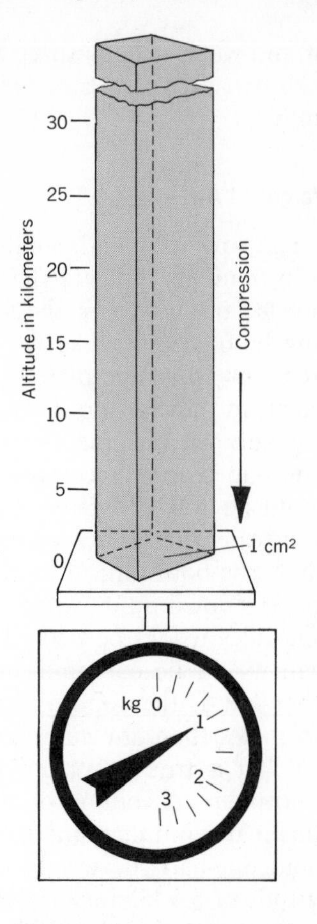

Fig. 2–5. Air exerts pressure.

The force with which the weight of the atmosphere presses down on your desk is much greater than the force pressing down on the sheet of paper. The question arises: Why doesn't your desk collapse under the enormous pressure that is pushing down on it? The answer is that the air pressure is not only pushing downward, the air pressure is pushing in *every* direction. The air pressure pushing upward against the bottom of your desk is equal to the air pressure pushing downward. These two pressures produce forces that balance each other.

By performing the experiment shown in Fig. 2–6, you can see for yourself that air pressure is being exerted in an upward as well as in a downward direction. You will need a small glass jar or bottle with a smooth rim, and a piece of stiff, light cardboard such as an index card. Fill the container to the top with water, and press the cardboard over the rim of the container.

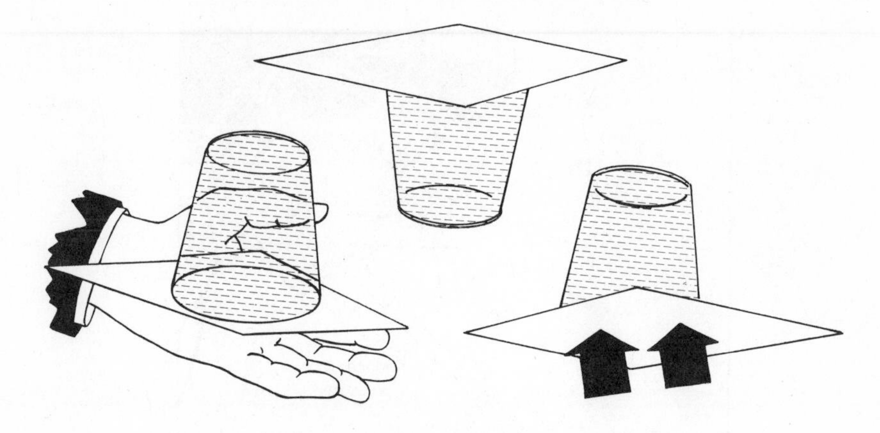

Fig. 2–6. Demonstrating that air exerts pressure.

Turn the container upside down. (Make sure you perform this experiment over a sink.) The cardboard will not fall off even if the glass is tilted. It remains pressed against the rim of the container, and the water is unable to escape from the container.

What is the explanation of this puzzle? The water in the container weighs very little—perhaps 250 grams. When you turn the container upside down, there is only the weight of the water pushing down against the cardboard. Against the other side of the cardboard, the air is pushing up with a force of 1 kilogram per square centimeter. The air pressure is more than sufficient to keep the cardboard pressed against the rim of the container.

USES OF AIR PRESSURE

We make use of air pressure to operate vacuum cleaners, to suck soda pop through drinking straws, and in many other devices.

In a vacuum cleaner, a motor-driven fan blows air from the inside of a tank to the outside of the tank. As air leaves the tank, the air pressure inside the tank is reduced so that it is less than the air pressure outside the tank. The outside air rushes into the tank through a hose connected to the tank. This rush of air carries along with it dirt, which collects in the tank, or bag, of the vacuum cleaner.

A drinking straw works according to the same principle. When you put a straw into a glass of liquid and suck through one end of the straw, you remove air from inside the straw. The removal of the air reduces the air pressure inside the straw. The outside air pressure is constantly pushing against the surface of the liquid. Because the outside air pressure is now greater than the air pressure inside the straw, the outside air pressure pushes the liquid through the straw and into your mouth (Fig. 2–7).

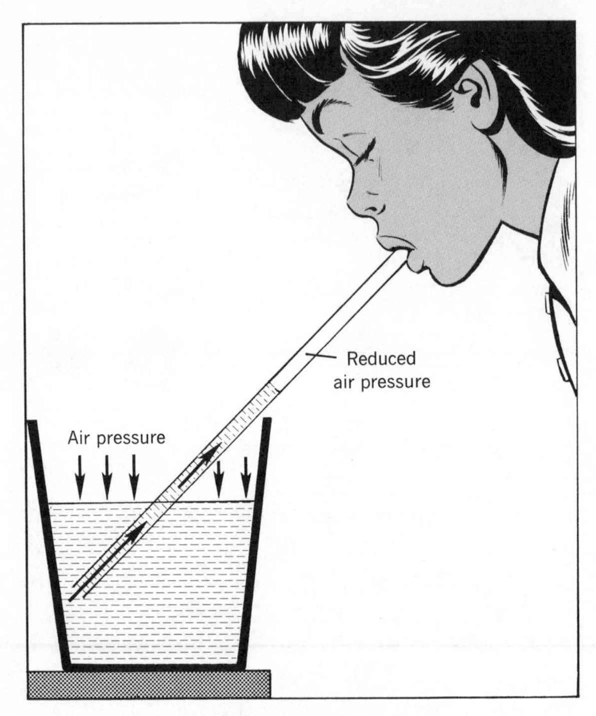

Fig. 2–7. A drinking straw.

The same thing happens when you squeeze the bulb of a medicine dropper, place the tip in a liquid, and then release the bulb.

MEASURING AIR PRESSURE WITH BAROMETERS

A *barometer* is an instrument that measures air pressure. The first barometer was invented in 1643 by an Italian physicist named *Evangelista Torricelli* (1608–1647). Torricelli completely filled a long glass tube (840 millimeters), sealed at one end, with mercury. Holding his thumb over the open end of the tube to prevent the escape of the mercury, Torricelli then turned the tube upside down and placed the open end of the tube in a dish of mercury. When Torricelli removed his thumb, the column of mercury inside the tube moved down a short distance and stopped when the top of the column of mercury was about 760 millimeters above the level of mercury in the dish (Fig. 2–8).

The space above the column of mercury became a vacuum because nothing replaced the mercury that sank downward. (This space is more accurately called a *partial vacuum,* since a few air molecules probably remain.) The column of mercury sank down inside the tube because its weight was greater than the weight of the column of air pressing down

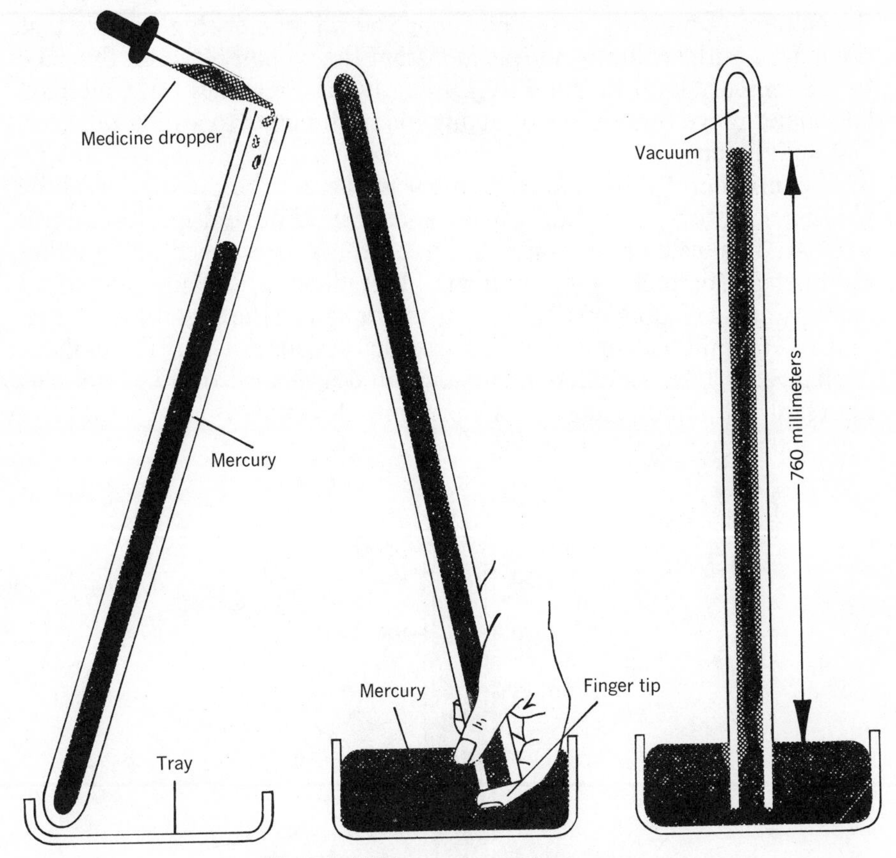

Fig. 2–8. Making a mercury barometer.

on top of the mercury in the dish. The column of mercury stopped moving downward only when the pressure it was exerting was equal to the pressure being exerted by the column of air against the surface of the mercury in the dish.

Mercury Barometer

The simple device we have been describing is called a *mercury barometer*. In a mercury barometer, the constant weight of a column of mercury is balanced against the constantly changing air pressure. The changing air pressure can be measured by noting how the mercury level in the column changes. When the air pressure decreases, the column of mercury drops in the tube. When the air pressure increases, the column of mercury rises in the tube.

If a meter stick were placed next to the glass tube shown in Fig. 2–8, the column of mercury would be about 760 millimeters high. Note that the length of the column is measured from the mercury level in the tube to the mercury level in the dish. Ordinarily, the readings on a mercury barometer range from a low of about 740 millimeters to a high of about 780 millimeters.

The *millibar* (abbreviated as *mb*) is the unit ordinarily used by weather scientists to measure air pressure. One thousand millibars equal one bar. The scale of a barometer, however, can be marked off in either millimeters (or inches) or millibars. A reading of 760 millimeters of mercury and a reading of 1013.2 millibars represent the same air pressure; that is, 760 millimeters of mercury exerts a pressure of 1013.2 millibars. A change of 10 millimeters of mercury and a change of 13.3 millibars represent the same change in air pressure. A comparison of these two barometer scales is shown in Fig. 2–9.

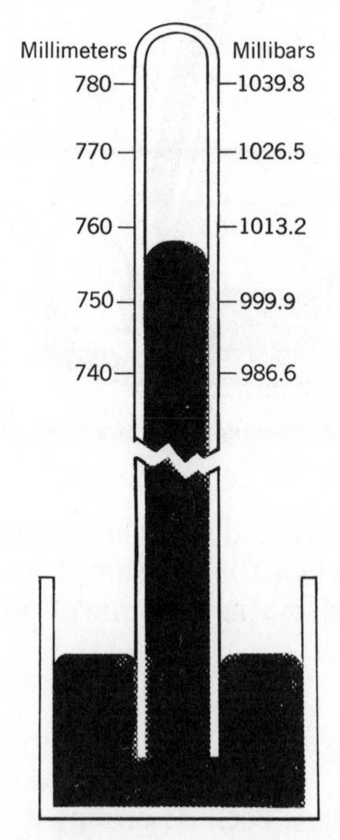

Fig. 2–9. A comparison of two barometer scales.

Can water be used to make a barometer instead of mercury? Water is nearly 14 times lighter (less dense) than mercury. Therefore, it would take a column of water that is 14 times taller than a column of mercury to measure the same air pressure. That is, a barometer using water instead of mercury to measure air pressure at sea level would have to be at least 10,640 millimeters high (760 millimeters $\times$ 14 = 10,640 millimeters or 10.64 meters).

In the seventeenth century, a German physicist named *Otto von Guericke* (1602–1686) made a water barometer that stood three stories high. Many people noticed that whenever the water level dropped, bad weather followed. The superstitious people of his town thought the barometer brought bad weather because of some strange magical properties it possessed. As a result, von Guericke was forced to remove the barometer.

Aneroid Barometer

An *aneroid barometer* contains neither mercury nor water nor any other liquid. The essential part of an aneroid barometer is a thin, round, sealed metal can from which most of the air has been removed.

The top and bottom of the can are flexible and can move in and out in response to changes in air pressure. An aneroid barometer can be made much smaller than a mercury barometer and is much more convenient to carry about.

An increase in air pressure pushes in the top of the can slightly. A spring attached to the top of the can keeps the can from collapsing completely. When the air pressure decreases, the spring pulls out the flexible side of the can.

As the top of the can moves in and out, its movement is transferred to an indicator through a series of levers and a chain. The levers and chain magnify the very slight in and out movements of the can. The indicator moves around a dial marked in units of pressure (Fig. 2–10).

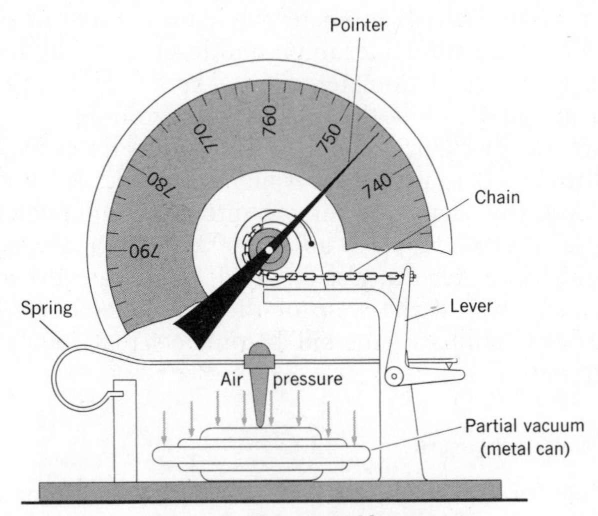

Fig. 2–10. The aneroid barometer.

Although aneroid barometers are convenient to use, they are not as accurate as mercury barometers. When an aneroid barometer is used in scientific work, or where great accuracy is needed, the barometer is checked against the readings of a mercury barometer.

Barograph

A *barograph* is an instrument that keeps a continuous record of changes in the barometric (air) pressure. The basic parts of a barograph are an aneroid barometer and a clock-driven drum that has a sheet of graph paper wrapped around it. A pen is attached to the levers of the barometer instead of a pointer. This pen touches the sheet of graph paper. As the drum turns, the pen draws a line that shows the changes in atmospheric pressure.

FACTORS THAT AFFECT AIR PRESSURE

Air pressure is caused by the weight of the air. Whenever the weight of the air changes, the pressure it exerts changes also. The weight of the air and, therefore, its pressure vary with changes in altitude, temperature, and humidity.

Altitude and Air Pressure

The higher you are above sea level, the less air presses down on you from above. Therefore, the air pressure decreases as the altitude increases. You can observe how air pressure changes with changes in altitude if your school has three or more stories.

Carefully read an aneroid barometer while on the roof or top floor of your school. Carry the barometer to ground level, or to the basement of the school, and read the barometer again. The barometric pressure will read about 1 millimeter more than the previous reading.

Air pressure usually changes about 25 millimeters for every 300 meters change in altitude. (Because the air at higher altitudes is less dense than it is at sea level, this change in air pressure of 25 millimeters per 300 meters is useful at altitudes up to about 3000 meters above sea level.)

The aneroid barometer can also be used to indicate the altitude, or height above sea level, if the scale of the barometer is marked off in meters instead of millibars. Aneroid barometers that indicate altitude are called *altimeters*.

Temperature and Air Pressure

It is possible for two cities, both at sea level but distant from each other, to have different air pressures. For example, New York City might have an air pressure of 775 millimeters of mercury, while Miami, Florida, has an air pressure of 737 millimeters of mercury. Since both cities are at sea level, we know that altitude is not a factor in the difference in pressures.

The lower pressure reading at Miami tells us that the air over Miami is lighter than the air over New York City. If the air were heavier at Miami, it would push down with greater force against the mercury in the dish of the barometer, causing the barometer to read higher.

Pressure differences are often caused by the differences in weight between masses of warm air and cold air. Smoke rising from an open fire or from a chimney shows us that hot air is lighter than cold air. You may have noticed that the air near the ceiling of a room is warmer than the air near the floor. The first balloons capable of carrying people into the air were filled with heated air. In 1783, a Frenchman floated over Paris in a balloon filled with heated air.

If you were to weigh a large metal container on a scale, you would be weighing both the container and the molecules of air inside the container. If you were to heat the container over a fire and weigh the container while it was still hot, as you did in the laboratory experience, the container would weigh less. The container loses weight because there are fewer molecules of air inside it when heated.

The heat causes the molecules of air inside the container to move faster. Because the molecules are moving faster, a greater number of molecules escape through the opening at the top of the container. That is, the heat causes the air to expand.

Heating a volume of air in the atmosphere also causes the air to expand and become lighter. On the other hand, when the volume of air cools again, it contracts and becomes heavier.

All other things being equal, a mass of warm air weighs less than a mass of cold air. Consequently, a mass of warm air exerts less pressure on the surface of the earth than does a mass of cold air.

Humidity and Air Pressure

Air pressure varies not only with the temperature of the air but also with the humidity. Recall that a given volume of water vapor weighs less than an equal volume of dry air at the same temperature. When water vapor enters the air, it displaces some of the heavier gases in the air. Therefore, the air weighs less than it did before. Thus, when the air is moist, lower air pressures are recorded than when the air is dry.

Furthermore, a mass of air that is both warm and moist exerts less pressure than a mass of air that is both cold and dry. Therefore, on a day when the air over Miami is warm and moist and the air over New

York City is cold and dry, Miami will have a lower air pressure than New York.

PRESSURE BELTS AROUND THE WORLD

Although the air pressure is changing continuously all over the world, certain parts of the world tend to have certain levels of air pressure that persist for long periods of time. On a map of the world these regions appear as belts of high or low air pressure that encircle the earth. Fig. 2–11 shows the names and locations of these pressure belts, which are also discussed in Chapter 4.

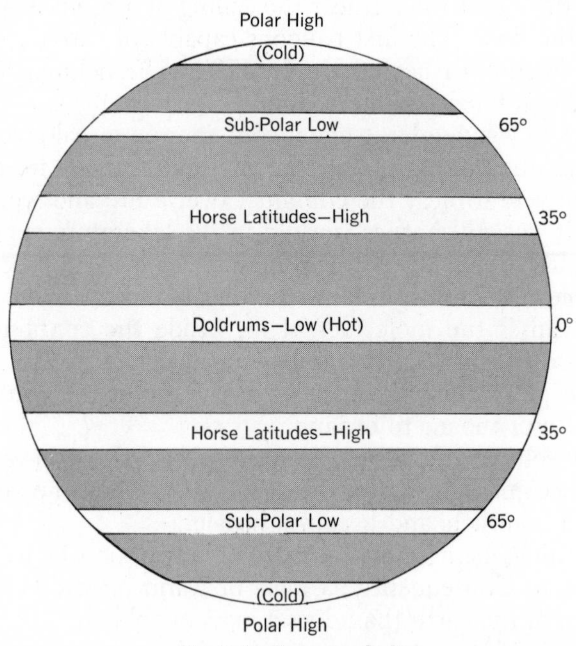

Fig. 2–11. Pressure belts.

The persistence of a belt of high pressure in the polar regions is easy to understand because the air in the polar regions is always extremely cold. In contrast, the air over equatorial regions is always very warm. As a consequence, a belt of low pressure persists in the region of the equator.

Temperature differences alone do not determine the location of a region of high or low pressure. Other factors are also important, including the location of land and water areas, the rotation of the earth, and the upward and downward movements of large masses of air as the air is heated or cooled. A great many additional factors affect air pressure, so that the pressure belts are not as simple as those shown on Fig. 2–11.

Even though the locations of air pressure belts vary, it is important to know the usual locations of these belts because they play an important part in determining the wind patterns of the world and the movements of storms. Winds are discussed in Chapter 4; storms are discussed in Chapter 6.

Looking Back

Air, or atmospheric, pressure is caused by the weight of the air above us. Our bodies depend on air for the oxygen it contains and the pressure it exerts. Air pressure that is much greater or much less than normal can injure our bodies. When we change air pressure artificially, we can make the air pressure work for us in certain devices. Examples of such devices are vacuum cleaners, drinking straws, and medicine droppers. The temperature and humidity of the air not only affect the operation of many mechanical devices, but also affect our health and comfort.

Looking Ahead

The air pressure in different regions of the earth is often different. One reason for the difference is the variation in the amount of heat energy each region receives from the sun. In the next chapter, we will consider why this is so and how heat affects the atmosphere.

Multiple-Choice Questions

1. About one-half of the total weight of the atmosphere is concentrated in that part of the atmosphere that extends from sea level to an altitude of about
   a. 1 kilometer c. 30 kilometers
   b. 5½ kilometers d. 100 kilometers
2. The air pressure that is normally exerted against every square centimeter of your body at sea level is about
   a. 1 kilogram b. 15 kilograms c. 30 kilograms d. 60 kilograms
3. Our bodies are not crushed by the outside air pressure because
   a. our bones are very strong
   b. our muscles push back against the air pressure
   c. body fluids absorb the pressure
   d. the air pressure inside our bodies balances the outside air pressure

4. Devices that depend on atmospheric pressure to function include vacuum cleaners and
   a. fire extinguishers
   b. radios
   c. drinking straws
   d. elevators
5. The space above the column of mercury in a barometer is
   a. filled with an inert gas
   b. nearly empty
   c. connected to the atmosphere through a small opening
   d. filled with alcohol
6. The mercury in a barometer tube moves downward until it
   a. is equal in weight to an equal volume of air
   b. is equal in weight to a column of air having the same diameter as the inside of the tube and extending to the top of the atmosphere
   c. reaches the level marked 740 millimeters
   d. fills the reservoir at the bottom of the column of mercury
7. The number of millibars equal to 10 millimeters of mercury is approximately
   a. 2.5 b. 13.3 c. 760 d. 1013.2
8. Water is not used in liquid barometers because
   a. water evaporates
   b. water stains the glass
   c. water is colorless
   d. barometers using water would be over 10 meters high
9. A type of barometer that is especially designed to make a written record of the air pressure is called
   a. a barograph
   b. an aneroid barometer
   c. a mercury barometer
   d. an altimeter
10. In an aneroid barometer, the device that expands and contracts as the air pressure changes is a
    a. sealed can
    b. coiled spring
    c. steel disk
    d. sensitive needle
11. A volume of air is lightest in weight when it is
    a. hot and moist
    b. hot and dry
    c. cold and moist
    d. cold and dry
12. The *least* important factor in the location of air pressure systems over the earth is
    a. the location of land and water areas
    b. the upward and downward movement of large masses of air
    c. the rotation of the earth
    d. the amount of rainfall in a given area

Modified True-False Questions

1. A liter of air weighs about *three* grams at sea level.
2. About *fifty percent* of the weight of the atmosphere is located below an altitude of 50 kilometers above sea level.

3. The barometer was invented in 1643 by the Italian physicist *Evangelista Torricelli.*
4. The column of mercury in a liquid barometer at sea level often stands at *850* millimeters.
5. The *millibar* is a unit that is used to indicate atmospheric pressure.
6. A liquid barometer using water would have to be about *one and one-quarter* times taller than a liquid barometer using mercury.
7. A type of barometer that does not use a liquid to measure air pressure is the *aneroid* barometer.
8. One type of barometer that can be used to measure altitude is the *hygrograph.*
9. High pressure systems are usually found at the *equator.*
10. The different pressure systems that persist in the atmosphere are caused by differences in temperature and *humidity.*

Increases—Decreases—Remains the Same

Write the term that correctly completes the statement.

1. As a volume of air in the atmosphere gets warmer, air pressure
   increases, decreases, remains the same
2. With increasing altitude, the weight of a liter of air
   increases, decreases, remains the same
3. As water vapor enters the air, the weight of the air
   increases, decreases, remains the same
4. As atmospheric pressure increases, the height of a column of mercury in a barometer
   increases, decreases, remains the same
5. When a volume of air is heated, the motion of its molecules
   increases, decreases, remains the same

Thought Questions

1. Explain how you can use a barometer to measure changes in altitude.
2. Explain why a cubic meter of air, several thousand meters above sea level, is lighter in weight than a cubic meter of air at sea level.
3. Explain why a barometer, inside a building, will measure the air pressure existing on the outside of the building.
4. What two conditions can cause a quantity of air at sea level to become lighter in weight? Explain how each of these conditions acts upon the quantity of air.
5. Explain why the interiors of continents become centers of high air pressure in the winter, whereas the interiors of continents become centers of low pressure in the summer.

CHAPTER 3
WHAT ARE THE SOURCES AND EFFECTS OF HEAT IN THE ATMOSPHERE?

When you have completed this chapter, you should be able to:

1. *Discuss* the effect on an animal of the temperature of its environment.
2. *Describe* what happens to the sun's rays upon reaching the earth.
3. *Explain* how air pollution and other factors affect the absorption of energy from the sun.
4. *Distinguish* between conduction, convection, and radiation.
5. *Account* for the "greenhouse effect."
6. *Give examples* of different regions that are each influenced mainly by a factor affecting the air temperature of the region.
7. *Relate* the dangers of air pollution to temperature inversions.

In the laboratory experience that follows, you will investigate the rates of warming and cooling of a solid and a liquid.

Laboratory Experience

HOW DO HEATING AND COOLING AFFECT THE SAME QUANTITIES OF SAND AND WATER?

A. Set up two thermometers and two beakers of the same size, as shown in Fig. 3–1. Adjust the thermometers so that each is about 25 millimeters above the bottom of its beaker.

Fill one beaker with water at room temperature. Fill the other beaker with sand at room temperature.

1. What is the temperature of the water?
2. What is the temperature of the sand?

Copy the two tables on page 35 into your notebook, and record both temperatures in the proper spaces of the table headed "Heating."

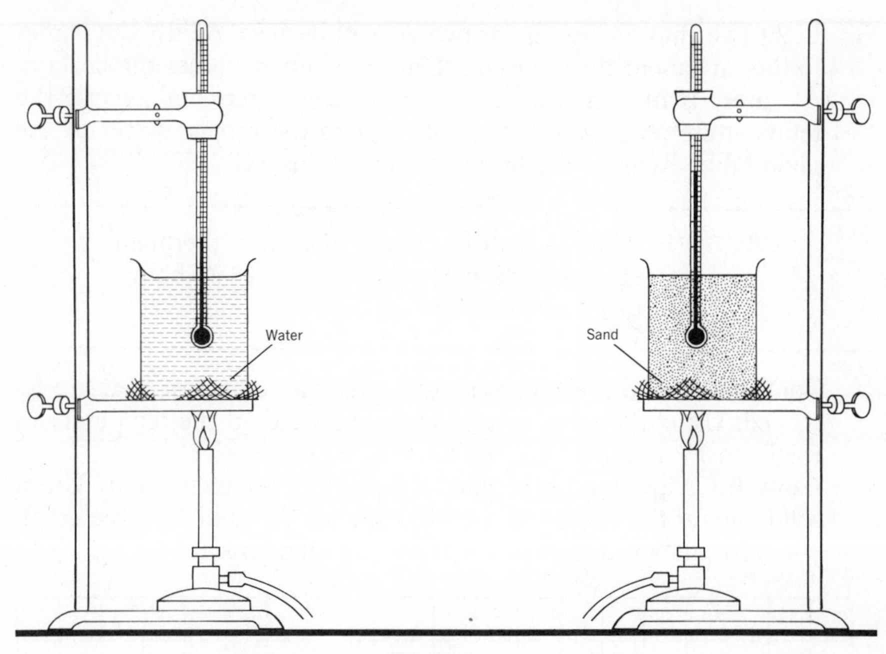

Fig. 3–1.

	Heating	
	Temperature	
Minutes	*Water*	*Sand*
Begin 0		
1		
2		
3		
4		
5		
6		
7		

	Cooling (Heat Removed)	
	Temperature	
Minutes	*Water*	*Sand*
1		
2		
3		
4		
5		
6		
7		
8		
9		
10		
11		
12		
13		
14		
15		

B. Light two Bunsen burners or two alcohol burners. Adjust the flames so they are about the same size. Place the burners under the beakers. At intervals of 1 minute, read the thermometers and record the temperature readings in your notebook in the proper spaces of the same table. Remove the burners after 7 minutes.

CAUTION: Remove both burners if the sand thermometer records a temperature of 65°C before the 7 minutes are up.

Continue to read the thermometers after the sources of heat are removed. Using the table headed "Cooling," record the temperatures for 10 to 15 minutes after the burners are removed.

C. Copy the graph, and plot your temperature readings on it. Use a solid line for the water and a dotted line for the sand. Use the graph you have drawn to answer the following questions:

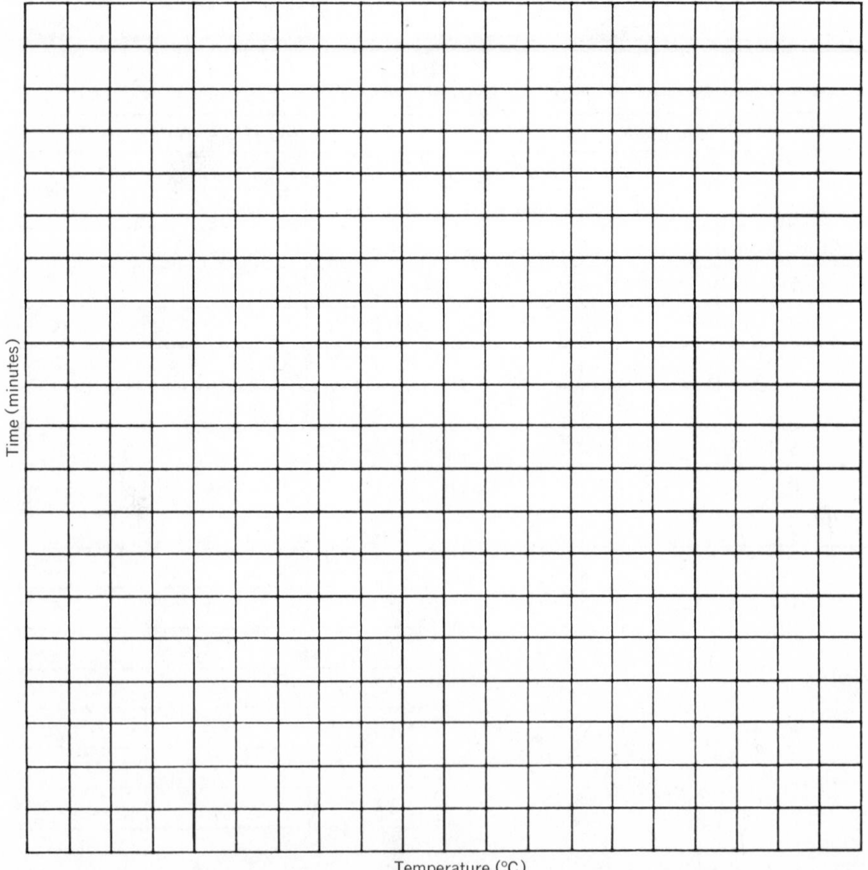

3. Over the entire heating period, which substance heats up faster, sand or water? How do you know?
4. Over the entire cooling period, which substance cools off faster, sand or water? How do you know?
5. Which of these two substances holds heat for a longer period of time? How do the temperature curves show this?
6. Which would probably heat up more quickly on a hot summer day, a sandy beach or a body of water? Why?
7. Which would probably cool off more quickly at the end of the summer, a large land mass or a large body of water? Why?
8. Discuss one application of your findings in this experiment.

Introduction

All of us are aware that the temperature of the air around us is always changing. The temperature of the air varies from hour to hour, from day to day, and from season to season. This variation depends upon climate and weather and occurs because the amount of heat in the atmosphere is continually changing.

The temperature of the air is a very important factor of the environment because temperature affects every organism. Each type of organism survives best where the temperature suits it. Should the usual temperatures of a region suddenly change, some living things would die. Other living things would *migrate*—that is, travel to a more suitable region. In tropical regions, where the temperature is warm and does not vary much from season to season, we find the greatest number and variety of plants and animals.

The temperature of a region depends upon how much heat energy the region receives and how much it loses. In turn, the amounts of heat energy received and lost depend upon the amounts of heat energy present in the land and water masses in the region and in the atmosphere above the region. In this chapter, we will study the major source of the earth's heat energy and how heat energy affects the atmosphere.

WHAT IS HEAT?

Heat is one form of energy. The particles—atoms and molecules—that make up all matter are in constant motion. *Heat energy* is a way of describing how fast these atoms and molecules are moving. The faster the atoms or molecules move in a particular substance, the hotter the substance, or the higher is its temperature. We then say the substance contains a large amount of heat energy.

The slower the motion of the atoms or molecules in a substance, the colder the substance, or the lower is its temperature. We then say the substance contains a small amount of heat energy. For example, the molecules in boiling water move faster than do the molecules in cold water. Therefore, a given quantity of boiling water contains more heat energy than does an equal amount of cold water.

The molecules of gases that make up the atmosphere are also in constant motion. The atmosphere, therefore, contains heat energy. In the same way, the rocks and soil on land and the water in the ocean also contain heat energy because their molecules are in motion.

ENERGY RECEIVED FROM THE SUN

The source of almost all the earth's heat energy is the sun, which is about 150 million kilometers from the earth. The sun gives off its heat in the form of *radiant energy*, which travels through space in the form of rays, or *radiation*.

When radiant energy strikes an object, part of the radiant energy is absorbed by the object. As a result, the radiant energy makes the molecules in that object move faster. As we just learned, when the molecules in an object move faster, the object becomes hotter—it acquires more heat energy. We say that the radiant energy of the sun has been transformed (changed) into heat energy. In this way, the heat produced by the sun warms the earth.

TYPES OF RADIANT ENERGY

There are several types of radiant energy, as shown in Fig. 3–2. *Ultraviolet radiation* (UV) is part of the radiant energy given off by the sun. This radiation is invisible. When ultraviolet radiation strikes our skin, some of the radiation is transformed into heat energy and warms the skin. If we stay in the sun too long, the ultraviolet radiation may produce painful sunburn. In extreme cases, ultraviolet radiation may even destroy tissue or cause skin cancer.

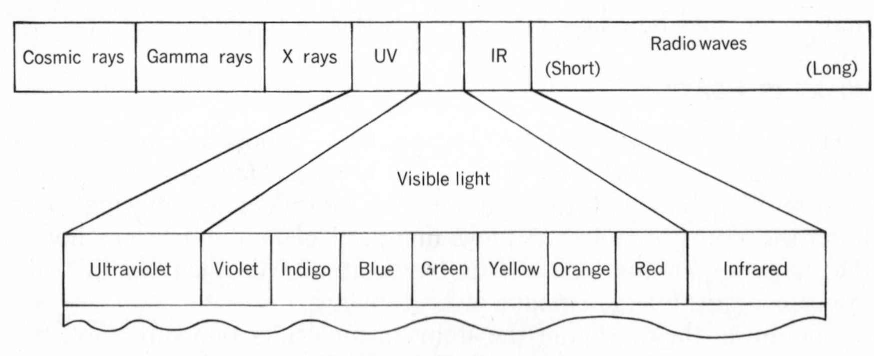

Fig. 3–2. Radiant energy.

Infrared radiation (IR) is another form of invisible radiant energy given off by the sun, as are radio waves (which cause static in radio receivers), and X rays.

Visible light is also a form of radiant energy given off by the sun. This part of sunlight is visible to us because our eyes are sensitive to this form of radiant energy. (In the same way, a radio receiver is sensitive to radio waves, and photographic film is sensitive to X rays.) Like all other forms of radiant energy, visible light is absorbed by many of the objects it strikes and thus warms them.

ABSORPTION OF RADIANT ENERGY

The sun's radiant energy reaches the earth almost unchanged after its long trip through the vacuum of space. However, of all the radiant energy entering our atmosphere, only about two-thirds ever reaches the surface of the earth. The remainder of the radiant energy is absorbed by the atmosphere and by the clouds. Some energy is also reflected back into space by clouds, water vapor, and dust particles suspended in the atmosphere (Fig. 3–3).

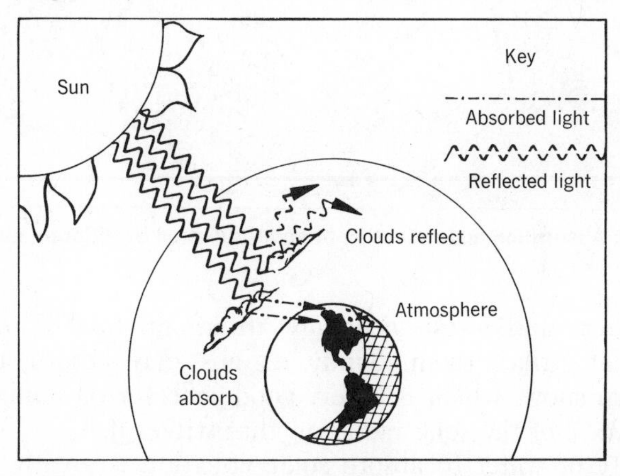

Fig. 3–3. Only a part of the radiant energy that enters the atmosphere reaches the earth.

The sun's radiations (also called solar radiations) that play the most important part in the heating of the earth are visible light and invisible infrared radiations. These radiations are changed to heat energy when they are absorbed by substances on the earth and in the atmosphere.

The amount of solar radiation absorbed by the atmosphere depends largely on the amount of water vapor, dust, and other substances present in the atmosphere. The atmosphere is heated most, however, by the solar radiation absorbed by the surface of the earth. In turn, the amount of solar radiation absorbed by the earth and converted into heat is determined mainly by (1) the kind of material present on the surface of the earth, (2) the substances in the atmosphere, and (3) the angle at which the solar radiation strikes the earth.

Energy Absorption by Land and Water

Different kinds of land surfaces differ in their ability to absorb solar radiation (Fig. 3–4). Dark-colored and rough land surfaces absorb solar radiation better than do light-colored and smooth land surfaces. Similarly, objects that are black in color and rough in texture absorb heat better than do objects that are light in color and smooth in texture. Thus, in a warm climate, white clothing is cooler than dark clothing.

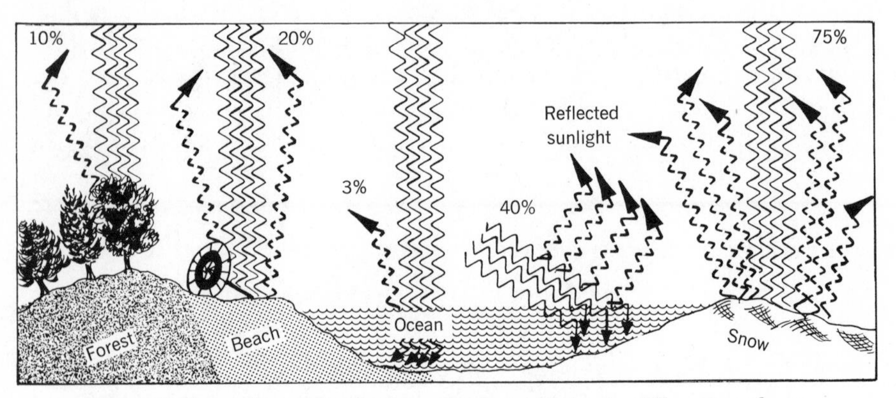

Fig. 3–4. Absorption and reflection of solar radiation by different surfaces.

Planted areas and forests generally absorb up to 90% of the solar radiation that strikes them. Sandy regions may absorb about 80%. Freshly fallen snow, which is a very good reflector of sunlight, absorbs only about 25% of the solar radiation that strikes it.

The ability of water to absorb solar radiation is greatly affected by the angle at which the radiation strikes the water. When the sun is low in the sky, water absorbs about half of the solar radiation that strikes it. Water absorbs about 97% of the solar radiation when the sun is directly overhead. Can you explain this difference?

Land and water areas differ greatly in their ability to absorb radiant energy. During a hot day at the beach, for example, the water will remain cool no matter how high the air temperature is, while the sand may become so hot that you cannot walk on it barefoot. However, when the sun sets in the evening, the sand cools off quickly, while the temperature of the water remains about the same.

Land and water differ greatly not only in their ability to absorb heat but also in their ability to hold heat. Land heats up quickly during the day, but it does not retain the heat. That is, the land gives up its heat just as quickly in the evening as it absorbs the heat during the day. On the other hand, water heats up slowly but retains the heat. This is the same as saying that water gives up heat slowly.

Even though land heats up more quickly than water, it is only the top layers of the soil or sand that heat up. On a hot beach, if you dig into the sand several centimeters, the sand that was protected from the solar radiation feels much cooler than the sand that was exposed directly to the sun. The same thing happened when the bulb of your thermometer was buried in sand in the laboratory experience. Then, after a few minutes of heating, the heat penetrated to the bulb, causing a rapid rise in temperature. This means that sand does not transfer heat uniformly as does an iron wire held in a flame. On the other hand, the temperature of the water increased at a steady rate over the heating period. This means that water transfers heat uniformly.

Water is somewhat transparent to solar radiation. The radiation can travel into the water for a distance, reaching a depth that depends on the amount of energy the solar radiation contains. For example, red light rays have less energy than blue and green rays. The red light is absorbed quickly by the top layers of water and is changed into heat energy, while the blue and green light travel deeper into the water before being absorbed. Most of the solar radiation is absorbed before it can travel more than 10 meters into the water. However, some light can be detected as far as 600 meters or more below the surface.

Because water is partially transparent to solar radiation, water can be heated to a much greater depth than land. This means that water can store a much larger quantity of heat energy than land can store. The amount of heat energy stored in the depths of the ocean is increased by currents which mix the warmer water on the surface with the colder water below.

Effect of Gases and Dust Particles

Sunlight, streaming through the atmosphere, is affected by clouds, dust, water vapor and various other gases in the atmosphere (Fig. 3–5, page 42). Clouds reflect solar radiation very well. On days when the sky is covered by thick clouds, large amounts of solar radiation are reflected by the clouds back into space. On cloudy days, only about 45% or less of the sun's radiant energy can reach the surface of the earth to heat it.

Water vapor and carbon dioxide in the atmosphere absorb some of the infrared radiation from the sun, which, in turn, heats these gases. Consequently, these gases radiate some of their heat energy back into the atmosphere.

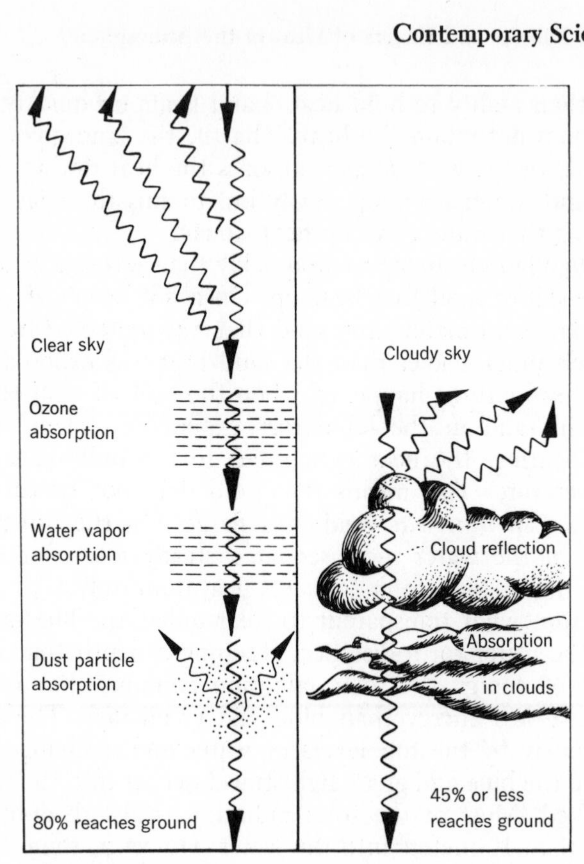

Fig. 3–5. Amounts of radiant energy reaching the earth on clear and cloudy days.

Recall that a layer of ozone, a special kind of oxygen, is present in the stratosphere. This layer absorbs most of the sun's harmful ultraviolet rays and prevents the rays from reaching the surface of the earth. Only a small part of these harmful ultraviolet rays reaches us. The absorption of large amounts of ultraviolet rays by the ozone layer is important because, if these rays reached the surface of the earth, they would soon destroy all forms of life.

Dust particles in the air block solar radiation. The radiation that strikes the dust particles may be absorbed by them, reflected back into space, or the radiation may be scattered through the atmosphere. As we have already shown, the scattering of sunlight by dust, and by the gases in the air, gives the sky its blue color. The radiation that is absorbed by dust is transformed into heat energy, which is added to the atmosphere.

Effect of Air Pollution

Over the ocean and over land areas far from cities and industrial centers, dust is a normal part of the atmosphere. Such dust particles include pollen, particles emitted by volcanoes, and fine soil. As we have noted before, these particles are responsible for the color of the sky and for the conversion of some solar radiation into heat energy.

What happens when modern civilization adds more dust particles of various sorts, such as ash and soot, to the dust particles naturally present? First, the color of the sky changes. It becomes a duller blue, or grayish. Second, more radiation is converted to heat. Third, the air near the surface of the earth becomes warmer than usual. If more and more dust particles are continuously added to the atmosphere, can you predict what will eventually happen to our environment?

Modern jet airplanes or supersonic transport planes travel long distances in the stratosphere. You have no doubt seen the "vapor trails," or exhausts, behind such high-flying planes. These exhausts from the burning of jet fuel consist of water droplets, carbon dioxide, and other substances. All of these substances are added to the substances normally present in the stratosphere. The additional substances can have indirect effects upon the surface of the earth. These effects may include reducing the amount of sunlight that normally reaches the earth's surface and increasing the possibilities for the formation of clouds.

Another source of air pollution is the compressed propellant gases in cans of hair spray, deodorant, and other types of sprays. These gases could eventually reach the stratosphere and destroy the ozone there. Our government has already acted to prohibit the use of these propellants. What other steps should our nation and others take to prevent pollution of the atmosphere 15 kilometers or more above us?

Angle of Radiation

The angle at which solar radiation strikes the surface of the earth is an important factor in the amount of heat any part of the surface receives. At the equator, the sun passes almost directly overhead most of the year. Therefore, the solar radiation strikes the earth with greatest intensity along the equator. As a result, the land and ocean areas along the equator absorb more of the sun's heat than do areas that are farther from the equator.

In the United States and Canada, the sun always appears lower in the sky than it does along the equator. In these regions, the surface of the earth curves away from the sun's radiation, and the radiation is spread out over a larger portion of the earth's surface than it is along the equator (Fig. 3–6, page 44). Because the radiation is less concentrated away from the equator, the United States and Canada receive less heat over the course of a year than do land and ocean areas along the equator. Furthermore, the rays which strike the earth at a greater angle must travel a greater distance through the atmosphere to reach the surface of the earth. As a result, more of the solar radiation is absorbed, reflected, or scattered by the atmosphere, which further reduces the amount of solar radiation received at the surface of the earth.

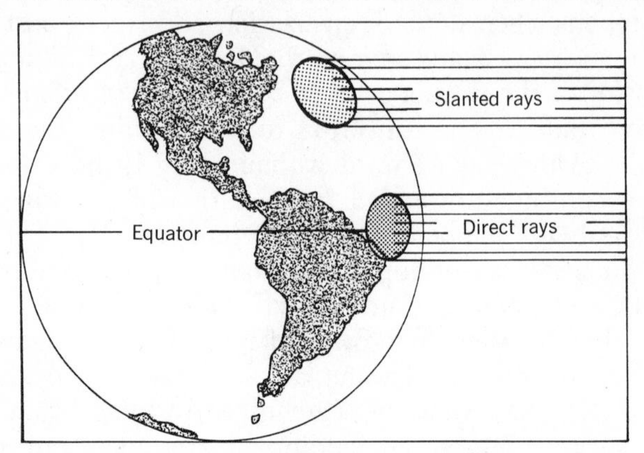

Fig. 3–6. The sun's rays are most intense at the equator.

In addition, because the earth's axis is tipped about 23½ degrees in relation to the sun, the Northern Hemisphere and Southern Hemisphere receive different amounts of solar radiation in the winter than they do in the summer. That is, solar radiation strikes the earth at different angles at different times of the year. The tilting of the earth's axis is responsible for the seasons, as described on pages 52–53.

TRANSFER OF HEAT ENERGY TO THE ATMOSPHERE

The light energy that is absorbed at the earth's surface and changed into heat is the most important factor in the heating of the troposphere, the air layer nearest the surface. The heat energy absorbed by the surface is transferred back to the atmosphere again by the processes of *conduction, convection,* and *radiation.*

Conduction

When a metal spoon is placed in a bowl of hot soup, the entire spoon soon becomes hot. This happens because the heat from the soup travels first to the bowl-shaped part of the spoon and then to the handle. In the same way, if you hold one end of a metal rod in your hand and place the other end of the rod in a flame, the heat from the flame will travel through the rod to your hand. This type of heat transfer by particles (either atoms or molecules) is called conduction.

Metals are made up of atoms. Heat travels through the metal spoon and metal rod because the atoms within the metal transfer heat energy from the heated end to the cold end (Fig. 3–7). This happens because the atoms in the heated end move faster as they absorb heat energy from the flame. The increased motion of these atoms causes them to collide with slower-moving atoms nearby, causing these slower-moving atoms to move faster. This process continues through the spoon or rod until eventually all the atoms are moving faster.

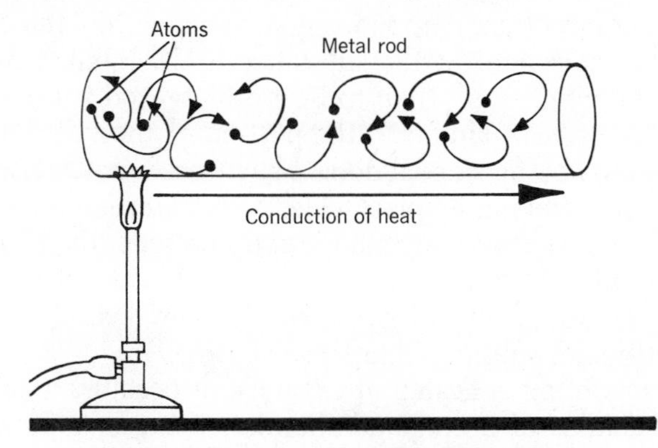

Fig. 3–7. Transfer of heat by conduction.

The hottest part of the metal, where the atoms are moving the fastest, will be at the source of the heat. The coldest part of the metal, where the atoms are moving the slowest, will be that end farthest away from the source of heat.

Some substances do not readily allow heat to pass through them. These substances are called *insulators*. Gases and liquids, unlike metals, are generally poor conductors of heat. We can account for this observation by assuming that the particles that make up gases and liquids are farther apart than are the particles in metals. Therefore, neighboring particles in a gas or in a liquid are less affected by the increased motions of heated particles, and consequently heat is not conducted rapidly. Substances such as wood or plastic are also poor conductors of heat, or good insulators. This is why they are used to make handles for metallic objects that are to be heated. The clothing we wear is also a poor conductor of heat, enabling us to retain body warmth. Porous material is generally nonconducting because it contains layers of trapped air, which do not permit heat transfer.

During the day, when solar radiation is heating the earth, the portion of the atmosphere touching the ground is heated by conduction. That is, heat energy from the warm surface of the ground is transferred directly to molecules of air. The atmosphere, however, is a poor conductor of heat because molecules of air are far apart. Consequently, the portion of the atmosphere not touching the ground cannot receive heat by conduction. The atmosphere that is not very close to the surface of the earth is heated by convection and radiation.

Convection

Heat is transferred through gases and liquids—poor heat conductors—by a process called convection. Convection is the transfer of heat through a substance (liquid or gas) by moving currents within the substance—that is, by the movement of the substance itself. It takes much longer to heat a container of water than to heat a metal rod because water is a poor conductor of heat. However, the portion of the water near a flame readily becomes hot by conduction. The heated water rises, and the colder water sinks, taking its place. The cold water is now heated, continuing the cycle. The moving water sets up currents that, in time, heat the entire sample of water (Fig. 3–8*a*). Convection occurs readily in liquids, such as water, and in gases, such as air, because currents can move easily through substances in these states.

When a mass of air is heated, it expands, or occupies a larger volume of space. The mass of air expands because the gas molecules, on absorbing heat, move faster and collide more strongly with each other. These collisions push the molecules farther apart from each other. This results in fewer molecules occupying the original volume of space. The volume of air in this space will, therefore, weigh less than it did before it was heated.

A given volume of cooler air, on the other hand, has less heat energy than the same volume of warm air. The molecules in the mass of cool

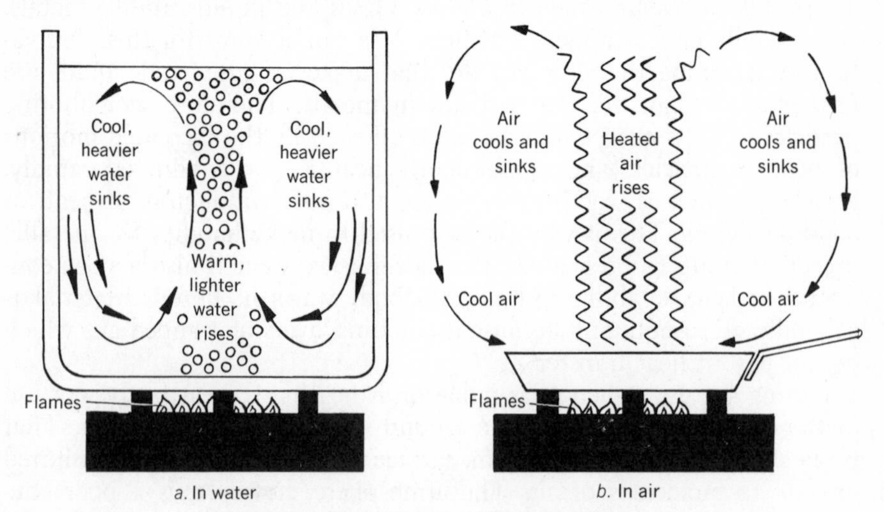

Fig. 3–8. Transfer of heat by convection.

air move slower and are closer together than the molecules in an equal mass of warm air. The cool air, therefore, weighs more than the same volume of warm air. Consequently, cool air is more dense than warm air.

Because a mass of warm air in the atmosphere is lighter than the same volume of cool air, the warm air *rises* into the atmosphere. Because a mass of cool air is heavier than the same volume of warm air, the cool air *sinks* towards the earth. The upward movement of warm air and the downward movement of cool air result in currents in the air. Such currents are called *convection currents.* A familiar example of a convection current is shown in Fig. 3–8*b*.

Another example of convection currents is seen in a room heated by a radiator. The air in contact with the radiator is heated by conduction and rises. Cooler air moves in from below to take the place of the air that has risen; this air becomes heated also and, in turn, also rises. The convection process continues as long as the air away from the radiator is cooler than the air surrounding the radiator (Fig. 3–9).

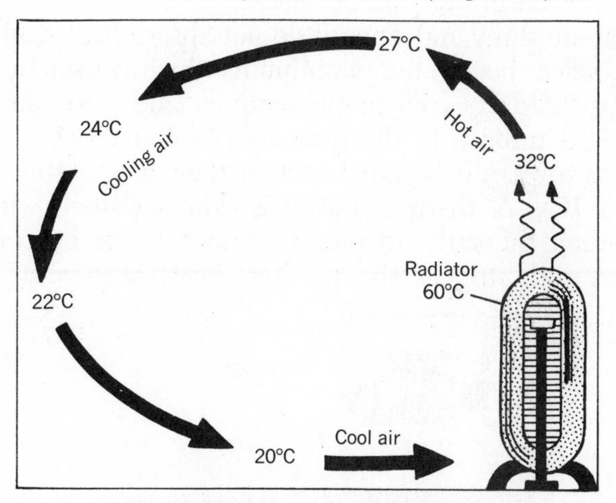

Fig. 3–9. Heating a room by convection.

Land and water surfaces act like the radiators in a house. The cooler air in contact with these surfaces is heated by conduction. The air expands and rises into the atmosphere. Cooler, heavier air then replaces the warmed air. This air is now heated, and it, too, rises upward. The movement of air in the atmosphere is similar to the convection current shown in Fig. 3–9.

The continuous upward movement of heated air transfers large amounts of heat energy through the troposphere. But as the heated air rises, it slowly cools. The farther the heated air rises from the surface of the earth, the cooler the air becomes.

Radiation

We know that energy travels from the sun to the earth through space, which is an almost perfect vacuum. This energy, traveling without the aid of atomic or molecular collisions, is transferred from the sun to the earth by radiation, that is, by means of rays, or waves. You can understand this method of energy transfer by standing a short distance from an open fire or by placing your hand a little to one side of, but not touching, a hot radiator. Since neither source of heat is being touched, you cannot receive heat by conduction. Since warm air rises vertically from the heat source, the heat cannot reach you by convection. The heat that is transferred to you from the fire or radiator reaches you by radiation.

Bodies that are rough and dark tend to radiate heat better than shiny smooth bodies. This is why steam radiators are often dark and have a roughened surface. It is for the same reason that coal-burning stoves are made of dark metal or are painted black.

Bodies that are shiny and smooth do not absorb heat readily. Instead, these bodies reflect heat. Thus, aluminum, which is sometimes used for roofing, keeps buildings cool in the summer and warm in the winter. This principle is utilized in the thermos (vacuum) bottle, which is so constructed as to permit liquids to retain their temperatures for a long time (Fig. 3–10). A thermos bottle is double-walled, with a partial vacuum between the walls to prevent heat transfer by conduction or convection. A cork stopper also prevents heat transfer by conduction.

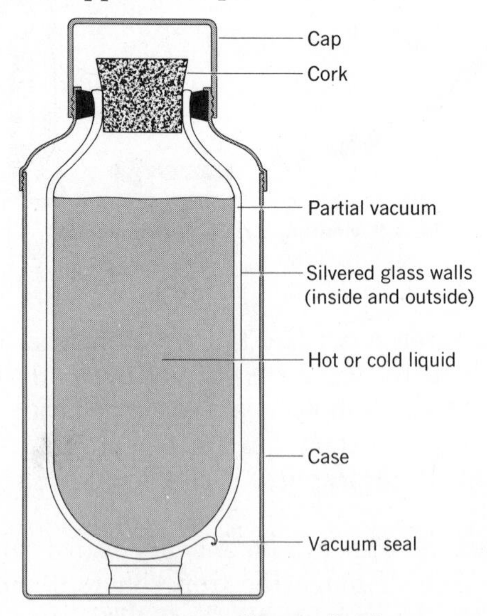

Fig. 3–10. A thermos bottle.

The inner glass walls are silvered to reflect radiant heat back into the liquid, thereby minimizing heat loss by radiation. Thus, a hot liquid remains hot because heat is lost very slowly. A cold liquid remains cold in thermos bottles because outside heat can enter only very slowly by conduction, convection, or radiation.

THE GREENHOUSE EFFECT IN THE ATMOSPHERE

We noted before that visible and ultraviolet light rays are absorbed by land and water and are transformed into heat energy. Then the heat energy is transferred to the atmosphere. In addition to this source of atmospheric heat, there is another. As visible and ultraviolet light rays travel through the water vapor and carbon dioxide present in the air, these gases also absorb the rays and transform them into heat energy. This source of heat adds to the warmth of the atmosphere.

At all times, the heat energy from the land, water, and atmosphere tends to radiate into space. This process is greater at night than during the day. As this process goes on at night, the earth becomes cooler and the temperature falls. However, not all of the heat energy reaches space because the heat is reflected back downward by the water vapor and carbon dioxide in the air. In other words, these two gases not only absorb rays and transform them into heat, but they also trap heat in the atmosphere.

The trapping of heat energy by water vapor and carbon dioxide in the atmosphere is known as the *greenhouse effect.* This effect is best illustrated by the greenhouses used by farmers and gardeners (Fig. 3–11). The glass roof of a greenhouse allows most of the solar radiation to

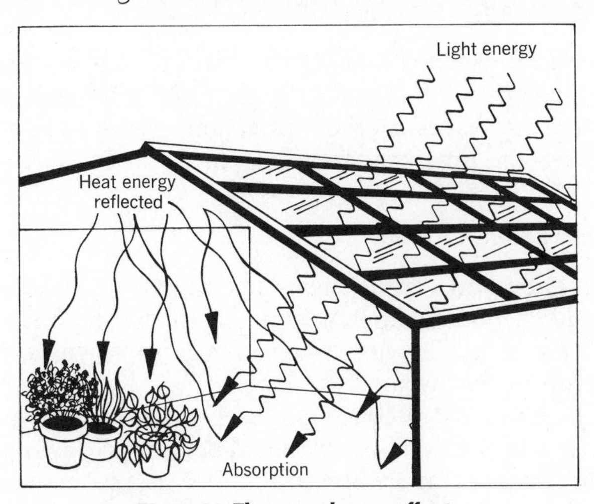

Fig. 3–11. The greenhouse effect.

pass into the greenhouse quite readily. The solar radiation is absorbed by objects inside the greenhouse. The radiation is thus changed into heat energy. The heated objects, in turn, radiate their heat in all directions. However, the glass roof of the greenhouse now prevents the passage of these radiations to the outside. Instead, the radiations remain trapped within the greenhouse.

In the atmosphere, carbon dioxide and water vapor act somewhat like the glass roof in a greenhouse. These gases allow most of the radiation to pass downward through them but, at night, prevent the escape of large amounts of heat energy from the atmosphere into outer space. During cloudy nights, the greenhouse effect is aided by the clouds which, like the carbon dioxide and water vapor, reflect a large portion of the escaping heat energy back to earth (Fig. 3–12).

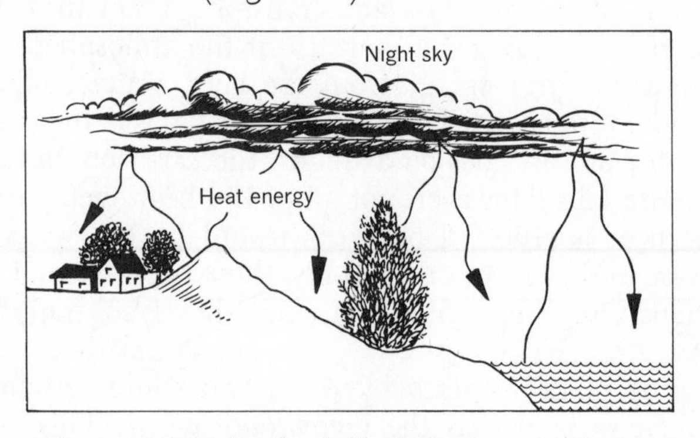

Fig. 3–12. At night, clouds block the escape of heat.

VARIATIONS IN AIR TEMPERATURE

In addition to the factors we have discussed, a number of other factors affect the temperature of the air at a particular time and place. Thus, air temperature may vary with the contraction or expansion of air masses, the time of day, the time of year, geographic location, and altitude.

Contraction and Expansion of Air

The contraction and expansion of large masses of air affect the temperature of the air immediately within the air masses. Such changes in temperature are especially noticeable in regions where air masses are moving upward or downward.

When air contracts, it becomes hotter. For example, if you have ever filled a bicycle tire with air, using a hand-held bicycle pump, you know that the barrel of the pump becomes hotter as you continue to force air into the tire. This is because the molecules of air entering the barrel are pressed together, or compressed, by the downward movement of the plunger. As the molecules of air are pushed together, the heat energy of the air inside the barrel increases. You feel this heat with your hand.

When air expands, on the other hand, it becomes cooler. You can feel this effect if you hold your hand in a stream of air escaping from an inflated bicycle tire. When the air was pumped into a tire, the air was compressed. When this air escapes from the tire, the molecules of air move rapidly away from each other. That is, the volume of the air that had been compressed increases. And as the distance between the molecules increases, the heat energy contained in the air decreases. Therefore, the escaping air feels cool as it blows against your hand.

The same kind of heating and cooling effect takes place on a gigantic scale in the atmosphere. When a current of air rises to higher levels in the atmosphere, the atmospheric pressure surrounding the mass of rising air decreases. This allows the mass of rising air to expand. As the air expands, it becomes cooler. If the mass of air does not contain any moisture, it will cool at a rate of about 1°C for every 100 meters of altitude it gains.

The opposite effect occurs when a mass of air sinks towards the earth. As the mass of air sinks to a lower altitude, the increasing atmospheric pressure compresses the mass of air. As the air is compressed, it warms up. If the mass of air does not contain moisture, it will heat up at a rate of about 1°C for every 100 meters of altitude it loses.

The heating and cooling of sinking and rising masses of air has a very important effect on the weather. This effect is described in Chapter 6.

Effect of Day and Night

The earth receives its greatest amount of heat during the daylight hours. The typical rise and fall in the daily air temperature is shown in Fig. 3–13, page 52. The air temperature begins to rise at sunrise. At 12 noon, when the sun is at its highest point in the sky, the temperature of the air is still increasing. The hottest time of the day usually occurs in the midafternoon between about 2 P.M. and 4 P.M. because the earth gains more heat than it loses during the early afternoon hours.

In the late afternoon, when the sun is much lower in the sky, the earth begins to lose the heat it has accumulated during the day. The temperature of the air begins to fall and continues to drop through the night, reaching its lowest point just before sunrise. At times, changes in the weather will affect the curve. Instead of temperatures rising at sunrise, a weather change might cause the temperatures to drop throughout the day (see the right end of Fig. 3–13).

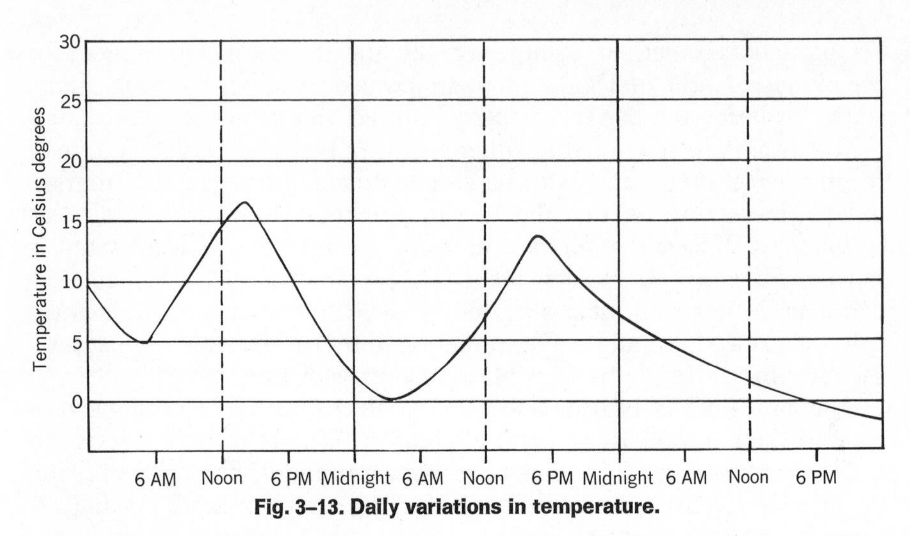

Fig. 3–13. Daily variations in temperature.

Effect of the Seasons

As we all know, winters are colder than summers. The temperature variations we experience from one season to the next occur because the axis of the earth is always tilted at an angle of $23\frac{1}{2}$ degrees to the orbit followed by the earth as it travels around the sun (Fig. 3–14).

During the summer, the North Pole is tilted toward the sun. The solar radiation is then concentrated over the Northern Hemisphere.

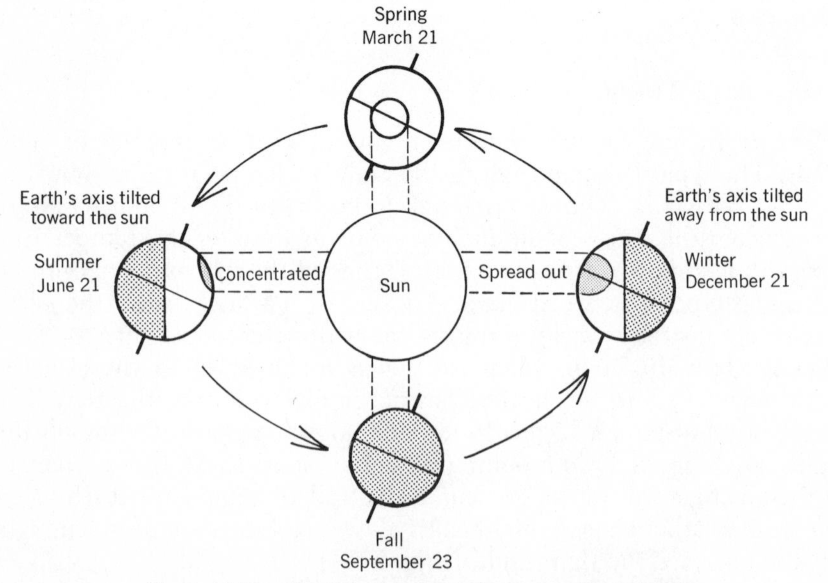

Fig. 3–14. The tilt of the earth's axis causes the seasons.

During the winter, the North Pole is tilted away from the sun, and the radiation strikes the Northern Hemisphere at an angle. Because the solar radiation is spread out over a larger area, it is less concentrated. Thus, any given region in the Northern Hemisphere is heated less strongly in the winter than in the summer.

When the Northern Hemisphere is tilted away from the sun in winter, sunlight reaches this part of the earth for fewer hours each day. Fewer hours of daylight means that less solar radiation reaches the earth's surface. This fact, combined with the angle of radiation, explains why winters in the Northern Hemisphere are colder than summers. In the Southern Hemisphere, for the same reasons, the seasons are exactly reversed.

At the beginning of spring and fall, the axis of the earth is not tilted either toward or away from the sun. (The axis is tilted in another direction.) Therefore, in the early spring and early fall, the solar radiation is divided about equally between the Northern Hemisphere and the Southern Hemisphere. Also, at these two times, days and nights are almost equal in length. Spring and fall temperatures in both hemispheres, therefore, are not as high as summer temperatures or as low as winter temperatures.

Effect of Geographic Location

In the summer, people living along the seashore usually enjoy cooler weather than people living inland. In the winter, people living along the seashore usually enjoy warmer weather than people living inland. It is the nearness of the ocean that makes the difference in temperature.

As you know, water absorbs and releases heat more slowly than does land. Thus, the ocean heats up slowly during the summer and cools off slowly during the winter. In midsummer, the temperature of the Atlantic Ocean near New York, New Jersey, and Connecticut reaches a high of about 20°C. During the day, the temperature of nearby land areas is often higher than 28°C. On summer days, then, the air over the ocean is usually cooler than the air over the land.

On hot summer days, when the air temperature several kilometers inland is about 35°C, the air temperature along the coast is often 5°C cooler. We could say that the ocean acts as a huge air conditioner in the summer, cooling the air along the coast. In the winter, the reverse is true—the ocean releases heat and acts as a huge radiator, heating the land along the coast. In the middle latitudes, when the land is frozen solid and the air temperature often drops below freezing, the ocean temperature may be approximately 10°C. The ocean then warms the air above it. The warmed air moves over nearby land areas. As a result, the air temperature over coastal regions is often several degrees warmer than the air temperature inland.

On a large scale, the heat energy stored in the ocean is distributed over the earth in several different ways. Large masses of air warmed by the ocean drift across the continents and give up their heat to the land. Ocean currents, such as the Gulf Stream, transport huge volumes of warm water northward from the Caribbean Sea and the Gulf of Mexico. The warm waters of the Gulf Stream help to produce mild winters in northerly regions such as Scandinavia and the British Isles.

Effect of Altitude

As one travels away from the surface of the earth, the temperature decreases as one approaches the boundary of the troposphere. The temperature drops with increasing altitude because the earth's surface, which is the major source of heat for the atmosphere, is farther away, and because the thinner air at high altitudes contains less water vapor, which is a heat absorber.

Picture a string of thermometers placed 300 meters apart, from ground level to the top of the troposphere. Each thermometer reads 2°C less than the thermometer placed 300 meters below it. If the thermometer on the ground reads 15°C, the thermometer 300 meters above it will read 13°C. The next thermometer in line will read 13°C−2°C, or 11°C, and so on (Fig. 3–15).

As Fig. 3–15 suggests, however, sometimes the air temperature decreases for several hundred meters and then begins to increase again. Such a condition of inverted (upside-down) temperature is called an *inversion*.

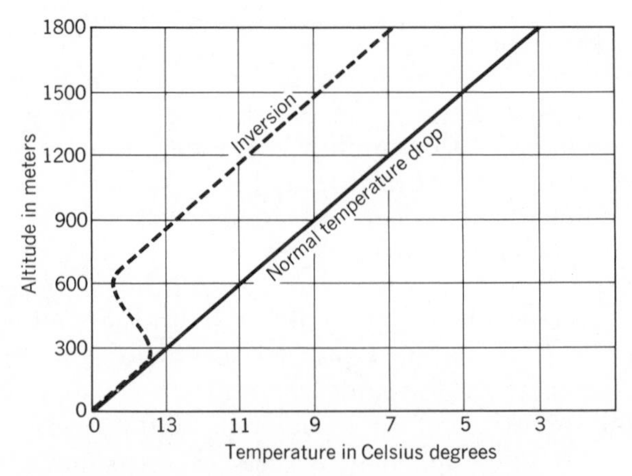

Fig. 3–15. Temperature changes with altitude.

TEMPERATURE INVERSIONS AND AIR POLLUTION

When a temperature inversion occurs, warm air is trapped near the surface of the earth. The warm air cannot rise because it is held down by a blanket of warmer air above. Where inversions occur, the air may be warmer than usual, but, ordinarily, it presents no particular threat to human health.

We have noted before that the air over large cities and industrial areas is generally warmer than the surrounding air and usually contains pollutants such as exhaust gases from burned fuels. In the absence of an inversion, such polluted air rises, and the pollutants in it are swept away by the winds at higher altitudes. When an inversion occurs, however, polluted surface air cannot rise. Instead, it becomes more polluted as more exhausts are added to it.

In this condition, the polluted air remains close to the surface of the ground, where it is continuously subjected to solar radiation. The radiation causes numerous chemical reactions to take place among the molecules of air pollutants. The result is called *smog*. Smog is a mixture of fog, smoke, and chemical products. Smog irritates the eyes and lungs and causes many people to become ill—some of them seriously. Smog occurs readily in certain cities, such as Los Angeles, California, and London, England, because the geography of these cities—along with the presence of polluted air—provides conditions favorable for the formation of atmospheric inversions.

Looking Back

Radiation from the sun heats the earth's atmosphere indirectly. In passing through the atmosphere, part of the radiation is reflected back into space by dust particles and gas particles. The same particles also absorb some of the radiation. However, most of the radiation passes through the air and reaches the earth's surface. The surface reflects some radiation and absorbs the rest. The absorbed radiation is changed into heat and then transferred to the atmosphere.

Polluted air contains more particles than does clean air; therefore, polluted air absorbs more radiation than does clean air. As a result, regions having polluted air receive less radiation from the sun than do other regions. When a temperature inversion occurs in the atmosphere, the action of radiation on polluted air causes harmful smog.

Looking Ahead

Fortunately for living things, polluted air over a region is usually swept away by moving air. We will study the movements of air next.

Multiple-Choice Questions

1. Of all the sun's radiations that enter the earth's atmosphere, the amount that reaches the surface of the earth is about
   a. 10% b. 33% c. 66% d. 98%
2. Which of the following land areas best absorbs the sun's radiations?
   a. farmland b. a sandy beach c. a snowfield d. a desert
3. When the sun is directly over a large body of water, the amount of the sun's radiations that the body of water will reflect back into the atmosphere is about
   a. 3% b. 40% c. 80% d. 97%
4. Which of the following factors is *least* important in distributing heat throughout the ocean?
   a. waves
   b. currents
   c. the transparency of the water
   d. the flow of rivers into the ocean
5. The greatest variety of living things can be found
   a. near the equator
   b. near the North Pole
   c. near the South Pole
   d. in temperate zones
6. Gases in the atmosphere that best absorb the sun's radiations are
   a. carbon dioxide and oxygen
   b. carbon dioxide and water vapor
   c. nitrogen and water vapor
   d. nitrogen and carbon dioxide
7. The blue color of the sky is caused primarily by the
   a. absorption of sunlight by particles in the atmosphere
   b. reflection of sunlight by the ionosphere
   c. reflection of sunlight from the ocean
   d. reflection of sunlight from particles in the atmosphere
8. Compared to other parts of the earth, the equatorial region is heated the most by the sun's radiations because the equator
   a. is closer to the sun
   b. has very large land masses along it
   c. has very large sea areas along it
   d. receives the sun's most direct rays
9. The increased motion of molecules that have absorbed part of the sun's radiations is measured in terms of
   a. radiation b. heat c. convection currents d. evaporation
10. Solids are better conductors of heat than gases or liquids because the molecules in solids are
    a. closer together
    b. opaque to radiations
    c. heavier than the molecules in gases or liquids
    d. in more rapid motion
11. The sun transfers its heat to other objects by
    a. conduction b. convection c. radiation d. expansion
12. When a quantity of air is heated, it expands because the gases in the air
    a. become lighter
    b. move faster
    c. decompose
    d. exert less pressure on each other

13. Heat is transferred from the surface of the earth to high altitudes by means of
    a. convection currents
    b. heat radiation
    c. winds
    d. cloud reflections
14. The method by which gases in the atmosphere trap the heat energy given off by the earth is known as the
    a. blocking effect
    b. heat sink
    c. greenhouse effect
    d. radiation trap
15. As a quantity of air expands, it becomes
    a. cooler b. warmer c. compressed d. denser
16. The coldest part of the day is usually around
    a. sunrise b. sunset c. midnight d. 2 A.M.
17. Strong winds have a beneficial effect on
    a. polluted surface air
    b. the ocean
    c. the seasons
    d. deep polluted water
18. As an airplane climbs into the sky, a thermometer in the airplane recording the outside air temperature should show that the air temperature decreases in °C at a rate of
    a. 3° per 300 meters
    b. 5° per 1000 meters
    c. 5° per 300 meters
    d. 15° per 300 meters

Modified True-False Questions

1. The types of electromagnetic radiation that are most important in heating the earth are visible light and *ultraviolet* light.
2. Water is usually heated to a much greater depth than land because water is *less dense.*
3. On a hot summer day, heat may penetrate up to several *meters* below the surface of your school yard.
4. Water vapor, *nitrogen,* and dust in the atmosphere help heat the atmosphere because they absorb part of the sun's radiations.
5. The great difference between summer temperatures and winter temperatures in most places over the earth is determined largely by the *angle* at which the sun's rays strike the earth at different times of the year.
6. The process by which heat travels from one part of a solid object to another part of the object is called *conduction.*
7. Cold air that touches the heated earth during the day is warmed by *convection.*
8. Daily air temperatures usually reach a peak at about *12:00 noon.*

Increases—Decreases—Remains the Same

1. As the depth of water increases, the amount of sunlight that reaches greater depths
   increases, decreases, remains the same
2. As the sun gets lower in the sky, the amount of sunlight that is reflected from the earth's surface
   increases, decreases, remains the same

3. As objects get darker and rougher, the amount of sunlight absorbed
   increases, decreases, remains the same
4. As air moves closer to the earth's surface, the likelihood of its being heated by conduction
   increases, decreases, remains the same
5. As the amounts of carbon dioxide and water vapor in the air increase, the amount of escaping heat radiation trapped by the atmosphere
   increases, decreases, remains the same
6. As a volume of rising air expands, its temperature
   increases, decreases, remains the same
7. From season to season, the amount of sunlight given off by the sun
   increases, decreases, remains the same
8. With increasing altitude, the temperature in the troposphere normally
   increases, decreases, remains the same
9. When a temperature inversion occurs, the likelihood of smog
   increases, decreases, remains the same

Thought Questions

1. Of all the sun's radiations that enter the earth's atmosphere, only two-thirds of those radiations reach the surface of the earth. Explain.
2. Give two reasons why large bodies of water heat up more slowly than land areas.
3. Name the three methods by which heat may be transferred through solid, liquid, and gaseous substances, and briefly describe each method.
4. How might the "greenhouse effect" account for the fact that an aerosol container stored in the trunk or glove compartment of an automobile explodes on a hot summer day.
5. Explain why containers that are filled with a gas under pressure, such as carbon-dioxide fire extinguishers and aerosol containers, get cold when the compressed gases are discharged from the containers.
6. Two boys live next door to each other. Outside their bedroom windows they have installed thermometers. Both thermometers are accurate. At the same moment, both boys read their thermometers. One thermometer reads 30°C; the other thermometer reads 35°C. How might you account for the difference in readings?

CHAPTER 4
WHAT CAUSES WIND?

When you have completed this chapter, you should be able to:

1. *Explain* the origin of air currents and winds.
2. *Account* for the change of direction of a wind.
3. *Describe* the major wind systems of the world.
4. *Distinguish* between sea breezes, land breezes, mountain breezes, valley breezes, and monsoons.
5. *Discuss* the formation of rotating wind systems.
6. *Relate* rotating wind systems to the weather.

In the laboratory experience that follows, you will investigate air currents.

Laboratory Experience

HOW CAN WE STUDY AIR CURRENTS?

A. Set up the candle and glass chimneys as shown in Fig. 4–1, page 60. Light the candle, and close the sliding glass front.
   1. Explain why the candle continues to burn even in a closed box.
   2. Hold your hands about 15 centimeters above the glass chimneys. What differences do you feel?

B. Hold a piece of lighted smoke-paper just above one of the chimney openings for 5 to 10 seconds. Do the same at the other chimney opening.
   3. What path does the smoke follow?
   4. Draw a diagram of the box in your notebook, and show the path followed by the smoke by means of arrows.

C. Blow out the candle. Place the candle in the opposite end of the box. Repeat steps *A* and *B* above.
   5. What is the path followed by the smoke now? Draw another diagram of the box and, by means of arrows, show the path followed by the smoke now.

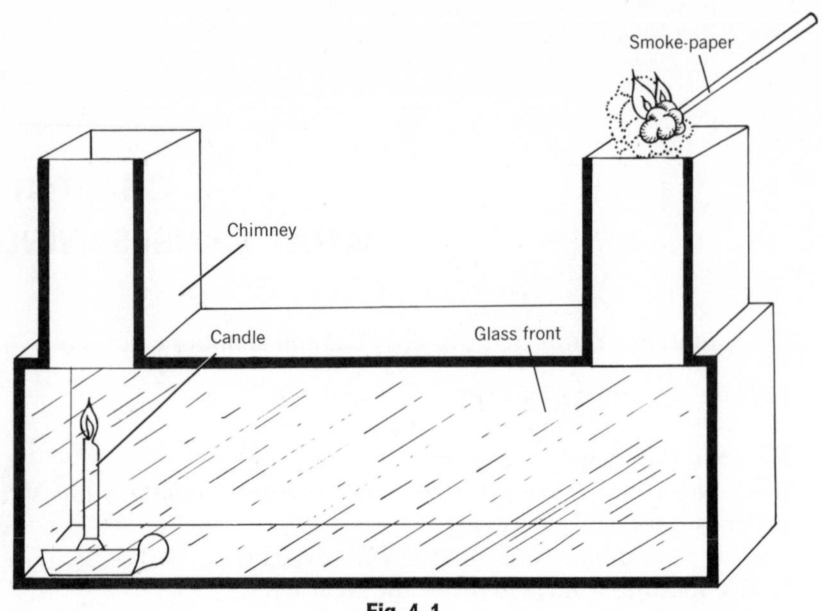

Fig. 4–1.

6. What path do you think the air flowing through the box would follow if no candle were burning? You can check your answer by repeating the experiment but without lighting the candle.

Introduction

The rotation (spinning) of the earth and convection currents in the atmosphere cause masses of air to move in different, yet regular, directions. A mass of air that moves parallel to the surface of the earth is called a *wind*. A mass of air that moves toward or away from the surface of the earth (that is, up or down) is called an *air current*. Winds and air currents are important because they transport large quantities of heat and moisture from one part of the atmosphere to other parts of the atmosphere.

For many city dwellers, to whom air pollution is an ever-present threat, winds carry away polluted air and bring in fresh, clean air. If the air were to stop moving, carbon dioxide and other harmful gases would accumulate near the surface of the earth, and life on the earth would be seriously threatened. However, differences in temperature, pressure, and humidity, as they exist in the atmosphere, are continually setting air in motion. We will now study the causes of the almost horizontal movement of air on the surface of the earth that we call wind.

HOW WINDS ARE MEASURED

Winds, although invisible, have definite characteristics. Identifying and measuring the characteristics of winds help us understand them and their relation to weather. Among the most important characteristics of winds are direction and speed.

Identifying Wind Direction

The instrument most often used to indicate the direction of the wind is the *wind vane*. Wind vanes are a common sight on top of weather stations, many church steeples, and other tall structures. Wind vanes (or *weather vanes*, as they are sometimes called) are usually arrow-shaped devices with extra-large tails. The vane is mounted so that it turns easily. When the wind blows, it pushes against the large tail surface until the head of the arrow points in the direction *from which* the wind is blowing (Fig. 4–2).

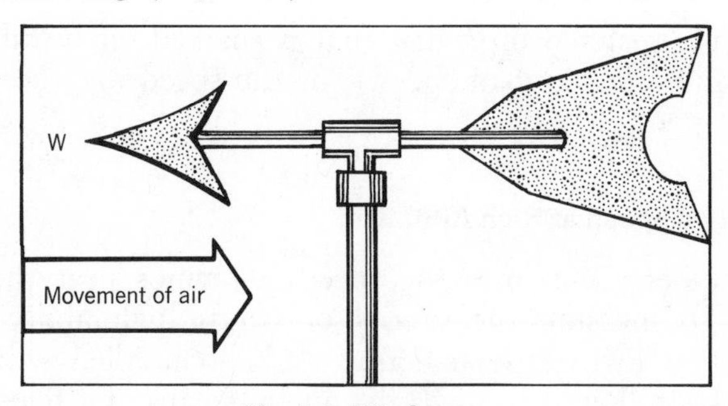

Fig. 4–2. Wind vane.

Because the wind vane of a weather station is usually located quite high above the ground, the wind vane is connected electrically to an indicating instrument inside the weather station. The movements of the wind vane are usually transmitted to a pen which records the direction of the wind on a chart moving beneath the pen. In this way, the meteorologist can see the direction from which the wind is blowing without going outside.

Measuring Wind Speed Near the Ground

Wind speed is measured by an instrument called an *anemometer* (Fig. 4–3, page 62). An anemometer consists of three or more small cups mounted on arms that are connected to the same shaft. The insides of the cups catch the wind, while the curved outsides of the cups pass through the air quite easily. The force of the wind pushing against the insides of the cups causes the shaft to rotate. The faster the wind blows, the faster the cups cause the shaft to rotate. The speed at which the

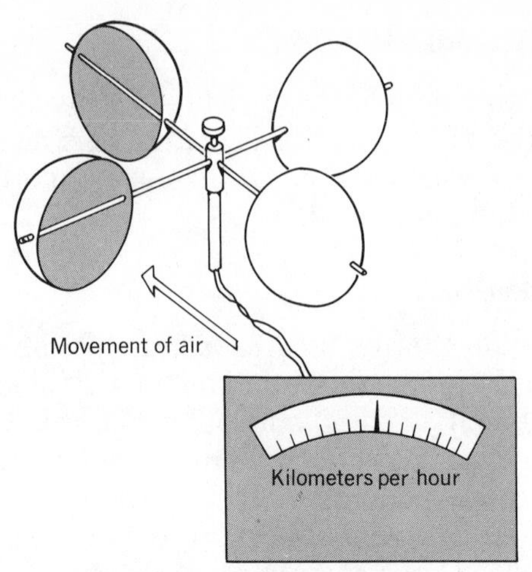

Fig. 4–3. An anemometer.

shaft turns is registered on a dial that is marked off in kilometers per hour (or some other unit of speed), or the speed may be recorded on a chart by a pen.

Measuring Wind Speed at High Altitudes

An anemometer measures the speeds of winds near the surface of the earth. To measure the speeds of winds high above the earth's surface, meteorologists use balloons. A balloon filled with helium is released and is followed through the air by means of a telescope. Markings on the telescope mounting indicate the angle and direction in which the telescope is pointing. The speed of the wind can then be calculated from the angle of the telescope. When winds are light, the angle between the telescope and the surface of the earth is wide. The stronger the winds, the smaller, or sharper, that angle becomes (Fig. 4–4).

Balloons are fairly accurate and are inexpensive; however, they cannot be followed visually through clouds or over great distances. For such purposes, radar is used to track the balloons.

Balloons that carry instruments are also sent aloft regularly. The instruments measure the temperature, humidity, and pressure of the air at high altitudes. The package of instruments is called a *radiosonde.* A tiny radio transmitter that is part of the radiosonde sends these measurements back to earth.

CAUSE OF WINDS

In Chapter 3, we described how solar radiation heats the earth. As you know, some parts of the surface of the earth absorb more heat

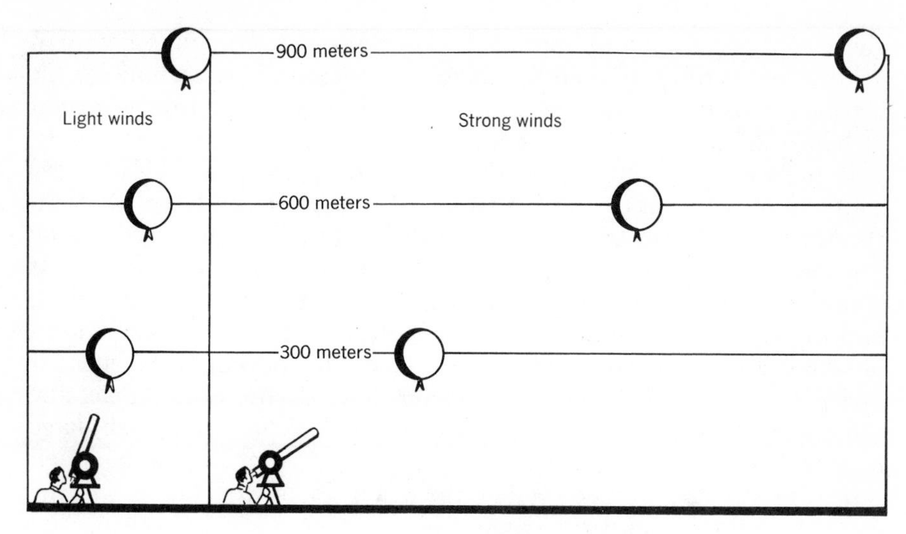

Fig. 4–4. Weather balloons.

than do other parts of the surface. Because the earth's surface is heated unequally, the atmosphere, which receives most of its heat from the surface, is also heated unequally. As a result, air in different sections of the atmosphere differs in density. These differences in air density, in turn, result in differences in atmospheric pressure. The chief cause of winds and air currents is these differences in atmospheric pressure.

Convection Cells

A simple experiment, such as the one you performed in the laboratory, shows how unequal heating of the earth results in movements of the atmosphere. The circulation of air into and out of the box is an example of a convection current, which was described in Chapter 3, pages 46–47.

Another example of a convection current is the circulation of air in a closed room, which was also described in Chapter 3. In the room, the air follows a circular path. The heated air rises from a radiator, flows across the ceiling to the far side of the room, cools, settles to the floor, and then flows along the floor to the radiator, where the air is heated again. This circular movement of air by means of convection currents is called a *convection cell.*

The part of the convection cell in which the air is warm contains air molecules that have been driven apart. As you know, a given volume of warm air contains fewer molecules than does an equal volume of cooler air and is, therefore, less dense. This volume of air becomes a region of low pressure. The part of the convection cell in which the air is cool contains air molecules that have been pushed together. A given volume of cool air contains more molecules than does an equal volume of warmer air and is, therefore, denser. This volume of air becomes a region of high pressure. Air will always flow from a region of high pressure to a region of low pressure.

If the earth did not rotate, the wind would circulate in two great convection cells, one in the Northern Hemisphere and the other in the Southern Hemisphere. At the equator, heat energy absorbed by the earth warms the air above the ground. The warmed air becomes less dense. As a result, the atmospheric pressure of the warmed air decreases, and the equator becomes a region of low-pressure air. The warm mass of low-pressure air then rises to the top of the troposphere, where it divides into two parts, one part flowing towards the South Pole, the other part flowing towards the North Pole. When two such large masses of air travel high in the troposphere, they gradually lose their heat and become denser. When these masses of cool air reach the poles, they flow toward the ground.

In the Northern Hemisphere, the mass of cold air then flows south toward the equator, gradually absorbing heat from the ground as it moves south. When the air reaches the equator, it is warmed and rises into the atmosphere again. In the Southern Hemisphere, the same thing happens, except that the mass of cold air flows north to the equator.

Thus, if the earth did *not* rotate, ground winds would always blow from the poles towards the equator, and high-altitude winds would always blow from the equator to the poles (Fig. 4–5).

A simple system of winds such as this does not actually exist because the earth *is* rotating. For this reason, the winds are deflected, or turned away, from their north-south paths, and the simple convection cells we have described become more complicated.

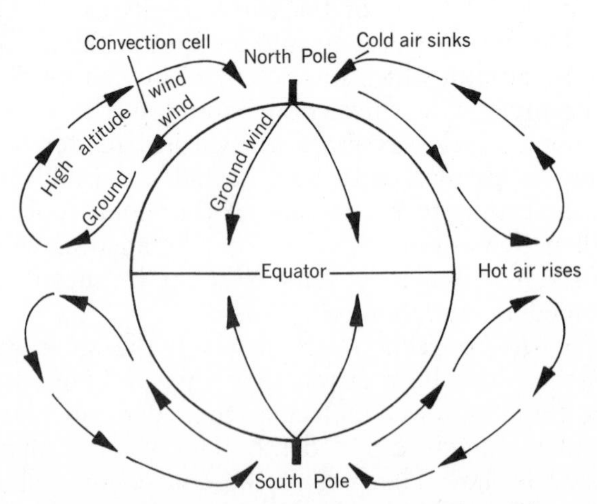

Fig. 4–5. Movement of air on a nonrotating earth.

Rotation of the Earth

A simple experiment will show you how winds are deflected by the rotation of the earth. You will need a globe of the earth mounted so that you can spin the globe. If you do not have a globe, you can make a substitute using a large rubber ball, a small saucer, and several marbles. Turn the saucer upside down. Place the marbles inside the rim of the saucer and place the ball on the marbles. The weight of the ball will push the marbles against the rim of the saucer. The marbles, in turn, will support the ball and allow it to spin quite freely.

When the globe (or ball) is stationary, drops of water falling on the top of the globe (the North Pole) will run straight down the globe (indicated in Fig. 4–6 by the dotted line). The paths followed by the drops are similar to the paths that would be followed by the surface winds in the Northern Hemisphere if the earth did not rotate.

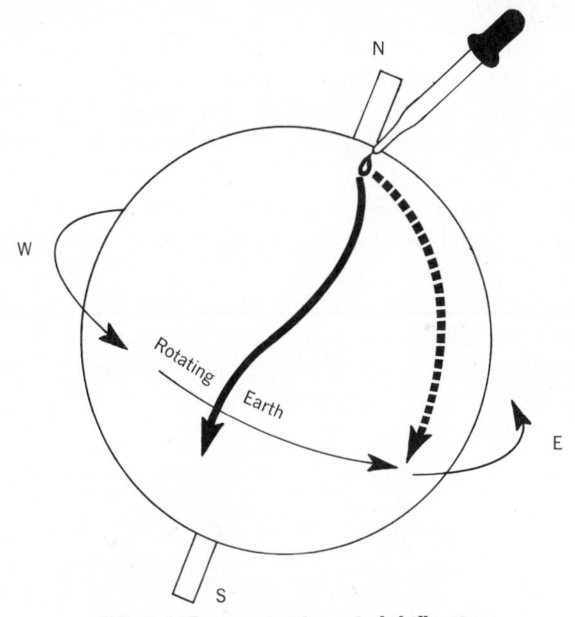

Fig. 4–6. Demonstrating wind deflection.

Now slowly spin the globe counterclockwise (moving the side near you from left to right), and again let drops of water fall on the top of the globe. Observe the path left by the water. You will see that the path curves in a direction opposite to the rotation of the globe (shown by the heavy solid line in Fig. 4–6).

Air moving over the surface of the earth behaves in much the same way. Fig. 4–6 illustrates in a simplified way what happens to the winds as they move along the surface of the rotating earth. As the earth rotates from west to east, the winds in the Northern Hemisphere do not follow direct north-south paths. Instead, the winds curve, or are deflected, towards the west. In the Southern Hemisphere, winds curve in the opposite direction.

A rule that helps us remember the direction toward which surface winds are deflected is called *Ferrel's Law.* This law states: In the Northern Hemisphere, winds are deflected to the right of their original path; in the Southern Hemisphere, winds are deflected to the left of their original path. Thus, in relation to the earth's surface in the Northern Hemisphere, air moving southward is deflected to the right of its path, or southwestward. In the Southern Hemisphere, air moving northward is deflected to the left of its path, or northwestward.

WIND SYSTEMS OF THE WORLD

The major wind systems existing in the earth's atmosphere are shown in Fig. 4–7. Notice that the wind systems in each hemisphere consist of three convection cells that encircle the earth. One cell circulates air between the equator and about 30° latitude, a second cell circulates air between 30° and about 60° latitude, and a third cell circulates air between 60° latitude and the pole. In addition, another convection cell circulates air high in the troposphere between the equator and the pole.

Each hemisphere has three major convection cells (instead of the single cell we have described earlier in this chapter) because of the complicated way in which the atmosphere is influenced by differences

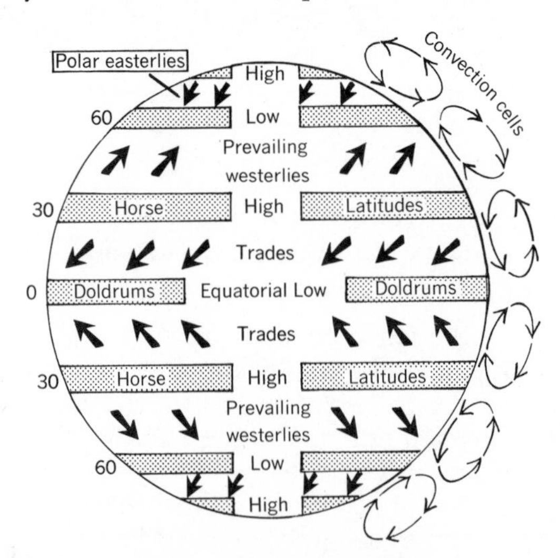

Fig. 4–7. Major wind systems.

in air temperature and pressure, and because of the rotation of the earth. These factors have resulted in the following major wind systems: (1) the *trade winds,* (2) the *prevailing westerlies,* and (3) the *polar easterlies.* The formation of these different wind systems depends upon the pressure patterns that develop in the *doldrums* and in the *horse latitudes.*

Doldrums

The region around the equator is known as the doldrums. In the doldrums, the heated air rises straight into the atmosphere, and there is little horizontal air movement. The heating of this region by the sun can be compared to the heating of the air around the candle flame in your laboratory experience. The warm air rising into the atmosphere creates a region of low-pressure air (the equatorial low in Fig. 4–7) called a *low-pressure belt.*

Horse Latitudes

The air heated at the equator slowly cools as it rises higher into the atmosphere. Many kilometers above the earth, this air current separates into two parts, one part moving north and the other part moving south. We will concentrate on the air moving north.

As the air moves northward, it continues to cool and, because of the rotation of the earth, the air is deflected toward the east. At about 30° N latitude, the air has cooled and its density has increased to the point where the air begins to sink toward the earth again. As the air sinks, it also warms up a bit.

The descending current of air forms a region of high-pressure air known as the horse latitudes. In Fig. 4–7, this is designated as a *high* at 30° latitude. Since the direction of the descending air is almost straight down, the horse latitudes represent a region of light winds and frequent calms. The horse latitudes are named from the days when sailing ships became becalmed and remained in these latitudes for weeks at a time. Occasionally, horses being transported from Europe to America on these ships were thrown overboard in order to conserve drinking water.

Trade Winds and Prevailing Westerlies

The air descending in the horse latitudes separates into two parts. One part moves toward the equator, and the other part moves toward the nearest pole. In each case, the air moves from a high-pressure region, the horse latitudes, to a low-pressure region located to the north or south of the horse latitudes.

The winds blowing toward the equator are called the trade winds. In the Northern Hemisphere, these winds are also called the *northeast trades* because they appear to be blowing from the northeast.

The winds that blow from the horse latitudes toward the pole are called the prevailing westerlies. In the Northern Hemisphere, these winds, blowing northward, appear to come from the southwest. In the Southern Hemisphere, the winds that blow southward from the horse latitudes appear to blow from the northwest. As they blow farther away from the horse latitudes, the prevailing westerlies become stronger. The open seas near the southern tip of South America (40° S latitude) were often called the "roaring forties" by sailors because of the force with which the winds blow there.

Polar Easterlies

The dense, cold air flowing from the polar regions produces wind belts called the polar easterlies. These winds make up part of the convection cell which, in the Northern Hemisphere, extends from about 60° N latitude to the North Pole. In the Northern Hemisphere, the polar easterlies flow toward the southwest and meet the prevailing westerlies in the region of northern Canada. The boundary between these two flowing air masses shifts continually northward and southward. These movements have an important effect on the weather in the United States, as will be described in Chapter 6.

LOCAL WINDS

Any area of the world is affected both by the major wind belt in which the area is located and by local winds such as *sea breezes, land breezes, monsoons, valley breezes,* and *mountain breezes.*

Sea Breezes

If you live near the ocean or the Great Lakes, you are probably familiar with the breezes that blow off the water many months of the year. These breezes are caused by the unequal heating of the land and the adjacent body of water.

We mentioned in Chapter 3 that land heats up much more quickly than does a body of water. For example, on hot summer days, a beach heats up much more rapidly than does the water. Therefore, the air over the beach becomes much hotter than the air over the water.

Because the air over the beach is hotter than the air over the water, a low-pressure area forms over the beach. Over the water, where the air is cooler and therefore denser, a high-pressure area forms. Under these conditions, the cool, dense air over the water flows towards the land, displacing the warm, less dense air over the beach.

The movement of cool ocean air toward the land is called a sea breeze (Fig. 4–8*a*). A sea breeze usually begins blowing in the late morning (about 10 A.M.) and continues until about sunset. Sea breezes off the ocean can be felt up to about 25 kilometers inland. Around the Great Lakes in summer, a lake breeze develops that can often be felt about 5 kilometers inland.

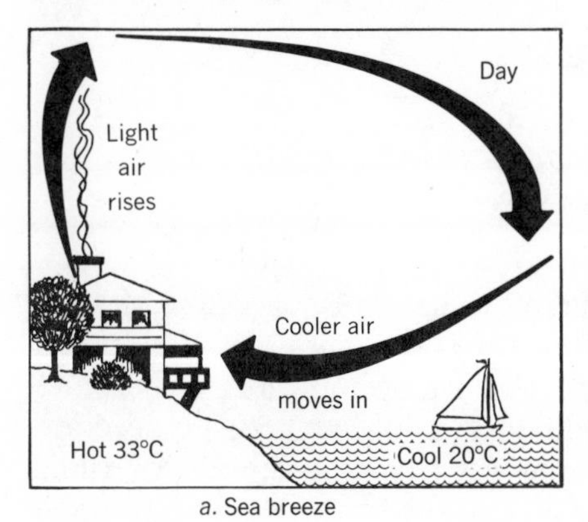

a. Sea breeze

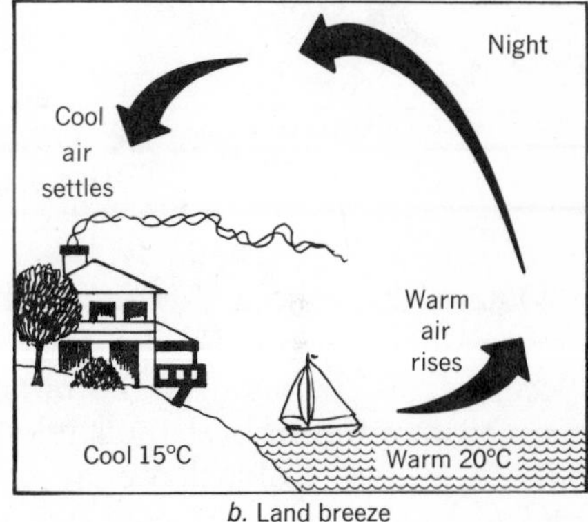

b. Land breeze

Fig. 4–8. Sea and land breezes.

Land Breezes

At night, the land cools faster than does the water. The air over the land becomes denser than the air over the water, and the air flows towards the ocean. This breeze that blows at night from the land to the sea is called a land breeze (Fig. 4–8*b*). The land breeze blows in the opposite direction to the sea breeze that blows during the day. Land breezes are usually much milder than sea breezes.

Monsoons

The famous monsoons of India are basically land and sea breezes, but on a much larger scale. In the summer, the interior of India becomes much hotter than the neighboring Indian Ocean. The interior of India becomes a region of low pressure.

The air over the Indian Ocean, being cooler than the air over India, becomes a region of high pressure. The denser cool air over the ocean moves towards the warmer land, producing a steady wind called the *summer monsoon* (Fig. 4–9*a*, page 70). Because the air carries with it a great deal of moisture, the summer monsoon brings with it heavy rainfalls. For this reason, the summer monsoon is also called the *wet monsoon.*

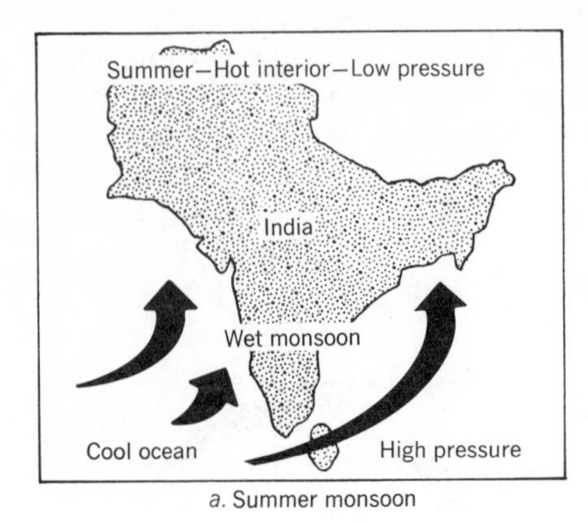

a. Summer monsoon

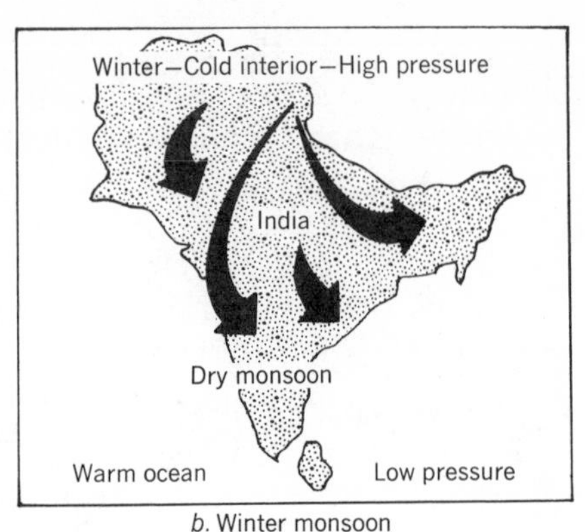

b. Winter monsoon

Fig. 4–9. Monsoons.

During the winter, as the interior of India cools, a region of high pressure develops inland. At the same time, the waters of the Indian Ocean warm the air over the ocean. The air over the ocean becomes warmer than the air over the land, and a region of low pressure develops over the ocean. Cold, dense air now moves from the interior of India toward the ocean. This cold air, which is also very dry, brings India a long period of cold, dry weather called the *winter monsoon*, or *dry monsoon* (Fig. 4–9*b*).

Sections of the United States, such as the central and eastern states, also experience a type of monsoon effect which plays an important part in the climate of these states. Throughout the year, air moving northward from the Gulf of Mexico brings warm, humid air to these states. However, from time to time, cold, dry air moving southward from Canada reverses this condition.

Valley and Mountain Breezes

In areas characterized by mountains and valleys, the sun heats the mountain slopes more rapidly than it heats the valleys. The air over the mountain slopes becomes warmer than the air in the valleys, and a convection cell develops. The heated air over the slopes rises into the atmosphere, and the cool, dense air in the valleys moves up the mountain slopes to replace it. The wind blowing up the side of a mountain from the valley below is called a valley breeze.

At night, the air on the mountain slopes cools more rapidly than does the air in the valleys. Cooling is more rapid on the slopes because the air at high altitudes contains less dust and moisture than the air in the valleys. The heat gained by the mountain slopes during the day is lost rapidly at night by radiation into the atmosphere. As the air over the mountain slopes becomes cooler, it also becomes denser than the air in the valleys. The cool, dense air on the mountaintops flows into the valleys. The movement of relatively cold, dense air into a valley from the mountain slope above is called a mountain breeze.

REVOLVING WIND SYSTEMS

Large masses of low-pressure and high-pressure air, hundreds or thousands of miles in diameter, drift slowly over the surface of the earth. The positions and shapes of these large masses of air, known as *high-pressure systems* and *low-pressure systems*, change continually. The masses of low-pressure air are called *cyclones*; the masses of high-pressure air are called *anticyclones*.

Cyclones

Within a low-pressure system, the air pressure is lowest at the center of the mass of air and highest along its outer edge. The higher-pressure air moves toward the area of lower pressure in the center of the air mass. If the earth did not rotate, the air would flow straight toward the center of the low-pressure system, as shown by the broken arrows in Fig. 4–10.

In the Northern Hemisphere, the earth's rotation causes the winds in a low-pressure system (shown by the solid black arrows in Fig. 4–10) to be deflected so that they spiral *toward* the center of the system in a *counterclockwise* direction. (In the Southern Hemisphere, these winds blow toward the center, but in a clockwise direction.) A low-pressure system in which winds rotate inward is called a cyclone.

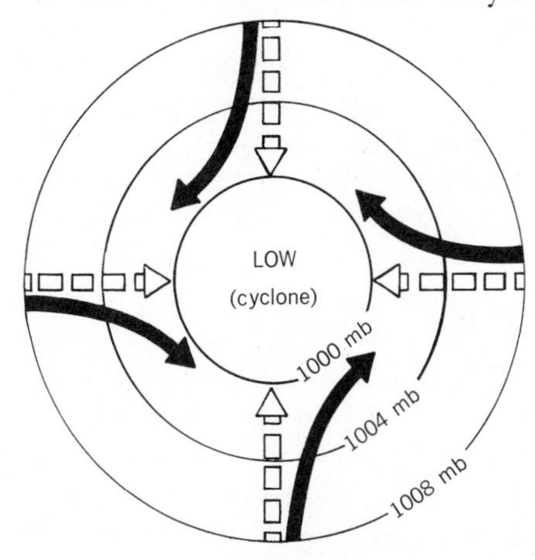

Fig. 4–10. Wind deflection in a cyclone.

Anticyclones

Within a high-pressure system, the air pressure is highest at the center of the air mass and lowest along the outer edge of the air mass. The air in the center of a high-pressure system, having a higher pressure, flows toward the outer edge of the air mass (Fig. 4–11).

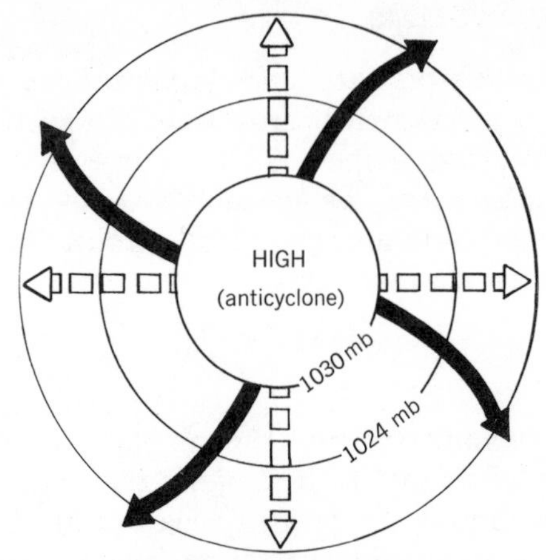

Fig. 4–11. Wind deflection in an anticyclone.

In the Northern Hemisphere, the rotation of the earth causes the winds in a high-pressure system to be deflected so that they spiral *outward* from the center in a *clockwise* direction. (In the Southern Hemisphere, these winds blow outward, but in a counterclockwise direction.) A high-pressure system in which winds rotate outward is called an anticyclone.

The movement of cyclones and anticyclones over the earth produces important changes in the weather in the places over which they pass. In general, cyclones bring stormy weather, and anticyclones bring clear or fair weather. The effect of these systems on the weather is discussed further in Chapter 6.

JET STREAMS

In the Northern Hemisphere, midway between the equator and the North Pole, usually 6 to 11 kilometers above the earth, we find swift-moving winds called *jet streams*. These winds travel in an easterly direction (Fig. 4–12). In winter, the jet streams are farther south than they are in summer. At one time, airplanes flying against these powerful winds were forced to stand still, or even to move backwards.

Jet streams were discovered during World War II, when B-29

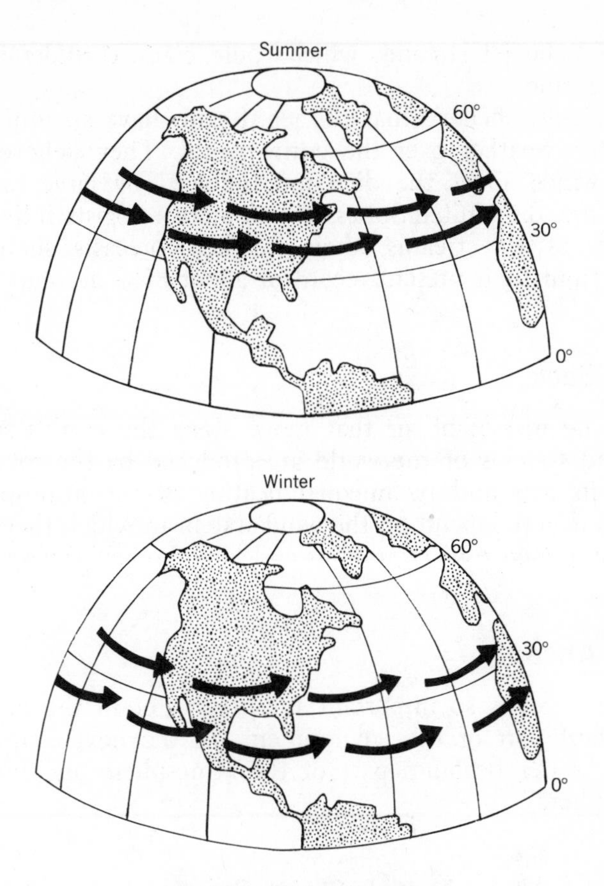

Fig. 4–12. The jet streams.

bombers on long-distance missions over the Pacific found that they were moving forward over the surface of the earth at about the same speed as a tramp steamer moving on the ocean. Their calculations indicated that they must be flying against a wind blowing nearly 480 kilometers per hour.

We now know that a typical jet stream is shaped somewhat like a large rectangular pipe. The pipe may be from 40 to 160 kilometers wide and more than a kilometer high. Although wind speeds of 640 kilometers per hour have been reported in the centers of jet streams, the usual wind speed ranges from 350 to 450 kilometers per hour.

Knowing the position and speed of a jet stream is important to airline pilots and weather forecasters. In winter, aircraft traveling from west to east may take advantage of these powerful winds to speed them to their destinations. During the summer, jet streams are too far north ordinarily to be used by most aircraft. On flights from east to west, pilots avoid the jet streams, which could cause considerable delay in their flying time.

Meteorologists believe that the jet streams have an important influence on the weather over the entire world. They believe that these powerful winds affect the direction followed by large masses of air moving across the United States. When meteorologists fully understand the causes of jet streams, their weather forecasts should improve markedly from their present record of about 85% accuracy.

Looking Back

Winds are masses of air that move along the earth's surface. The major wind systems of the world are produced by the rotation of the earth on its axis and by unequal heating of the atmosphere. Local winds in a region depend on the wind system in which they are located and on the presence of mountains and large bodies of water.

Looking Ahead

Because water is so important for life, water in the atmosphere is an important part of the environment. In the next chapter, we will learn how water becomes part of the atmosphere and how it leaves the atmosphere.

Multiple-Choice Questions

1. The continuous replacement of warm, lightweight air by cooler, heavier air produces movements of the atmosphere called
   a. whirlpools b. drifts c. convection cells d. doldrums
2. If the earth did not rotate, the winds high in the atmosphere of the Northern Hemisphere would be
   a. east winds b. west winds c. south winds d. north winds
3. Winds are deflected to their right in the Northern Hemisphere, a fact that is summarized in a law stated by
   a. Ferrel b. Galileo c. Newton d. Torricelli
4. The region of the earth in which warmed air results in a low-pressure belt is called the
   a. horse latitudes c. Arctic
   b. doldrums d. south temperate zone
5. Air moving northward from the horse latitudes produces a belt of winds called the
   a. trades b. northwesterlies c. southeasterlies d. westerlies
6. In the Northern Hemisphere, the trade winds blow from the
   a. southeast b. southwest c. northeast d. northwest

7. Dense, cold air flowing from the polar regions produces wind belts called the
   a. polar northerlies
   b. polar westerlies
   c. polar southerlies
   d. polar easterlies
8. Sea breezes result when
   a. land areas heat up more quickly than water areas
   b. water areas heat up more quickly than land areas
   c. warm ocean currents heat coastal areas
   d. warm land currents blow over the sea
9. Sea breezes usually begin blowing about
   a. 8 A.M. b. 10 A.M. c. noon d. 3 P.M.
10. The summer monsoon of India is also called the
    a. wet monsoon
    b. dry monsoon
    c. hot monsoon
    d. cold monsoon
11. In the winter, the interior of India is the center of a high-pressure area because
    a. India is in the center of the doldrums
    b. India cools off more quickly than the nearby Indian Ocean
    c. there is little snowfall in India
    d. warm ocean currents move offshore
12. A sinking mass of air heats up because it is
    a. expanding
    b. compressing
    c. losing water vapor
    d. condensing
13. An important factor in the counterclockwise motion of the air in a low-pressure system is the earth's
    a. revolution
    b. rotation
    c. tilt on its axis
    d. equatorial bulge
14. Wind systems in which the winds rotate outward are called
    a. hurricanes
    b. cyclones
    c. anticyclones
    d. low-pressure troughs

Modified True-False Questions

1. Because the earth rotates, southerly winds in the Northern Hemisphere are deflected to the *north*.
2. Sinking masses of air produce two belts of very calm winds at 30° N and *60° S* latitudes.
3. The horse latitudes are regions of *high* air pressure.
4. In the Northern Hemisphere, winds blowing from the horse latitudes toward the equator are called *westerlies*.
5. The winds of the "roaring forties" are located near the southern coast of *Alaska*.
6. Sea breezes usually begin at *sunrise* and end shortly before sunset.
7. Sea breezes can be felt up to *fifty kilometers* inland.
8. The monsoons of India are basically *valley and mountain* breezes.
9. Winds that blow up the slopes of mountains are called *mountain* breezes.

10. A low-pressure system in which the winds rotate inward is called *a cyclone.*
11. Anticyclones are associated with *clear, dry* weather.

Thought Questions

1. Make a drawing of your classroom showing the location of all radiators, windows, and doors. Indicate on this drawing the paths followed by heated and cold air when the heating system is in operation.
2. If you were to place a drop of water on top of a slowly rotating globe, the drop would curve toward one side of the globe. When the drop of water reached a point halfway between the top and bottom of the globe, it would curve to the opposite side of the globe. Explain why the drop of water follows two different curved paths on the globe.
3. Draw the major wind belts of the earth on a circle representing the earth. Label each wind belt, and explain briefly how the trade winds and westerlies originate.
4. Account for the origin of the term *trade winds* for the winds blowing over the Atlantic Ocean.
5. Describe how a sea breeze originates on a hot summer day.
6. Explain how cool, dense air can rise up the side of a mountain.
7. Name the type of pressure system—high or low—associated with each of the descriptions below.
   a. The air surrounding a hot radiator
   b. The air at the equator
   c. Horse latitudes
   d. The air over the ocean in the summer
   e. The interior of India in the summer
   f. The air on mountain slopes during the day
   g. Pressure system in which the winds rotate outward

CHAPTER 5
WHAT IS THE ORIGIN OF MOISTURE IN THE ATMOSPHERE?

When you have completed this chapter, you should be able to:

1. *Account* for the presence of atmospheric moisture.
2. *Relate* humidity to atmospheric temperature.
3. *Determine* the relative humidity with the aid of a table of relative humidity.
4. *List* the forms of condensation.
5. *Discuss* the types of clouds and the type of weather associated with each.
6. *Describe* the major types of precipitation and how they are measured.
7. *Explain* how air pollution affects precipitation.

In the laboratory experience that follows, you will produce conditions leading to the condensation of water from the air.

Laboratory Experience

UNDER WHAT CONDITIONS DOES WATER COME OUT OF THE ATMOSPHERE?

A. Using a cloth or paper towel, thoroughly dry the outside of a metal cup. Half-fill the cup with water. Place a thermometer in the cup, as shown in Fig. 5–1*a*, page 78.
   1. Describe the appearance of the outside of the cup.
   2. What is the temperature of the water?

B. Add cracked ice or ice cubes to the water. As shown in Fig. 5–1*b*, stir the ice-water mixture gently with the thermometer until the outside of the cup changes in appearance. As soon as you notice this change, read the thermometer.
   3. What is the temperature of the water?
   4. Describe the appearance of the outside of the cup.

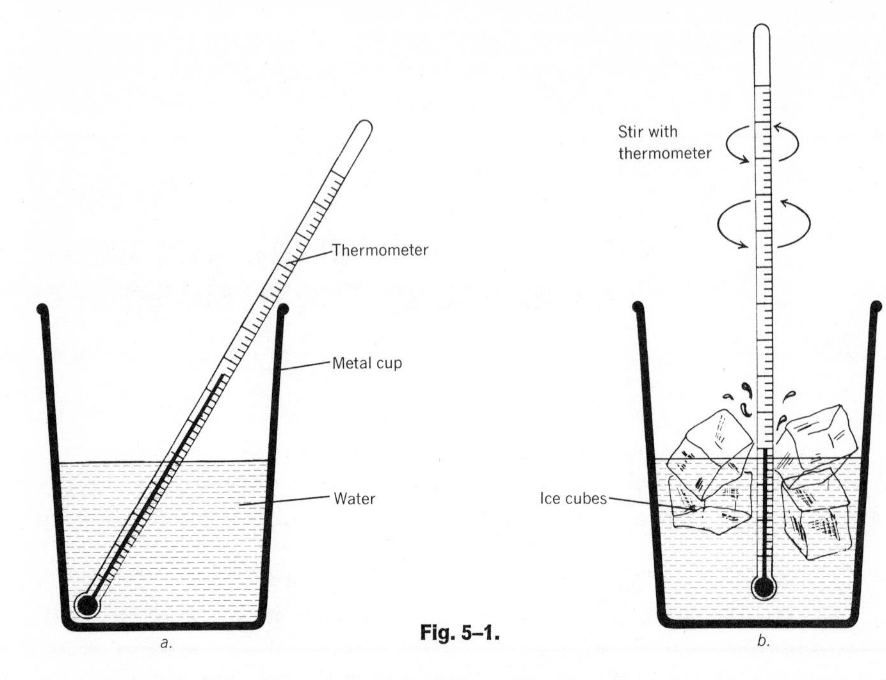

Fig. 5–1.

5. What is the relation between the change in temperature and the change in the appearance of the outside of the cup?

C. Obtain a wide-mouthed jar and a piece of rubber sheeting large enough to cover the mouth of the jar. Stretch the rubber sheet over the mouth of the jar, and fasten the sheet in place by winding a long piece of string tightly around the neck of the jar several times. Tie the loose ends of the string together with a bow knot.

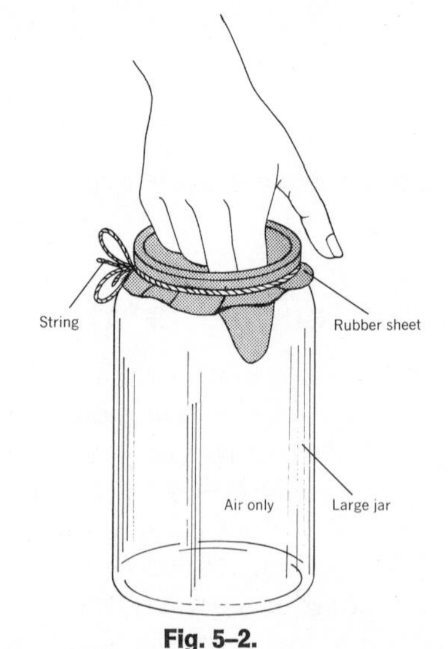

Fig. 5–2.

With two or three fingers, push the rubber sheet about 5 centimeters into the jar, as shown in Fig. 5–2. Quickly release the rubber sheet, at the same time carefully observing the appearance of the air inside the jar. Repeat this procedure.

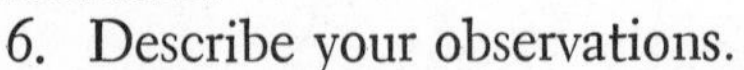

6. Describe your observations.
7. What happens to the volume of air inside the jar when you push on the rubber sheet?

8. What happens to the volume of air when you release the sheet?

D. Untie the string and remove the rubber sheet. Cover the bottom of the jar with a little water. Replace the rubber sheet and tie it in place as you did in part C.

Gently swirl the water around the bottom of the jar for about 1 minute. Repeat the procedure you followed in part C.

9. Describe your observations.

E. Remove the rubber sheet again. Light a match, blow it out, and quickly drop it into the jar. Very quickly replace the rubber sheet and tie it in place again. Repeat part C again.

10. Describe your observations.
11. What is the relation between the changes of volume inside the jar and the changes you observed inside the jar?
12. What effect did the smoke produced in part E have on the experiment?

Introduction

Water is present in oceans, rivers, lakes, glaciers, in the ground, and in the bodies of all plants and animals. From these sources, millions of tons of water enter the atmosphere every hour. The water enters the atmosphere as water vapor. When conditions in the atmosphere are suitable, the water vapor changes into clouds, fog, dew, frost, rain, or snow and returns to its original sources.

The total amount of water vapor in the atmosphere is always about the same. Water in the atmosphere that falls to earth in some places as rain or snow is replaced by water that enters the atmosphere in other places as water vapor.

Both the visible and invisible forms of water in the atmosphere affect us in many ways. The part played in our lives by fog, snow, and rain is obvious. The way in which water vapor influences the weather is not so obvious. By absorbing heat energy during the day and releasing this heat energy at night, the water vapor in the atmosphere helps prevent the daily air temperature from varying too greatly.

Recall that moist air is less dense than dry air. Thus, when the amount of water vapor in the air changes, it causes the atmospheric pressure to change. These changes in the temperature, pressure, and amount of water vapor in the atmosphere are closely related to changes in weather. It is by studying these changes that meteorologists have learned to understand what causes the weather and how to predict changes in the weather. In this chapter, we will study how moisture enters and leaves the atmosphere. In the following chapter, we will study the relationship between atmospheric moisture and the weather.

SOURCES OF MOISTURE IN THE ATMOSPHERE

The origin of most of the moisture in the atmosphere is the water vapor that evaporates from the surface of the ocean. Smaller, but still important, quantities of water vapor also evaporate from the surfaces of lakes and streams and from the land. In addition, plants and animals release water vapor into the air as a waste from their life activities.

Evaporation

Evaporation is the process by which a liquid changes into a gas. Since most of the water in the atmosphere enters the atmosphere as the result of evaporation, it is important to understand this process and the conditions that affect it.

Like the molecules of any other substance, molecules of water are always in motion. At the surface of a body of water, therefore, when water molecules bump into one another, some of the water molecules are pushed into the atmosphere, where they become water vapor (Fig. 5–3).

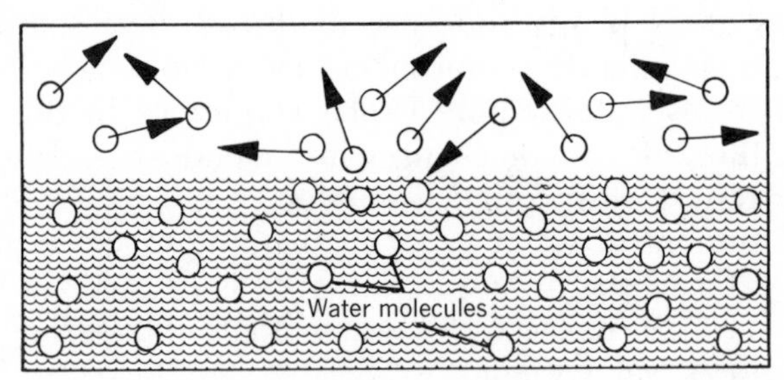

Fig. 5–3. Evaporation.

As heat energy is added to water, the motion of the water molecules increases. This means a corresponding increase in the speed of the molecules. In turn, this results in a larger number of water molecules escaping into the air. Thus, the rate of evaporation increases as the temperature of the water increases.

At the same time that heat energy causes the water to become warmer, water molecules escape by evaporation and remove heat energy, thus causing the water to become cooler. If the rate at which heat energy is removed by evaporation (or other cooling process) is faster than the rate at which heat energy is added, the water becomes cooler.

There are a great many examples of the cooling effect of evaporating water. Dip your hand in water, and then wave your hand through the air. Your hand feels cooler because the water, as it evaporates, removes some of the heat from your skin. For the same reason, you feel chilly when you get out of a swimming pool or bath—the water, evaporating from your body, removes some of the heat from your body.

The wind speeds up the evaporation process because it helps carry away the molecules of water vapor that have escaped into the air. The removal of water vapor then allows other water molecules to escape into the air. For example, wet clothes hanging on a line dry much faster on a windy day than on a calm day. And as you know, when you go swimming on a windy day, you feel much chillier when you leave the water than you do on a calm day.

Transpiration

Through their roots, plants absorb large quantities of water from the soil. Some of this water takes part in the life activities of plants, but most of the water does not. The excess water evaporates from the leaves of plants through the large number of stomates present in the leaves. *Stomates* are microscopic openings, or pores, in the epidermis (skin) of all leaves. The process by which water evaporates from the stomates of leaves is called *transpiration*. The amount of water added to the air by transpiration is tremendous. For example, a tree of average size may release through its leaves about 100,000 liters of water a year. An acre of corn may transpire about 1,000,000 liters of water in a growing season.

Activities of Animals

Animals release water from their bodies by expelling liquid wastes, by the evaporation of sweat, and by the exhalation of water vapor during breathing. Human activities, such as the burning of fuels, also release a great deal of water throughout the world.

HUMIDITY

The amount of water vapor in the atmosphere is called *humidity*. The humidity in the atmosphere varies continuously. Where the sun shines strongly on a large body of water, such as the Gulf of Mexico, the humidity is very high. Where the sun shines strongly in a place where there is little or no water present, such as the Sahara Desert, the humidity is very low. The amount of water vapor in the atmosphere ranges from a high of almost 4% (by volume) to a low of almost zero.

Humidity and Temperature

The amount of water vapor the atmosphere can hold depends greatly on the temperature of the atmosphere. As the temperature of the atmosphere increases, its ability to hold water vapor increases.

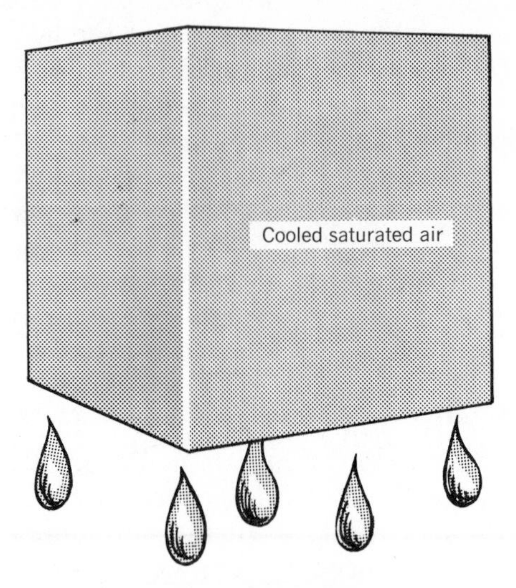

Fig. 5–4. Condensation.

On the other hand, as the temperature of the atmosphere decreases, its ability to hold water vapor decreases.

The amount of water vapor present in a given volume of air is measured in small units of weight called *grains*. There are about 15 grains to a gram. At any given temperature, the amount of water vapor that a given volume, or *parcel*, of air can hold is limited. The maximum number of grains of water vapor that a parcel of air can hold is called its *capacity*. When a parcel of air is holding all the water vapor it can, the air is said to be *saturated* (Fig. 5–4). At this point, the absolute humidity and capacity are equal. When a parcel of saturated air is cooled, the maximum amount of water vapor it can hold decreases. As a result, the excess amount of water vapor *condenses* —turns into tiny droplets of liquid.

The effect of temperature on the water-vapor capacity of a parcel of air is shown in Table 5–1. (Since the U.S. Weather Bureau continues to use the customary system of measurement, we will use customary units in our discussion of weather data and in tables and illustrations throughout this chapter.) Note that at higher temperatures the capacity of the air increases at a much greater rate than it does at lower temperatures. For example, when the air temperature increases from 80°F to 100°F, the capacity of the air increases by about 9 grains.

When the air temperature increases from 30°F to 50°F, the capacity of the air increases only by about 2 grains.

Table 5–1. Maximum Water Vapor Content of 1 Cubic Foot of Air

Temperature (degrees Fahrenheit)	*Water Vapor (grains)*
30°	1.9
40°	2.9
50°	4.1
60°	5.7
70°	8.0
80°	10.9
90°	14.7
100°	19.7

Relative Humidity

Humidity is measured by comparing the amount of water vapor actually present in the air with the maximum amount of water vapor that the air can hold at that temperature. For example, a parcel of air at 50°F has a capacity of 4.1 grains of water. If this parcel is filled to capacity, it is saturated. If this parcel of air is holding only 2 grains of water vapor, it is holding only about half of its capacity (Fig. 5–5). The meteorologist expresses this comparison as a percent and calls it *relative humidity*. Thus, a parcel of air that contains one-half its

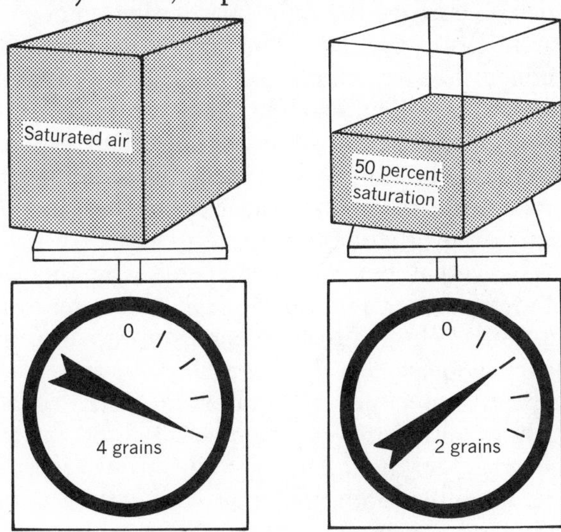

Fig. 5–5. Relative humidity.

capacity of water vapor (2 grains out of 4 grains) is said to have a relative humidity of 50%.

Let us take another example: Suppose a parcel of air with a capacity of 8.0 grains of water vapor actually contains only 2.0 grains of water vapor. Since this parcel of air contains only one-fourth of its capacity, it has a relative humidity of 25%. If the amount of water in the air remains the same, but the air is cooled, the relative humidity will increase. For this reason, relative humidity is usually higher at night.

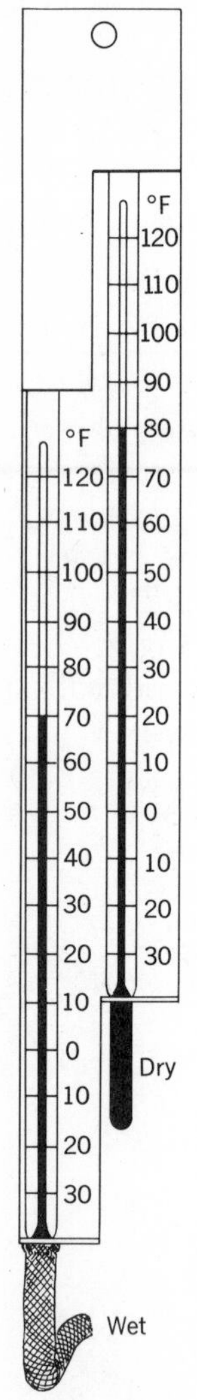

Fig. 5–6. A psychrometer.

MEASURING RELATIVE HUMIDITY

The relative humidity can be determined by means of an instrument called a *hygrometer*. One type of hygrometer, called a *psychrometer*, depends on the fact that evaporation is a cooling process. Another type of hygrometer, called a *hair hygrometer*, depends on the fact that a human hair stretches when it is damp.

Psychrometer

A psychrometer consists of two thermometers mounted side by side on the same frame (Fig. 5–6). One thermometer is called the dry-bulb thermometer—it records the existing temperature of the atmosphere. The other thermometer is called the wet-bulb thermometer—it records a temperature that depends upon the humidity of the atmosphere. A cloth wrapped around the bulb of this thermometer is soaked in water. Both thermometers are either fanned or whirled through the air at the same time. The motion does not affect the dry-bulb thermometer, but it causes the water to evaporate from the cloth of the wet-bulb thermometer. The evaporation of the water cools the cloth, which results in a lower temperature reading on the wet-bulb thermometer than on the dry-bulb thermometer.

The actual temperature recorded by the wet-bulb thermometer depends on how quickly the water evaporates from the cloth. This, in turn, depends on how much water vapor is already present in the atmosphere. If the air is very humid, very little moisture will evaporate from the cloth, and the readings on the two thermometers will be about the same. If the air is very dry, a large amount of water vapor will evaporate from the cloth, and the wet-bulb temperature reading will be very low.

Thus, the factor that determines the temperature recorded

by the wet-bulb thermometer is the amount of water vapor in the atmosphere. By comparing the difference between the temperature readings of the dry-bulb and wet-bulb thermometers, a meteorologist can determine the relative humidity with the aid of a table such as Table 5–2.

Table 5–2. Finding Relative Humidity in Percent

Difference in degrees between wet-bulb and dry-bulb thermometers

Air temperature (reading of dry-bulb thermometer) in degrees Fahrenheit	1	2	3	4	5	6	7	8	9	10	11	12	13	14	15	16	17	18	19	20	21	22	23	24	25	26	27	28	29	30
30°	89	78	68	57	47	37	27	17	8																					
32°	90	79	69	60	50	41	31	22	13	4																				
34°	90	81	72	62	53	44	35	27	18	9	1																			
36°	91	82	73	65	56	48	39	31	23	14	6																			
38°	91	83	75	67	59	51	43	35	27	19	12	4																		
40°	92	84	76	68	61	53	46	38	31	23	16	9	2																	
42°	92	85	77	70	62	55	48	41	34	28	21	14	7																	
44°	93	85	78	71	64	57	51	44	37	31	24	18	12	5																
46°	93	86	79	72	65	59	53	46	40	34	28	22	16	10	4															
48°	93	87	80	73	67	60	54	48	42	36	31	25	19	14	8	3														
50°	93	87	81	74	68	62	56	50	44	39	33	28	22	17	12	7	2													
52°	94	88	81	75	69	63	58	52	46	41	36	30	25	20	15	10	6													
54°	94	88	82	76	70	65	59	54	48	43	38	33	28	23	18	14	9	5												
56°	94	88	82	77	71	66	61	55	50	45	40	35	31	26	21	17	12	8	4											
58°	94	89	83	77	72	67	62	57	52	47	42	38	33	28	24	20	15	11	7	3										
60°	94	89	84	78	73	68	63	58	53	49	44	40	35	31	27	22	18	14	10	6	2									
62°	94	89	84	79	74	69	64	60	55	50	46	41	37	33	29	25	21	17	13	9	6	2								
64°	95	90	85	79	75	70	66	61	56	52	48	43	39	35	31	27	23	20	16	12	9	5	2							
66°	95	90	85	80	76	71	66	62	58	53	49	45	41	37	33	29	26	22	18	15	11	8	5	1						
68°	95	90	85	81	76	72	67	63	59	55	51	47	43	39	35	31	28	24	21	17	14	11	8	4	1					
70°	95	90	86	81	77	72	68	64	60	56	52	48	44	40	37	33	30	26	23	20	17	13	10	7	4	1				
72°	95	91	86	82	78	73	69	65	61	57	53	49	46	42	39	35	32	28	25	22	19	16	13	10	7	4	1			
74°	95	91	86	82	78	74	70	66	62	58	54	51	47	44	40	37	34	30	27	24	21	18	15	12	9	7	4	1		
76°	96	91	87	83	78	74	70	67	63	59	55	52	48	45	42	38	35	32	29	26	23	20	17	14	12	9	6	4	1	
78°	96	91	87	83	79	75	71	67	64	60	57	53	50	46	43	40	37	34	31	28	25	22	19	16	14	11	9	6	4	1
80°	96	91	87	83	79	76	72	68	64	61	57	54	51	47	44	41	38	35	32	29	27	24	21	18	16	13	11	8	6	4
82°	96	91	87	83	79	76	72	69	65	62	58	55	52	49	46	43	40	37	34	31	28	25	23	20	18	15	13	10	8	6
84°	96	92	88	84	80	77	73	70	66	63	59	56	53	50	47	44	41	38	35	32	30	27	25	22	20	17	15	12	10	8
86°	96	92	88	84	80	77	73	70	66	63	60	57	54	51	48	45	42	39	37	34	31	29	26	24	21	19	17	14	12	10
88°	96	92	88	85	81	78	74	71	67	64	61	58	55	52	49	46	43	41	38	35	33	30	28	25	23	21	18	16	14	12
90°	96	92	88	85	81	78	74	71	68	64	61	58	56	53	50	47	44	42	39	37	34	32	29	27	24	22	20	18	16	14
	1	2	3	4	5	6	7	8	9	10	11	12	13	14	15	16	17	18	19	20	21	22	23	24	25	26	27	28	29	30

For example, suppose the dry-bulb reading is 80° F and the wet-bulb reading is 70° F. The difference between the readings is 10°. Look across the top or bottom of Table 5–2 and find the column showing the 10° F difference. Look down the left-hand side of the table and find the row showing a dry-bulb reading of 80° F. Where this column and this row intersect, we find the relative humidity to be 61%.

Table 5–3, page 86, shows the typical dry-bulb and wet-bulb temperatures that may be obtained in a dry climate and in a damp climate.

Table 5–3. Some Sample Psychrometer Readings

	Painted Desert, Arizona (dry)	*Okefenokee Swamp, Florida (humid)*
Dry-bulb temperature	90° F	90° F
Wet-bulb temperature	65° F	88° F
Difference between dry- and wet-bulb temperatures caused by evaporation (cooling effect)	25 F°	2 F°
Relative humidity	24%	92%

Hair Hygrometer

Hair stretches when it is damp. The more moisture there is in the hair, the more the hair stretches. A hair, therefore, will indicate changes in the relative humidity of the atmosphere.

A hair hygrometer consists of a long bundle of hairs, one end of which is fixed in position and the other end of which is attached to an indicator (Fig. 5–7). The indicator reads the relative humidity directly. A permanent record of the relative humidity can be made by attaching a hair hygrometer to a pen that writes on a chart wrapped around a slowly rotating drum.

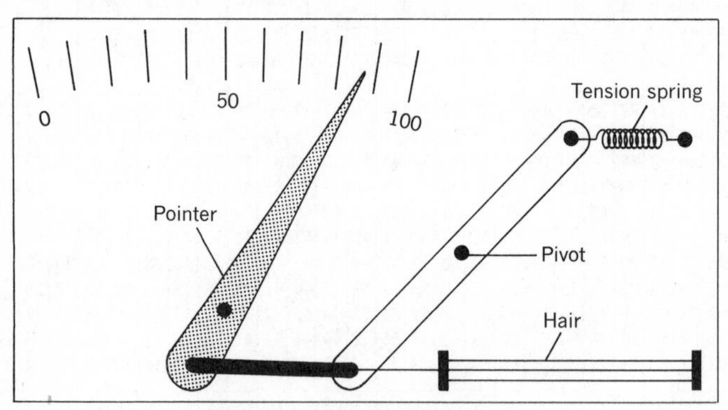

Fig. 5–7. A hair hygrometer.

CONDENSATION OF WATER VAPOR

When the water vapor in the atmosphere cools sufficiently, it condenses. That is, some of the water vapor changes from a gas into a liquid. When water vapor condenses at the surface of the earth, it forms *dew* or *frost*. When water vapor condenses above the ground, it forms *fog* or *clouds*.

Condensation Near the Ground

The water vapor that condenses on solid objects is called dew. For example, in hot weather, the water vapor that condenses on the outside of a glass of cold water is dew.

The temperature at which water vapor begins to condense is called the *dew point*. The dew point depends on (1) the amount of water vapor present in the atmosphere, and (2) the air temperature. Water vapor changes into a liquid when the air temperature falls low enough for the air to become saturated. In other words, at the dew-point temperature, the water-vapor capacity of the air has decreased to the point where part of the water vapor condenses into a liquid. You observed this in part B of your laboratory experience.

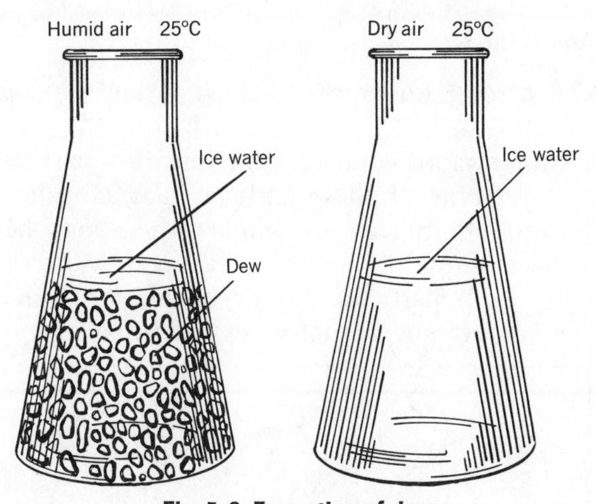

Fig. 5–8. Formation of dew.

If samples of humid air and dry air having the same temperature are cooled at the same rate, by coming into contact with a flask of ice water, the humid air will become saturated first (Fig. 5–8). Some of the water vapor will then condense in the form of dew. Table 5–1 (page 83) tells us that at 80°F a sample of air has a capacity of about 11 grains of water vapor. If a sample of air at 80°F is holding 11 grains, it is saturated, or holding all the water vapor it can. If this very humid air cools to 70°F, the table shows that its capacity would drop to 8 grains. In this case, 3 grains of water vapor would condense into liquid.

In contrast, consider a sample of dry air at 80°F that contains 4.1 grains of water vapor. According to Table 5–1, page 83, the temperature must reach 50°F for the capacity of air to be 4.1 grains. Before any of the water vapor in this air will condense, the air would have to be cooled from 80°F to 50°F or below.

Dew usually forms at night, after the ground has radiated the heat it absorbed during the day. The ground radiates its heat best during a calm, clear night in the absence of clouds or wind. During such nights, the ground becomes cold enough to cool the air above it to the dew point.

At times, the air may reach its dew point after the temperature falls below 32°F, the freezing point of water. When this happens, the water vapor in the air condenses to form ice crystals. This condensation is called frost. Frost forms when water vapor changes directly from a gas into a solid. (When dew freezes, it does not form frost, but frozen dew.) As with dew, frost is most likely to form on calm, clear nights.

Condensation Above the Ground

Water vapor often condenses above the surface of the earth, where there are no large objects upon which water can collect. In such cases, the water vapor condenses on very tiny particles present in the air (Fig. 5–9). Some of these particles may be salt crystals from ocean spray blown into the air by wind. Others may be smoke and dust particles from fires and active volcanoes. When water vapor condenses around such particles, *fog* or *clouds* are formed. You observed this in part E of your laboratory experience.

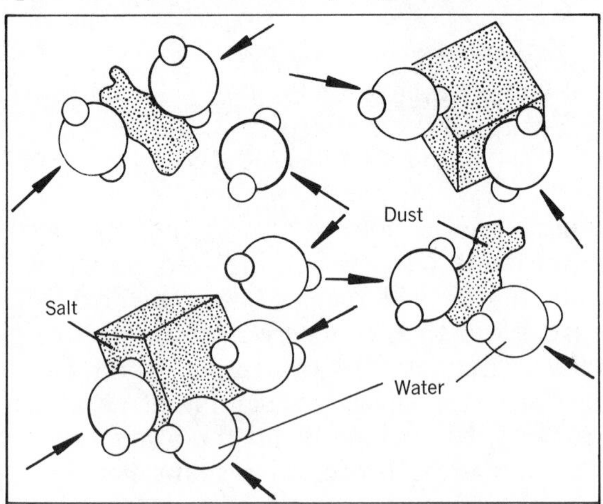

Fig. 5–9. Condensation on particles.

Fog consists of drops of moisture that are small and light enough to remain suspended in the air. Like dew and frost, fog usually forms when the air temperature falls at night.

When air close to the ground is cooled below its dew point and a slight wind or air current keeps the condensed droplets in motion, the droplets will remain suspended just above the surface of the earth. Fog of this type is called *ground fog,* or *radiation fog,* because it forms on clear nights after the earth has lost heat by radiation and because the fog usually extends less than 100 feet (30 meters) above the ground. Ground fog usually forms during the hours of darkness and "burns away" by late morning as the sun's warmth causes the water droplets to evaporate.

Fog also forms when warm moist air is cooled as it passes over a cold surface. Fog of this type often occurs along seacoasts when warm air from over the ocean flows inland and is cooled as it comes in contact with colder land surfaces (Fig. 5–10). This type of fog also forms when warm moist air is cooled as it moves over cold ocean currents.

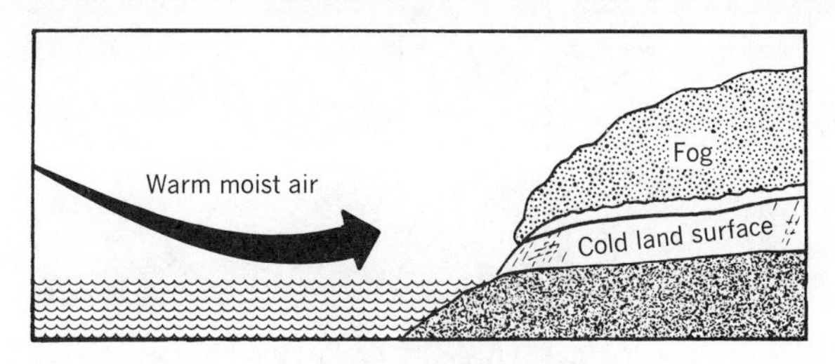

Fig. 5–10. Fog.

Clouds, like fog, result when water vapor in the atmosphere condenses on tiny particles suspended in the air. However, the process that produces clouds is usually quite different from the process that produces fog.

As you know, when air expands, it cools (see Chapter 3, pages 50–51). Another example of this process may be seen in the small carbon dioxide cylinders that are used to inflate life jackets and to charge bottles of water with carbon dioxide gas. When the gas is released from the cylinder, the gas expands greatly. As a result, the cylinder becomes very cold to the touch, sometimes so cold that frost forms on the outside of the cylinder.

In the atmosphere, as a parcel of warm air rises, the atmospheric pressure surrounding the parcel lessens. Therefore, the parcel of air expands in volume as it rises. As it expands, it becomes cooler. When the temperature of this parcel of air falls to its dew point (say, at 3000 feet), the water vapor in the air condenses, and a cloud appears in the sky (Fig. 5–11, page 90). If there are a great many smoke or salt particles in the air, the water vapor may condense even before the dew point is reached.

There are a number of ways in which air may rise, cool, and reach its dew point. The air may rise because it passes over a hot surface;

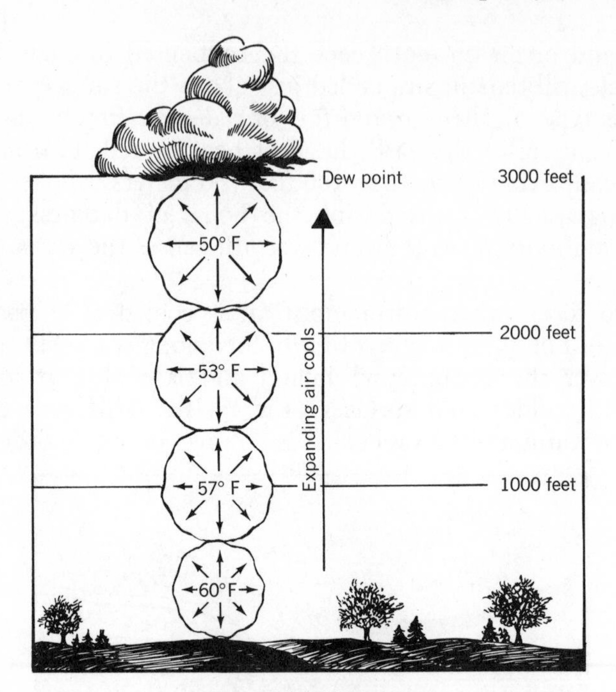

Fig. 5–11. Cloud formation.

it may be forced to rise to pass over a mountain in its path; or it may be lifted upward by a wedge of cooler air that forces its way beneath it. Each of these methods of raising a mass of air higher into the troposphere plays an important part, alone or in combination, in the formation of different types of clouds.

TYPES OF CLOUDS

The type of cloud that forms depends mainly on the way in which a mass of air rises into the troposphere. If the mass of air rises straight up, the clouds will be puffy, like balls of cotton. If the mass of air rises diagonally, along a gentle upward slope, the clouds that form will be sheetlike, or flat.

Clouds are classified according to their shape and their distance above the ground. If the base of a cloud is above 20,000 feet, the cloud is classified as a *high cloud*. If the base of a cloud is between 6500 feet and 20,000 feet, the cloud is classified as a *middle cloud*. If the base of a cloud is between sea level and 6500 feet, the cloud is classified as a *low cloud*.

Descriptions of some of the more common types of clouds follow.

Stratus clouds are sheetlike, or flat.

Cumulus clouds are fluffy, like cotton wool.

Cirrus clouds resemble tufts of hair, or feathers. Cirrus clouds occur at great altitudes where the temperature is very low. Consequently, these clouds always consist of ice crystals.

Nimbus clouds are rain clouds.

Several cloud names are a combination of two names, for example, *cumulonimbus, altostratus,* and *cirrostratus.* A cumulonimbus cloud is a dark rain cloud that is piled up in a huge mound; an altostratus cloud is a flattened cloud at a middle altitude; and a cirrostratus cloud is a flattened cloud at high altitude. Some of these clouds are illustrated in Fig. 5–12, page 92, together with other common types of clouds. Note how each name describes the appearance of the cloud.

Clouds are often important weather indicators. Certain types of clouds are signs of good weather; other types of clouds are signs of poor weather. A brief description of the kind of weather usually associated with different types of clouds is given in Table 5–4.

Table 5–4. Clouds and the Weather They Bring

Cloud	*Weather*
Cirrus	Fair, generally clear skies; little chance of rain or snow
Cirrostratus (covering a large part of the sky)	Possibly rain or snow within 24 hours
Altostratus (covering most of the sky)	Possibly rain or snow within a few hours
Altocumulus (covering a large part of the sky)	Fair, but with some chance of rain or snow
Cumulus	Fair
Stratocumulus (covering a large part of the sky)	Chance of rain or snow
Cumulonimbus	Thunderstorms, hail
Nimbostratus	Rain or snow

TYPES OF PRECIPITATION

To a meteorologist, *precipitation* means the falling of rain, drizzle, sleet, hail, or snow from the atmosphere to the ground. In some way, not yet fully understood, the very small droplets of water that make up clouds increase in size until they are heavy enough to fall to earth. A general description of the most common forms of precipitation is given in Table 5–5, page 93.

Altocumulus — *Cumulus*

Cumulonimbus — *Cirrus*

Stratocumulus — *Nimbostratus*

Fig. 5–12. Types of clouds.

Table 5–5. Common Forms of Precipitation

Drizzle	Fine drops of water (diameter less than 1/50 inch)
Rain	Drops of water larger than for a drizzle
Sleet	Frozen drops of rain
Hail	Frozen drops of water having a layered or onionlike structure
Snow	Ice crystals having a branched structure

Sleet, hail, and *snow* are solid forms of precipitation that form under different conditions.

Sleet

Sleet consists of pellets of ice that form when falling rain freezes. This may happen when rain falls from a warm region at a high altitude to a colder region at a lower altitude. You recall that such a condition of reversed temperature is called a temperature inversion (see Chapter 3, page 55). If the temperature at the lower altitude is below freezing, the raindrops may freeze before they reach the ground.

Hail

Hail forms in cumulonimbus clouds in which there are strong updrafts of air. A hailstone begins as a raindrop which is carried high into the cloud by a strong updraft of air. When the raindrop reaches a level in the cloud where the temperature is below freezing, the raindrop turns to ice and then begins to fall. As the frozen raindrop falls through the cloud, it reaches a warmer level where ice begins to melt and the frozen raindrop acquires a coat of water. Another strong updraft lifts the raindrop up again to a level where the coat of water freezes again. This process of freezing, melting, and freezing again may be repeated several times. Each time, the hailstone acquires a new layer of ice. As a result, if you cut a hailstone in two, you will discover that it usually consists of a number of layers of ice, like the layers of an onion.

Snow

Snow forms in the same way that frost forms. You recall that frost occurs at ground level whenever water vapor changes directly into ice. In the same way, water vapor in the clouds gathers on particles suspended in the air and changes directly into the crystals of ice we call snowflakes. The basic form of these crystals is hexagonal, or six-sided. Large snowflakes result when a number of ice crystals clump together at temperatures that are not too much below freezing. In general, the colder the temperature, the smaller are the snowflakes that form.

MEASURING PRECIPITATION

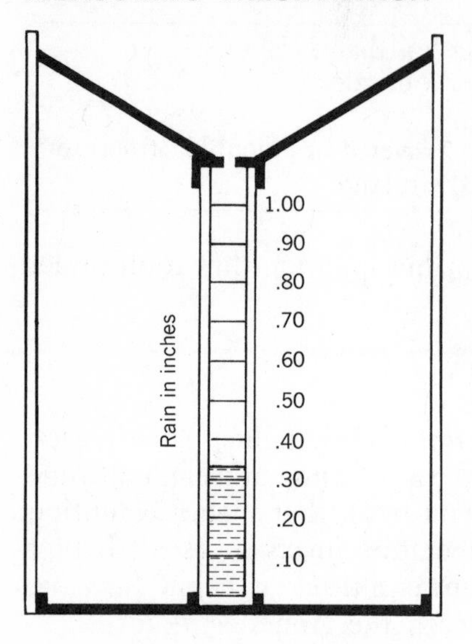

Fig. 5–13. A rain gauge.

The amount of rainfall is measured by catching the rain in a *rain gauge* (Fig. 5–13). This device consists of a funnel leading into a cylindrical container. The diameter of the funnel is ten times the diameter of the cylinder. Thus, when 0.1 inch of rain falls into the funnel, it fills the cylinder to a depth of 1 inch. That is, the cylinder magnifies the amount of rainfall 10 times. A rainfall of 0.2 inch fills the cylinder to a depth of 2 inches; a rainfall of 1 inch fills the cylinder to a depth of 10 inches. As soon as the cylinder becomes full, it is automatically emptied, thus allowing heavy continuous rains to be measured. In Fig. 5–13, the cylinder is filled to a depth of 3.2 inches, indicating 0.32 inch of rainfall.

Snowfall is measured by pushing a ruler into freshly fallen snow. Since snowfall does not ordinarily cover the ground evenly, measurements are taken in several places. The average of these measurements is recorded as the depth of the snow. A rain gauge can be used to determine the amount of rainwater in a snowfall by allowing melted snow to pass through it. In general, 1 foot of melted snow equals about 1 inch of rain.

PRECIPITATION AND POLLUTION

You will remember that when water vapor high in the atmosphere condenses, it does so on tiny particles present in the air. These particles may be composed of harmful substances—air pollutants. In some regions, human activities continuously add smoke particles to the air. In other regions, where atomic (nuclear) bombs are exploded, radioactive particles are added to the air.

What happens when water vapor condenses on these added particles, as well as on natural particles? Studies have shown that, in regions where excessive amounts of airborne particles are present in the atmosphere, precipitation is heavier than elsewhere. Raindrops and snowflakes that form in such regions often form around these particles and rapidly carry them down to the earth's surface. Although the precipitation "washes" the air clean, the particles pollute the earth's surface.

Rain and snow bearing soot particles, if they do nothing else, soil clothes and other materials on which they land. Should harmful radioactive particles reach reservoirs or food plants, the particles pollute the water and the plants. When plants absorb such polluted water, they become radioactive. When animals eat radioactive plants, the animals become polluted in turn. In order to reduce this danger, a number of nations (but not all) have signed a treaty banning the testing of nuclear bombs in the atmosphere. The problem of radioactive materials and other pollutants in the atmosphere is one with which all of us must be concerned if the human race is to survive.

Looking Back

Moisture enters the atmosphere by evaporation from bodies of water and from the bodies of animals, and by transpiration from plants. Moisture leaves the atmosphere by condensing into dew, frost, fog, or clouds. After condensing, the moisture returns to the earth's surface by precipitation as rain, sleet, hail, or snow. The forms of precipitation are important to us because they are the source of the water we, and all other living things, use daily. Precipitation may also bring with it pollutants that had been suspended in the atmosphere.

Looking Ahead

If you think back over Chapters 1 through 5, you will note that we have really been discussing different weather factors under separate headings. Knowledge concerning changes in these factors enables us to make weather forecasts, which are the subject of Chapter 6.

Multiple-Choice Questions

1. The amount of water that a tree of average size returns to the atmosphere in the course of one year is about
   a. 1000 liters
   b. 10,000 liters
   c. 100,000 liters
   d. 1,000,000 liters
2. Evaporation involves the changing of molecules of liquid water into
   a. separate atoms of water
   b. molecules of solid water
   c. molecules of water vapor
   d. tiny drops of water
3. Water evaporates most rapidly on days when the air is
   a. hot, dry, and still
   b. muggy, hot, and windy
   c. hot, dry, and windy
   d. cold, dry, and still

4. On an average day in the summer, the humidity is usually highest during the
   a. late morning b. early afternoon c. late afternoon d. night
5. The water-vapor content of the atmosphere is usually highest over
   a. plains b. tropical oceans c. swamps d. mountains
6. As air pollution over an area increases, we can expect the annual precipitation in the region to include
   a. more snow than rain
   b. more hail than rain
   c. more sleet than rain
   d. more of all forms of precipitation
7. When a sample of air that has a capacity of 6 grains of water vapor contains only 1 grain of water vapor, the relative humidity of the air is about
   a. 17% b. 60% c. 83% d. 92%
8. The principle of the wet-bulb and dry-bulb thermometers is that
   a. evaporation causes cooling
   b. evaporation causes heating
   c. moving air cools objects
   d. the dry-bulb thermometer absorbs water from the wet-bulb thermometer
9. Which of the following cities would you expect to have the highest humidity?
   a. Butte, Montana—dry bulb, 50° F; wet bulb, 49° F
   b. Biscayne, Florida—dry bulb, 80° F; wet bulb, 60° F
   c. Sacramento, California—dry bulb, 75° F; wet bulb, 55° F
   d. Gallup, New Mexico—dry bulb, 90° F; wet bulb, 85° F
10. An important factor in the formation of ground fog is the loss of heat from the earth by
    a. evaporation b. radiation c. strong winds d. frost
11. Clouds form when the air cools as a result of
    a. expansion b. conduction c. evaporation d. condensation
12. The words that best describe a cirrocumulus cloud are
    a. thin, heaped up, consists of ice crystals
    b. thin, flattened out, consists of ice crystals
    c. thick, flattened out, consists of water
    d. thin, feathery, consists of water
13. The cloud formation that is always associated with rain or snow is the
    a. altostratus
    b. cirrostratus
    c. stratocumulus
    d. nimbostratus
14. Which of the following is *not* a form of precipitation?
    a. hail b. snow c. sleet d. frost
15. Which of the following statements is *incorrect*?
    a. snow is a solid form of precipitation
    b. rain cannot form from snow
    c. rain may change to sleet
    d. sleet may form from hail
16. In a standard rain gauge, five inches of water in the narrow cylinder connected to the funnel is equal to a rainfall of
    a. 0.10 inch b. 0.50 inch c. 5 inches d. 1 inch

Modified True-False Questions

1. The source of most of the water vapor in the atmosphere is the *ocean.*
2. The transfer of water from the leaves of plants into the atmosphere is called *transpiration.*
3. Heating water increases its rate of evaporation because the individual molecules of water *expand.*
4. The maximum amount of water vapor that a given parcel of air can hold is known as *humidity.*
5. The wet-bulb and dry-bulb thermometers together make up *an anemometer.*
6. Moisture in the atmosphere that condenses on solid objects, such as grass, is called *dew.*
7. Ground fogs usually "burn away" about *an hour* after sunrise.
8. *Cumulus* clouds ordinarily form in a mass of air that rises vertically.
9. A type of cloud that is usually associated with fair weather is *nimbostratus.*
10. *Snow* is rain that freezes after it has left the cloud.
11. Hailstones form in *cirrus* clouds.
12. Snow forms when water vapor in the atmosphere changes directly from *liquid* to solid.
13. One foot of snow, when melted, produces the same amount of water as *one inch* of rain.

Matching Questions

Write the letter of the item in column B which is most closely related to the item in column A.

Column A

1. humidity
2. capacity
3. saturation
4. hygrometer
5. dew point
6. radiation
7. stratus
8. sleet
9. cirrus
10. rain gauge
11. hail

Column B

a. instrument that measures relative humidity
b. method of heat loss that results in ground fog
c. sheetlike clouds
d. the maximum amount of water vapor that a given parcel of air can hold
e. clouds composed of ice crystals
f. moisture in the air
g. form of precipitation composed of a number of layers of ice
h. temperature at which water vapor condenses on objects
i. point at which a parcel of air is holding all the water vapor it can
j. instrument used to measure precipitation
k. frozen raindrops

Thought Questions

1. Describe two conditions that will cause water to evaporate rapidly.
2. Account for the fact that a wet cloth that freezes on a clothesline will dry even though the air temperature remains below freezing.
3. Explain the difference between capacity and saturation.
4. Give the relative humidity in each of the following cases:

	Amount of Water Vapor in the Air (in grains)	*Capacity of the Air (in grains)*
a.	2.0	6.0
b.	2.0	8.0
c.	4.0	8.0
d.	8.0	10.0

5. Use Table 5–2 on page 85 to determine the relative humidity when the dry-bulb and wet-bulb temperatures are as follows:
   a. 40°F and 30°F
   b. 80°F and 70°F
   c. 40°F and 38°F
   d. 90°F and 88°F
6. Explain how a hair hygrometer functions.
7. On a very hot, muggy day, large drops of water appear on a cold-water pipe. A hot-water pipe nearby remains perfectly dry. Account for the difference.
8. Describe the conditions that are necessary before dew or frost will appear on the ground.
9. Describe how two different kinds of fog form.
10. Describe three different ways in which a mass of air may rise into the air from ground level.
11. What is the difference between the following pairs of clouds?
    a. stratus and cumulus
    b. cirrostratus and altostratus
    c. stratocumulus and cumulonimbus
12. What is the difference between the following pairs of precipitation?
    a. drizzle and rain
    b. rain and snow
    c. sleet and snow
    d. hail and sleet
13. Explain why rainfall may increase at times when air pollution increases.

CHAPTER 6

WHAT DO WE NEED TO KNOW ABOUT THE ATMOSPHERE FOR WEATHER FORECASTING?

When you have completed this chapter, you should be able to:

1. *Identify* the symbols used on a weather map.
2. *Describe* the formation and movements of the different types of air masses.
3. *List* the kinds of weather fronts, and state the characteristics of each.
4. *Contrast* thunderstorms, tornadoes, and hurricanes.
5. *Predict* weather by studying a weather map.
6. *Distinguish* weather from climate.

In the laboratory experience that follows, you will observe a difference in humidity, which is an important weather factor.

Laboratory Experience

HOW DOES CHANGING THE CONDITIONS WITHIN A SAMPLE OF AIR AFFECT HUMIDITY?

A. Dip a strip of blue cobalt chloride paper in water. Exhale upon another strip of cobalt chloride paper several times.
   1. Describe what happens in each case.
   The change in color is a reliable test for the presence of water.

B. Tape a thermometer to the inner side of each of two dry battery jars, as shown in Fig. 6–1, page 100. Position the thermometers so that the bulbs are about 5 centimeters from the bottoms of the jars. Make sure you can read the scales on the thermometers. Hang a strip of dry cobalt chloride paper from the rim of each jar. Cover each jar with a piece of cardboard. Label one jar A and the other jar B.
   2. What is the color of the paper strip in jar A? What is the temperature of the air in jar A?

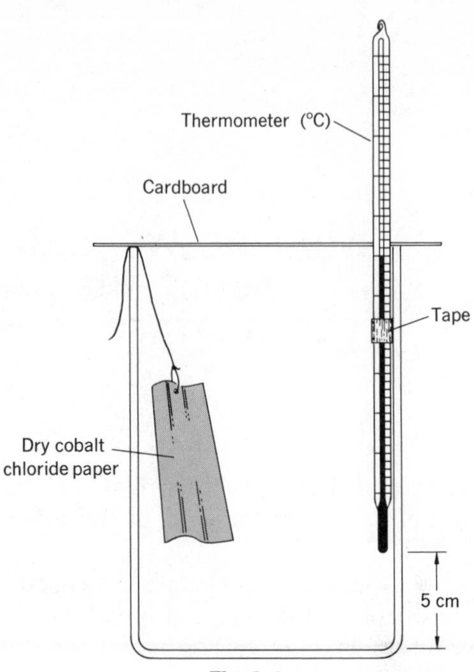

Fig. 6–1.

3. What is the color of the paper strip in jar B? What is the temperature of the air in jar B?

Copy the table below into your notebook. Record your results so far in the first row of the table.

	Jar A		*Jar B*	
Minutes	*Color of Cobalt Chloride Paper*	*Temperature*	*Color of Cobalt Chloride Paper*	*Temperature*
0				
1				
2				
3				
4				
5				
6				
7				
8				

C. Remove the strip of cobalt chloride paper from jar A. Cover the bottom of the jar with a layer of crushed ice cubes or cracked ice. Make sure the ice does not touch the thermometer. Replace the strip of cobalt chloride paper, and again cover the jar with the piece of cardboard.

D. Remove the strip of cobalt chloride paper from jar B. Pour about 2½ centimeters of warm water (about 40°C) into the jar. Make sure the water does not touch the thermometer. Replace the strip of cobalt chloride paper, and again cover the jar with the piece of cardboard.

At 1-minute intervals, read the thermometer in each jar, and note the color of the cobalt chloride paper. Record your observations in the table. Continue your observations for about 8 minutes.

4. What happens to the air temperature in jar A? What happens to the air temperature in jar B?
5. What happens to the humidity in jar A? What happens to the humidity in jar B?
6. Why should there be a difference in humidity between jar A and jar B?
7. Over what parts of the earth are the conditions in the atmosphere similar to the conditions in jar A? Why?
8. Over what parts of the earth are the conditions in the atmosphere similar to the conditions in jar B? Why?
9. Which atmospheric condition affects humidity?

Introduction

The pressure, temperature, and humidity of the atmosphere are constantly changing and affecting our lives. These changes, together with the changing seasons, are the sources of our daily weather. The weather is important for our health and comfort, for the plants and animals we use as food, and for some of our means of transportation. Knowing in advance what the weather will be helps us adjust to it. Such knowledge can be used to save crops and even lives when severe storms threaten us.

DEVELOPMENT OF WEATHER FORECASTING

To be able to predict the weather accurately has been a dream of people for thousands of years. However, until the middle of the nineteenth century, most weather forecasting was based on superstition or was just guesswork. For example, certain animals and plants were believed to be capable of anticipating weather changes. By watching how they behaved, one was supposed to be able to predict the coming weather. If a farmer's pigs returned to the barn with straw in their mouths, rain was supposed to fall shortly.

Weather forecasting was often based on the appearance of the sky. This type of forecasting was somewhat more reliable than watching animal behavior. These forecasts were usually expressed in the form of jingles, such as

Red sky at night,
Sailor's delight;
Red sky in the morning,
Sailors take warning.

When *Benjamin Franklin* was Postmaster General of the United States, he contributed to our knowledge of the weather by noting that storms moved from one place to another. From letters he received from friends in other cities, he learned that the storms described in these letters occurred on dates that differed from the dates on which the storms occurred in his city. Franklin concluded that the same storm passed over different cities in succession as it passed over the United States. As you will see later, Franklin's conclusions are those on which modern weather forecasting is based.

Improved weather forecasting became possible with the invention of the telegraph in 1844. Weather information could now be collected and sent to widely separated areas almost as soon as changes in the weather occurred. Today, with our modern means of communication, a network of hundreds of weather stations can communicate rapidly with one another over the entire world.

In the United States, at regular intervals throughout the day, weather observers at hundreds of weather stations throughout the country transmit weather data to the National Weather Service in Washington, D.C. Specialists at this central weather bureau compile different kinds of weather charts from this data. Exact copies of these weather charts are then transmitted to weather stations all over the country. Meteorologists at each of the weather stations use these charts to prepare the daily forecasts for their community.

The *weather map* is the key to the daily weather forecast for the country as a whole and for any local community. Therefore, to understand how meteorologists forecast the weather, it is necessary to know how weather maps are prepared and how to read them.

UNDERSTANDING WEATHER MAPS

A weather map for the United States gives an overall picture of the weather throughout the country at a particular time of day. The preparation of a weather map begins with a blank map of the United States on which every weather station in the country is shown as a small circle. At regular intervals throughout the day, each weather station observes and records weather data such as the local (1) temperature, (2) dew point, (3) atmospheric pressure, (4) winds, (5) clouds, and (6) precipitation.

At prearranged times, each station sends a report of its observations to the central weather bureau in Washington, D.C., where meteorologists then summarize all the reports on one map. This is the weather map, copies of which are transmitted to each weather station.

In Washington, D.C., the weather data reported by each station is recorded on the weather map as a group of numbers and symbols, called a *station model* (Fig. 6–2). Each number and each symbol describes one aspect of the weather observed at each local weather station. When all the station models have been recorded on a weather map, the map may show as many as 10,000 items. (As the Weather Service continues to use customary units of measurement on weather maps, we will do the same on the weather maps in this chapter.)

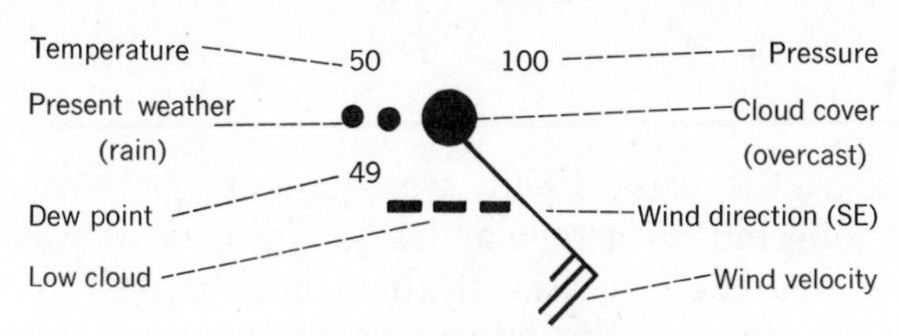

Fig. 6–2. Station model.

In Fig. 6–2, the numbers labeled *temperature* and *dew point* are in degrees Fahrenheit. The number labeled *pressure* is an abbreviated form of millibars, the unit used by weather scientists to measure atmospheric pressure (Chapter 2). In the abbreviation of the millibar reading, only the last three digits of the number are used. A decimal point belongs between the last two digits. For example, in the model, the number *100* is a shortened form of 10*10.0* millibars. In the same way, a pressure of 1*000.0* millibars (mb) is shown as 000 on a weather map; the number 995 on a map means a pressure of 999.5 mb; and so on. Some of the symbols used on weather maps are explained in greater detail in Fig. 6–3, page 104.

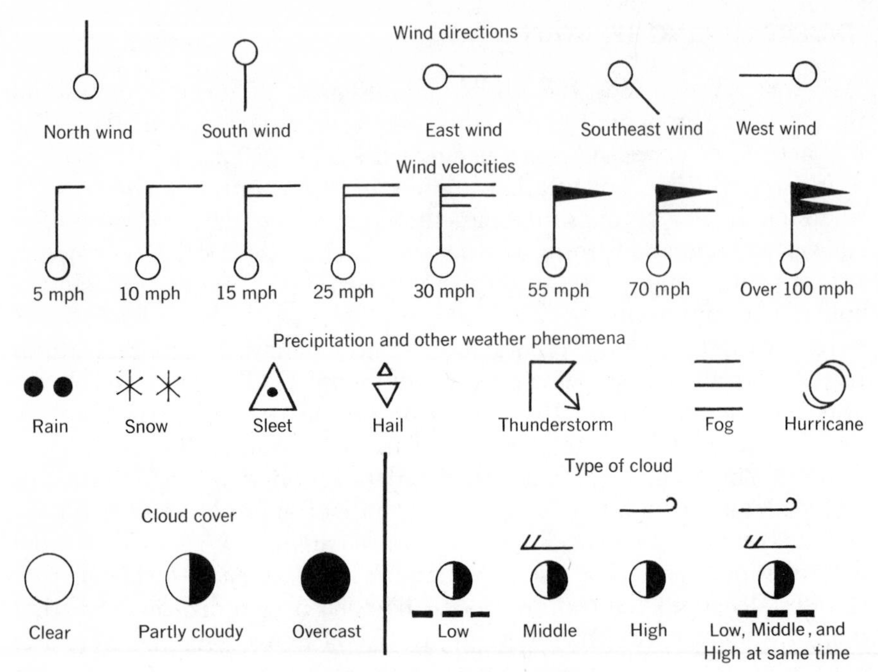

Fig. 6–3. Common weather symbols.

AIR MASSES

As far back as the early 1900s, weather data from many weather stations were collected on a regular basis. However, it was difficult to make accurate weather forecasts at that time because meteorologists did not fully understand the effects of temperature, humidity, and pressure on weather.

Today, as a result of many years of study, meteorologists do understand how these factors influence weather. We now know that the atmosphere is divided into huge masses of air, each mass having characteristics that are different from the characteristics of the other masses.

An *air mass* is a large section of the troposphere in which the temperature and humidity at a particular level are fairly uniform. Air masses may extend several kilometers into the atmosphere and may cover areas that vary in diameter from hundreds to thousands of kilometers. Air masses consist of either high-pressure systems or low-pressure systems. The boundary between any two pressure systems is often very clear-cut and is marked by distinct changes in the weather.

It is the movements of these air masses, and the changing positions of the boundaries between them, that change the weather of the communities over which they pass. Since different types of air masses have different characteristics, tracing the paths of these air masses as they move over the surface of the earth enables meteorologists to predict what the weather will be.

How Air Masses Are Formed

A particular type of air mass originates in a part of the world where surface conditions are much the same for relatively long periods of time. For example, many air masses originate in the Gulf of Mexico and in the central part of Canada. Air masses remaining over these regions for some time take on both the temperature and humidity characteristics of the surface below. In your laboratory experience, you observed on a small scale how the temperature and humidity of a sample of air can change.

A mass of air that remains over the warm water of the Gulf of Mexico for a long period of time slowly becomes warm and moist. On the other hand, an air mass that remains over the interior of Canada for a long period of time, especially in the winter, becomes very cold and dry.

Types of Air Masses

Air masses are named according to the nature and location of the surface over which they form. Air masses that form over land areas are called *continental* air masses; those that form over bodies of water are called *maritime* air masses. Air masses are also given names such as *polar*, *arctic*, and *tropical*, depending on the type of region over which they form.

The names given to air masses are usually abbreviated on weather maps according to the nature of the surface and region over which the air masses were formed. Thus, continental polar is shortened to cP, maritime polar is shortened to mP, maritime tropical is shortened to mT, and continental tropical becomes cT. Some of the principal types of air masses of North America and the paths they follow across the United States are shown in Fig. 6–4.

Movement of Air Masses

Our day-to-day weather depends mainly on the type of air mass that is passing over our community. For example, in the winter, if a continental polar (cP) air mass moves southward from Canada into the United States, it brings cold, dry weather to the regions over which

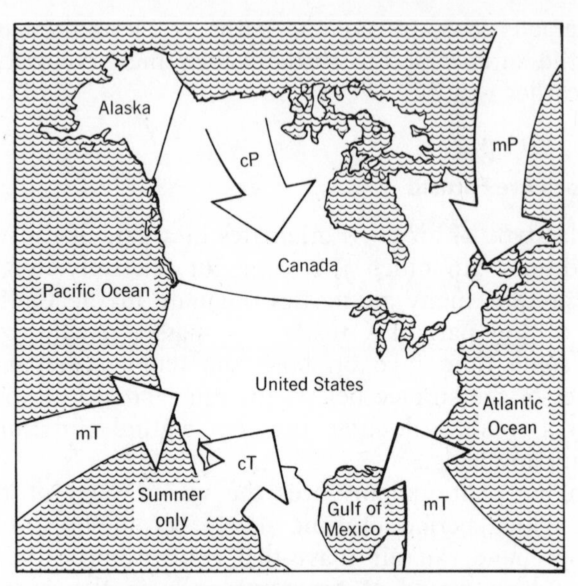

Fig. 6–4. Air masses of North America.

it passes. In the summer, continental polar air from Canada brings cool, dry weather to the United States. The kinds of weather that some common types of air masses bring with them are listed in Table 6–1.

Table 6–1. Air Masses and the Weather They Bring

Name	Source	Weather
Continental polar (cP)	Canada	Clear, cold, dry
Continental tropical (cT)	Southwestern U.S. and Mexico	Clear, hot, dry
Maritime tropical (mT)	Gulf of Mexico and Caribbean; Atlantic and Pacific Oceans close to equator	Cloudy, warm, rain, thunderstorms
Maritime polar (mP)	Atlantic and Pacific Oceans near polar regions	Cloudy, cold, rain or snow

WEATHER FRONTS

The boundary between two air masses is called a *weather front*. Storms are frequent along a weather front. Even if a storm does not occur, the weather is usually uncertain.

Fronts are named according to the relative positions and movements of the air masses that meet at a front. A *cold front* is the boundary along which a cold air mass overtakes a slower-moving mass of warm air. A *warm front* is the boundary along which a warm air mass overtakes a slower-moving mass of cold air. A *stationary front* is the boundary between two air masses that are not moving relative to each other. When two cold air masses force a warm air mass caught between them completely off the ground, the boundary between the cold air masses is called an *occluded front*. The symbols used on weather maps to indicate these types of fronts are shown in Fig. 6–5.

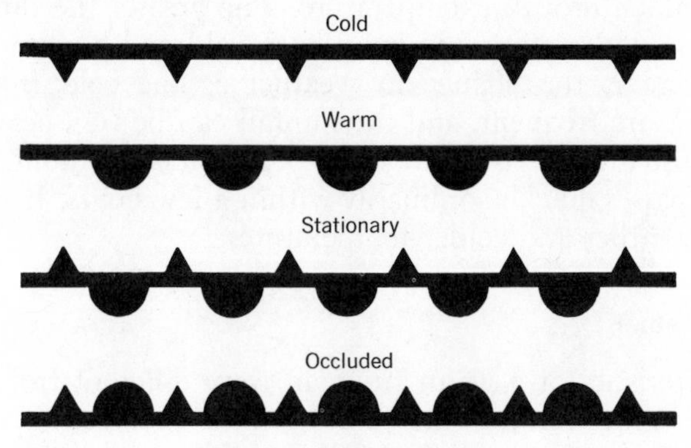

Fig. 6–5. Types of fronts.

Since a front always separates two air masses having different characteristics, a meteorologist following the movements of fronts can use this information to forecast the weather.

Cold-Front Weather

Ordinarily the air behind a cold front is cold and dry (cP), and the air ahead of the cold front is warm and moist (mT), as shown in Fig. 6–6. The cold, dry air is denser than the warm, moist air. Since

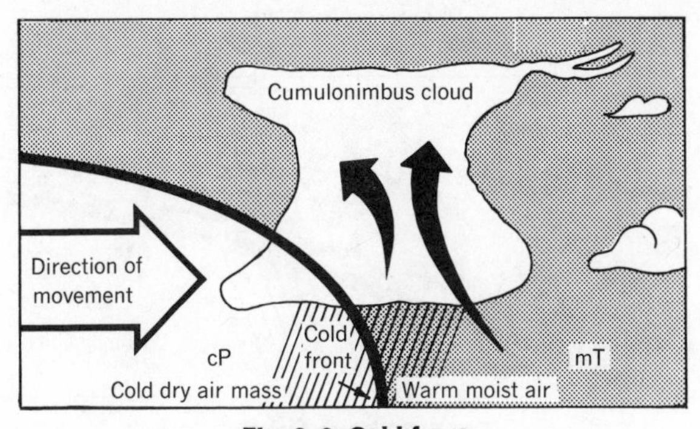

Fig. 6–6. Cold front.

the cold air is denser than the warm air mass it is meeting, the cold air mass behind a cold front stays close to the ground. The cold air mass forces its way under the warm air mass and lifts the warm air mass above it. Since the warm air mass is usually quite moist, the water vapor in the warm air mass condenses into clouds as the air ahead of the cold front rises into the air. Cumulonimbus clouds form because the warm moist air is lifted nearly vertically by the steep wall of approaching cold air. Heavy precipitation is common along a cold front.

Cold fronts are usually accompanied by heavy rain or snow, high winds, and sudden drops in temperature. The greater the difference in air temperature and air pressure between a cold and a warm air mass, the more severe is the change in weather as the cold front passes. Thunderstorms are frequent, and the rainfall can be very heavy. A cold front, which usually travels at about 50 kilometers per hour, often approaches and passes quickly, ordinarily within a few hours. It is followed by clear, dry weather and colder temperatures.

Warm-Front Weather

The characteristics of a warm front are very different from those of a cold front. With warm fronts, the air mass that causes the warm, moist air (mT) to rise upward, as in Fig. 6–7, is maritime polar air ahead of the front. The slope at which the warm moist air (mT) rises over the maritime polar air (mP) into the atmosphere is very gentle. For this reason, the clouds that form ahead of a warm front are of the stratus type.

Stratus clouds appear high in the sky, often as far as 1500 kilometers ahead of the warm front itself, and 24 hours or more in advance. To an observer on the ground, cloudiness increases gradually as the warm front approaches. When the clouds become thick enough to obscure the sun or moon, rain or snow usually begins to fall. It may rain or snow for 24 hours or more. After the warm front, which usually travels

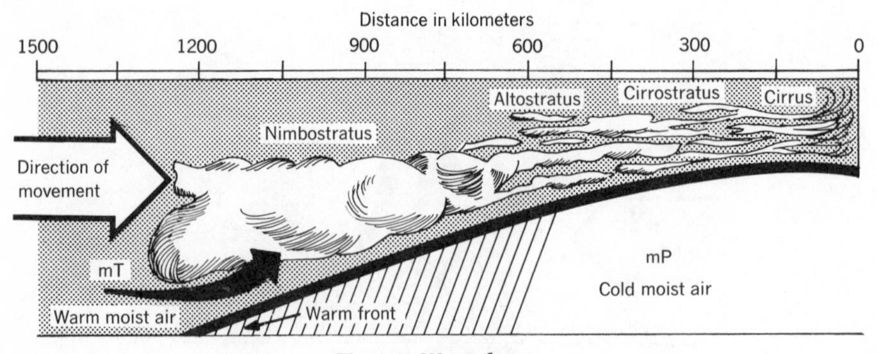

Fig. 6–7. Warm front.

at about 25 kilometers per hour, has passed, and as the center of the warm air mass reaches the observer, the air temperature increases, the wind direction shifts, the steady rain or snow ends, and the skies become partly cloudy.

Stationary-Front Weather

A cold air mass and a warm air mass may remain in the same relative positions for a time. In this case, a stationary front develops. At a stationary front, the warm air rises into the atmosphere but at a gentle slope. Therefore, the weather along the stationary front resembles the weather along a warm front.

Occluded-Front Weather

It often happens that a cold front catches up to a warm front which has another cold air mass ahead of it. Then, the warm air mass that was in between the two colder air masses is lifted completely off the ground. At this point, the cold air mass that was preceding the warm front now touches the cold air mass behind the cold front. The boundary where the two cold air masses meet—with the warm air mass above them—we have already called an occluded front. As you can see in Fig. 6–8, the weather along an occluded front is a combination of the weather along a cold front and a warm front.

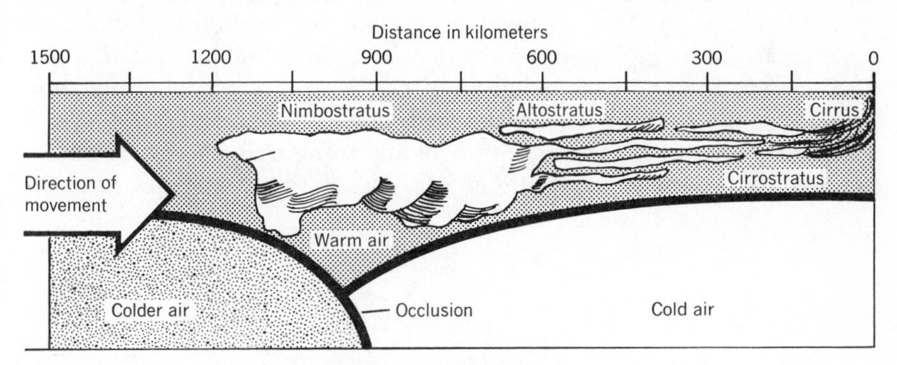

Fig. 6–8. Occluded front.

SPECIAL STORMS

Under certain conditions, a storm may develop within an air mass. The most destructive storms are those formed in maritime tropical air masses because these air masses are laden with warm, moist air. Common among such storms are *thunderstorms, tornadoes,* and *hurricanes.*

Thunderstorms

A thunderstorm is a local storm of short duration that is produced by the rapid movement of air within a cumulonimbus cloud. Thunderstorms are noted for the lightning, thunder, strong gusts of wind, and heavy rain or hail that accompanies them.

Within a cumulonimbus cloud, warm, moist air rises rapidly into the atmosphere resulting from one of two conditions. Either the air mass has become very warm because the earth's surface below has been strongly heated by the sun, or a mass of cool, heavy air has slid under the warm air mass, forcing it upward. Usually, the warm air contains much moisture and, as the warm air rises rapidly, the moisture condenses into a towering cumulonimbus cloud. The height of such clouds may reach about 12,000 meters above the earth. Within the cumulonimbus cloud, the air rushes upward and downward in strong currents, or drafts (Fig. 6–9). When a thunderstorm passes overhead, we may become aware of the downdrafts as very strong gusts of wind blowing around us.

As raindrops form in a cumulonimbus cloud, the strong air currents are believed to split them into drops of varying sizes. The larger droplets move downward, and the smaller, upward. As this happens, electrical charges build up at different levels in the cloud, as shown in Fig. 6–9. When the differences in charge become great enough between the parts of the cloud, between two clouds, or between the cloud and the ground, an electrical discharge in the form of *lightning* passes between them. This discharge produces so much heat that the air around it suddenly expands as in an explosion, producing the loud sound we call *thunder*.

The next time you see a lightning discharge, try to determine how many seconds elapse between the flash and the sound of the thunder. Each second that separates a flash of lightning and its accompanying thunder, when the temperature is 5°C, means that a distance of about

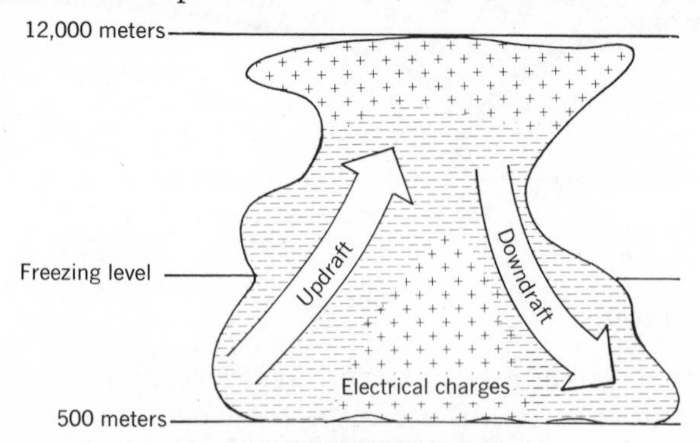

Fig. 6–9. Typical thunderstorm.

330 meters separates you from the lightning. For example, if you hear thunder about six seconds after seeing lightning, the lightning discharge has taken place about 2000 meters from you, or about 2 kilometers away. (To determine the distance of lightning at other temperatures, see page 227.)

It has been estimated that more than 10,000,000 thunderstorms occur over the earth every year. In the United States, most thunderstorms occur from April through September. They are rare in the winter, especially in the northern parts of the United States.

Tornadoes

Tornadoes, or twisters, are severe, whirling storms in which the winds reach speeds of hundreds of miles per hour. Tornadoes form under conditions similar to those that produce thunderstorms: the lifting and condensation of warm, moist air. Thus, tornadoes are most likely to occur when very hot, humid air gives rise to cumulonimbus clouds and thunderstorms. At times during violent thunderstorms, a funnel-shaped swirling current of air twists downward from a cumulonimbus cloud and reaches the earth as a tornado.

Wherever the tip of the tornado touches the ground, it destroys almost everything in its path. The destruction is caused by a combination of very high winds, which may reach speeds of from 300 to 800 kilometers per hour, and the very low pressures that exist within the funnel. When a tornado passes over a building, the air pressure outside the building drops sharply, enabling the normal air pressure inside the building to push the walls outward with great force. At the same time, the winds act against the building. The combination of both these forces may tear the building apart with explosive violence.

The area of destruction left by a tornado is usually very narrow, since most funnels are usually less than 400 meters in diameter. Most tornadoes in the United States travel in a northeasterly direction at an average speed of 55 to 70 kilometers per hour. They usually occur in the midwestern states, but they may occur elsewhere. Although tornadoes ordinarily occur in the spring and during the afternoon hours, they may occur at any hour of the day during any season of the year.

Hurricanes

A hurricane, or tropical cyclone, is a large, low-pressure system in which precipitation is heavy and the winds strong. In some parts of the world, such as the Pacific Ocean, hurricanes are called *typhoons*.

Hurricanes originate in the hot, moist air over tropical oceans. The moist, hot air rises, cools at higher altitudes, and condenses. The condensation of the water vapor releases a large amount of heat. This additional heat added to the rising air causes the air to rise even more rapidly. As this process continues, a very low-pressure system forms. The air surrounding this system rushes toward its center at great speed. As is true of any moving body of air, this moving air is deflected by the earth's rotation. As a result, the air begins to rotate in a counterclockwise direction (in the Northern Hemisphere). When the winds within this type of low-pressure system reach a speed of at least 120 kilometers per hour, the system is classified as a tropical cyclone, or hurricane.

A large hurricane may cover an area having a diameter of about 650 kilometers. Seen from above, the clouds spiral in toward the center of the hurricane. At the center of the storm there is a clear section of sky called the *eye* of the hurricane. This eye may be from 25 to 65 kilometers wide. The winds within the eye are nearly calm.

Heavy showers and thunderstorms occur in the clouds that encircle the eye. Wind speeds are highest just outside the eye, where they often exceed 150 kilometers per hour and may be as high as 300 kilometers per hour.

In the Northern Hemisphere, a hurricane travels in a westerly direction at first, and then it usually curves northward and eastward. The paths usually followed by hurricanes in the vicinity of the United States are shown by the arrows in Fig. 6–10. Hurricanes eventually die out as they reach higher latitudes, or when they move inland. Because the air over the ocean is colder at higher latitudes, the hurricane loses the heat required to maintain it. A hurricane that moves inland, however, dies out sooner than one that remains over the ocean. This happens because the friction with the land slows down the hurricane winds, and because the land areas do not contain enough moisture to keep the hurricane going.

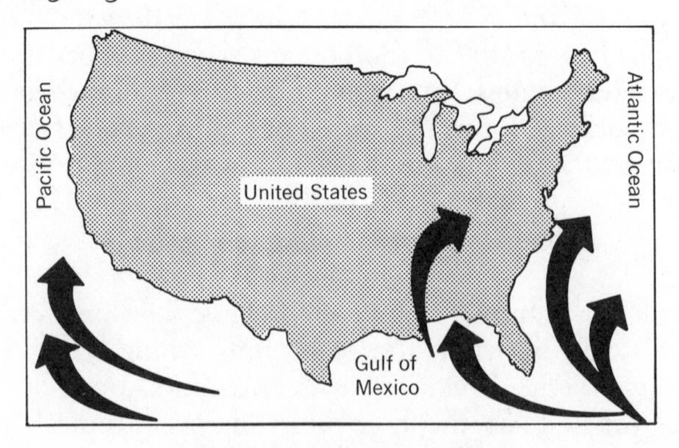

Fig. 6–10. Hurricane paths.

LOCATING FRONTS

An important part of weather forecasting is predicting the movement of fronts. Before this can be done, the fronts must be located and charted on a weather map.

One way of locating fronts is to study the *isobars* on a weather map. Isobars are the lines that connect the weather stations reporting the same air pressures. As shown in Fig. 6–11, isobars have sharp bends (kinks) wherever they cross a front.

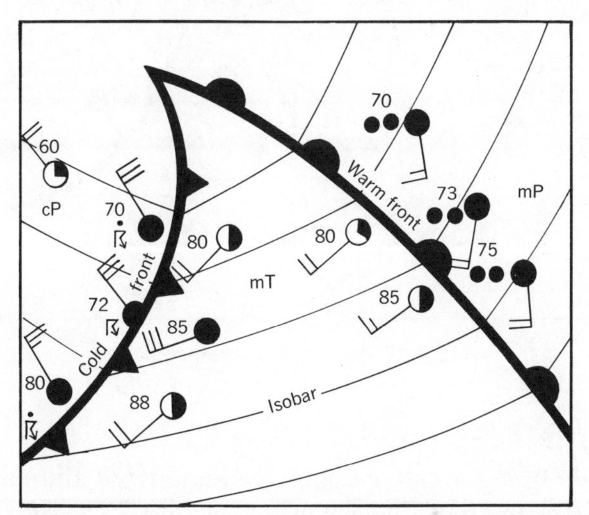

Fig. 6–11. Differences in winds and temperatures mark the locations of fronts.

Fronts may also be located on a weather map by looking for weather stations close to each other that have marked differences in winds and air temperatures. For example, note the differences in temperatures and wind directions between the stations on either side of the cold front and the warm front in Fig. 6–11.

Fig. 6–12, page 114, represents a simplified weather map. This map contains many of the essential features shown on all surface weather maps: weather stations, isobars, high-pressure areas (H), low-pressure areas (L), and fronts.

FORECASTING THE WEATHER

Meteorologists make two kinds of weather forecasts. *Short-range forecasts* attempt to predict what the weather will be 24 to 48 hours in advance. *Long-range forecasts* attempt to predict the weather for a week to a month or more in advance. Using computers, meteorologists are now trying to predict the weather for as much as a year in advance.

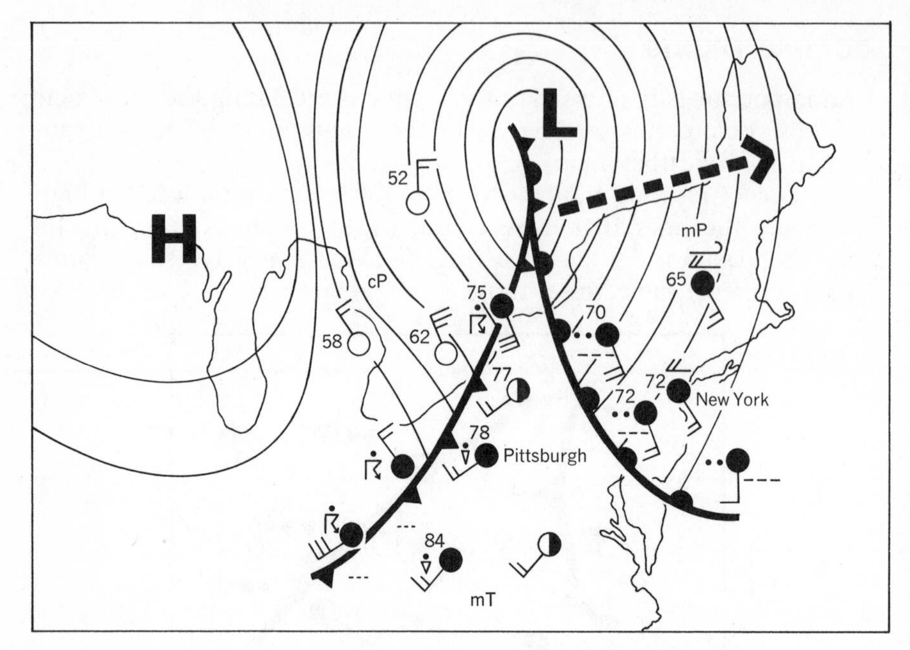

Fig. 6–12. A simplified weather map.

Short-Range Forecasts

The short-range forecast for your community is the daily weather report that you read in the newspaper or hear over the radio or see on television. These forecasts are much more accurate for the first 12 hours of a 48-hour period than for the last 12 hours.

A short-range forecast is made after a series of surface maps have been prepared that show how the weather is changing over regular six-hour periods. From these weather maps, the meteorologist estimates how fast and in what direction the front shown on the map is moving. Once he knows the speed and direction of the front, the meteorologist can predict what the position of the front will be in the future, and the kind of weather the front will bring with it.

Let us see how a meteorologist works. In the simplified weather map in Fig. 6–12, assume that the low-pressure system (marked L) and the cold and warm fronts associated with it are traveling eastward along the path shown by the arrow. Weather stations ahead of this low-pressure system have received reports concerning it. Knowing the speed at which the system is traveling, meteorologists can calculate when it will reach particular communities. The meteorologists then predict what the winds, temperatures, and sky conditions will be, and the chances that it will rain. Sample forecasts for New York City and Pittsburgh, two cities in the path of the low-pressure system, might read as follows:

June —, 19—, 6:00 A.M.

New York City and vicinity. Increasing cloudiness, rain beginning in the early afternoon, ending by tomorrow morning. Partly cloudy tomorrow with possibility of showers. The low tonight 70 to 75 and the high tomorrow in the upper 80s.

In making up the New York forecast, the meteorologist has taken these factors into account:

1. A warm front is moving toward New York.
2. The weather ahead of the warm front will pass over New York before the front itself.
3. The weather ahead of the warm front is cloudy and rainy.
4. This cloudy and rainy weather will take about twenty hours to pass over New York.
5. After the warm front passes, the warm, moist air mass (mT) will pass over New York, bringing with it partly cloudy skies, higher temperatures, and scattered showers.
6. The warm air mass is expected to remain over New York for the remainder of the forecast period.

In Pittsburgh, which is farther west than New York, the warm front has already arrived. Thus, the Pittsburgh forecast begins with items 5 and 6 of the New York forecast.

June —, 19—, 6:00 A.M.

Pittsburgh and vicinity. Partly cloudy today with the possibility of scattered showers [item 5]. Temperatures in the high 80s or low 90s today [item 6]. Probable thunderstorms late tonight, followed by rapid clearing. Mostly clear tomorrow with cooler temperatures. High tomorrow in the low 70s.

The Pittsburgh meteorologist has taken the following factors into account in making his forecast:

1. The warm, moist air mass (mT) with its high temperatures and scattered showers will be passing over Pittsburgh all day.
2. Sometime during the night, a cold front will pass over Pittsburgh. The passage of a cold front often results in thunderstorms.
3. After the cold front passes, a cold, dry air mass (cP) will pass over Pittsburgh. The center of the cold, dry air mass is represented by the

large letter H, which stands for high pressure. A cold, dry air mass is usually accompanied by clear skies and cooler weather.

In general, the daily weather forecasts are accurate about 85% of the time.

Long-Range Forecasts

Meteorologists cannot predict the weather accurately for an entire month or year. However, they are attempting to predict what the average weather would be for such periods of time. These attempts are based on the observation that certain kinds of weather usually follow each other in cycles. For example, after a cold front passes, certain kinds of weather patterns usually develop until the next cold front passes. However, there are many different kinds of weather patterns and many irregularities within these patterns.

Accurate long-range forecasts can be made only for the first week of the period. Thereafter, the accuracy of the forecast diminishes rapidly. Modern weather forecasting is not completely accurate because we do not yet completely understand the complex movements and energy changes that take place within the atmosphere.

In the future, as more data are gathered and analyzed by computers, meteorologists will learn more about the complicated ways in which forces work in the atmosphere. Once they know how these forces act, they should be able to improve their long-range weather forecasts considerably.

WHY CLIMATES DIFFER

Climate is the general character of the weather that exists over a particular region of the earth for a long period of time. Unlike the weather, which represents the hour-to-hour and day-to-day changes in the atmosphere over a region, climate is the average of all the weather changes over a region for a great many years.

The major factors that are often used to characterize the climate of a region are temperature and precipitation. Because the surface of the earth is not heated evenly, and because land masses, oceans, and polar ice masses are not distributed evenly over the surface of the earth, the climate varies greatly from region to region.

Climates may be divided into three main groups according to the average temperatures existing in a region. One main group would include the arctic and antarctic regions, where temperatures are very low throughout the year. A second group would include the belt around the equator, in which temperatures are very high throughout the year.

The third group would include the middle latitudes, in which the temperatures vary greatly throughout the year.

Thus, climates can be described as *polar* (for the arctic regions), *tropical* (for the equatorial regions), and *temperate* (for the middle latitude regions). Each of these climatic regions can be classified further according to the amount of precipitation that falls within each region.

The United States has many climatic regions. A simplified description of the climates of the continental United States is given in Table 6–2.

Table 6–2. Major Climates of the United States

Location	*Name*	*Temperature Range (approximate)*	*Annual Precipitation (approximate)*
East Coast and Midwest	Humid continental	Below zero to above 100° F	20 to 40 inches
Southeast	Humid subtropical	About freezing to over 100° F	60 inches
Northwest Pacific Coast	Humid marine	Slightly below freezing to about 80° F	40 to 60 inches
Southwest	Desert	Below zero to about 110° F	Less than 10 inches
West Coast	Mediterranean	About 40° F to 80° F	20 to 30 inches
Great Plains	Steppes	Below zero to about 110° F	Less than 20 inches

Looking Back

To forecast weather for a particular region, we need to know the condition of the atmosphere with respect to factors such as air pressure, temperature, and humidity, as well as the speed and direction of the wind. In some regions, the presence of air pollutants must also be taken into account.

Looking Ahead

You have noted how important the sun is to our environment on earth. The moon, planets, and other bodies outside the earth also affect our environment. We will discuss the effects of such bodies in Unit II.

Multiple-Choice Questions

1. The person who first brought attention to the fact that storms move from place to place was
   a. Edison b. Franklin c. Jefferson d. Morse
2. A barometric pressure reading of 1005.0 millibars would appear on a weather map as
   a. 005 b. 050 c. 500 d. 1005
3. The temperature and humidity within any given air mass are
   a. fairly uniform at any given altitude
   b. quite different between the center and edges of the air mass at any given altitude
   c. likely to vary widely within the center of the air mass
   d. always very different from the temperature and humidity within nearby air masses
4. An air mass that forms over a body of water is a
   a. polar air mass
   b. tropical air mass
   c. continental air mass
   d. maritime air mass
5. An air mass that forms over the Gulf of Mexico would be identified on a weather map as
   a. cP b. aM c. mT d. mP
6. Cumulonimbus clouds may form when warm, moist air is lifted into the atmosphere by
   a. strong winds
   b. expanding air
   c. condensation
   d. a mass of cold air below
7. Meteorologists believe that lightning is caused by the discharge of electricity built up in clouds as a result of
   a. friction between rain clouds
   b. friction between cumulonimbus clouds and layers of moist air
   c. the splitting of raindrops into drops of different sizes
   d. the scattering of moist air within clouds by thunder
8. If you hear a clap of thunder about three seconds after seeing a flash of lightning, the distance of the lightning to the observer is about
   a. 100 meters b. 1000 meters c. 2000 meters d. 5000 meters
9. Thunderstorms are least frequent during the
   a. summer b. winter c. spring d. fall
10. The type of cloud that is associated with tornadoes is the
    a. altostratus b. cumulus c. cumulonimbus d. stratus
11. The most important factor in the formation of a tornado is the
    a. barometric pressure in the clouds
    b. location of the clouds over the earth
    c. height of the clouds above the earth
    d. rise and condensation of warm, moist air
12. Most tornadoes occur during the
    a. afternoon hours in the spring
    b. afternoon hours in the fall
    c. early morning hours in the summer
    d. late afternoon in the winter

13. A tropical storm is classified as a hurricane when the wind speed reaches about
    a. 60 km/hr b. 120 km/hr c. 180 km/hr d. 240 km/hr
14. Hurricanes die out most rapidly when they pass over land areas that are
    a. cold and dry
    b. cold and wet
    c. warm and wet
    d. warm and dry
15. The type of weather front that is at the leading edge of a warm air mass is a
    a. warm front
    b. cold front
    c. occluded front
    d. stationary front
16. The type of weather that follows the passage of a cold front is
    a. continental tropical
    b. superior polar
    c. superior maritime
    d. continental polar
17. A cold front usually travels at a speed of about
    a. 25 km/hr b. 50 km/hr c. 75 km/hr d. 100 km/hr
18. Of the following, the statement that is *true* is
    a. cold fronts move more slowly than warm fronts
    b. precipitation may extend hundreds of kilometers in front of a warm front
    c. tornadoes are usually associated with the passage of a warm front
    d. a stationary front forms where a cold front overtakes a warm front
19. A sharp bend in an isobar on a weather map indicates the presence of a
    a. warm air mass
    b. high-pressure system
    c. low-pressure system
    d. front
20. Shortly after a warm front passes over your neighborhood, which of the following *does not* occur?
    a. the temperature rises
    b. the humidity remains high
    c. scattered showers occur
    d. steady rain continues to fall
21. Hours after a cold front passes over your neighborhood, which of the following *does not* occur?
    a. the humidity decreases
    b. the temperature decreases
    c. the rainfall increases
    d. the sky clears rapidly

Modified True-False Questions

1. An air mass that stagnates over the Gulf of Mexico should become warm and *dry*.
2. An air mass that originates over the Atlantic Ocean off the coast of Canada is indicated on a weather map by the abbreviation *cP*.
3. Hurricanes originate in *maritime tropical* air masses.
4. The winds within the center of *a hurricane* may reach a speed of 500 kilometers per hour.
5. Most hurricanes originate over the *southeastern states* during the late summer.
6. The leading edge of a cold mass of air is called *a cold front.*
7. The boundary between two different masses of air that are not moving relative to each other is called *a stationary front.*

8. Strong winds and heavy precipitation are common along *cold* fronts.
9. The weather associated with cold fronts usually takes *24 hours* to pass over a given weather station.
10. Isobars are lines drawn on a weather map to indicate areas of equal air *temperature.*

Thought Questions

1. List five different weather factors that each weather station records at regular intervals.
2. Name the kind of region from which each of the following types of air masses originate. Describe the temperatures and humidity you would expect to find in each air mass:
   a. maritime tropical b. maritime polar c. continental polar
3. Explain how a thunderstorm develops. Account for the strong gusts of wind and the electrical discharges that are associated with a thunderstorm.
4. Explain why the thunder that accompanies a flash of lightning is always heard after the lightning discharge.
5. What steps would you take to avoid being injured by an approaching tornado?
6. Explain how a hurricane develops, and state one factor that determines its path.
7. What is the difference between weather and climate?
8. Study the weather stations shown in the weather map below. Then, for each description of weather conditions, give the letter (or letters) of the weather station(s) where those conditions exist.

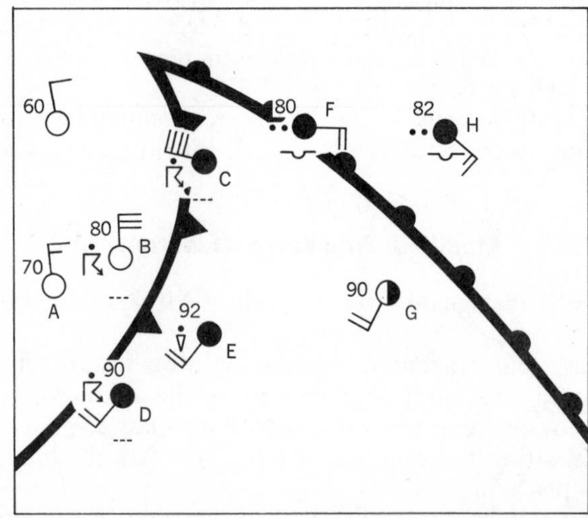

a. Wind WNW at 40 mph
b. Wind SE at 15 mph
c. Overcast; rain falling
d. Clear sky
e. Thunderstorm
f. Closest to the warm front
g. Closest to the cold front
h. Location of a mT air mass

UNIT II
Our Planet's Environment

Overview

Astronomy and space exploration have revealed that the earth is not alone in the *universe*. The universe includes the solar system of which the earth is a part, all the stars, everything else in space that consists of matter, and all forms of energy. The universe is the environment of the earth.

Even though the nearest bodies to the earth are very distant, these bodies influence the earth and its inhabitants in many ways. Examples of such influences are gravitation, tides, magnetism, and various kinds of radiations. Ordinarily we are not aware of these influences. However, they are an important part of our environment because they contribute to the daily life of every living thing.

CHAPTER 7
WHAT IS THE PLACE OF THE EARTH IN THE SOLAR SYSTEM?

When you have completed this chapter, you should be able to:

1. *Identify* the solar system and the major theories dealing with its origin.
2. *Describe* the sun, stating its composition, structure, and source of energy.
3. *Indicate* methods of using solar energy that help decrease environmental pollution.
4. *List* the planets in their order of increasing distance from the sun and describe each of them.
5. *Compare* the contributions of the following astronomers: Ptolemy, Copernicus, Galileo, Kepler.
6. *Distinguish* between (*a*) rotation and revolution; (*b*) comets, meteoroids, meteors, and meteorites.

In the laboratory experience that follows, you will learn how substances can be analyzed with a spectroscope. This instrument can detect matter present in the solar system.

Laboratory Experience

HOW DO WE USE THE SPECTROSCOPE TO ANALYZE SUBSTANCES?

A. Set up the equipment as shown in Fig. 7–1. Place a small crystal of rock salt on the wire gauze. Heat the crystal for about one minute.
   1. What is the color of the flame?

B. Allow the gauze to cool, and remove the remainder of the crystal. Repeat using crystals of potassium chloride, calcium chloride, lithium chloride, and copper sulfate. Be sure to place each crystal on a clean portion of the wire gauze.
   2. Copy and fill in the table that follows Fig. 7–1.

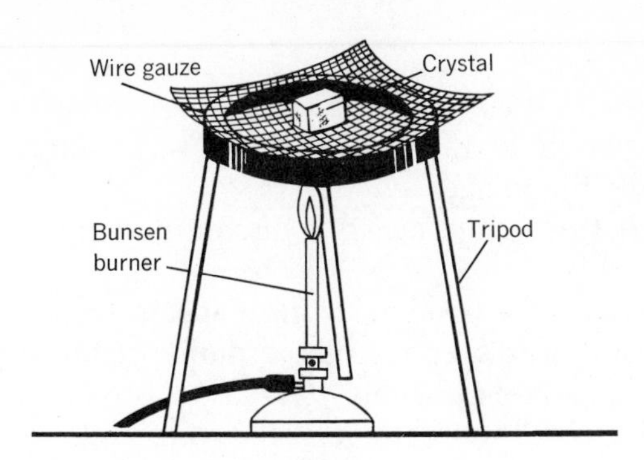

Fig. 7–1.

Crystal	*Color of Flame*
Potassium chloride	
Calcium chloride	
Lithium chloride	
Copper sulfate	

C. (*Note to the teacher*: This part of the laboratory experience should be presented as a demonstration lesson in a darkened room.) Set up the equipment as shown in Fig. 7–2. To strike a carbon arc, use two carbon rods and a 110-volt direct-current source in series with one 660-watt resistor. To strike a metallic arc, such as copper, use two copper rods and increase the number of resistors to three or four (connected in parallel).

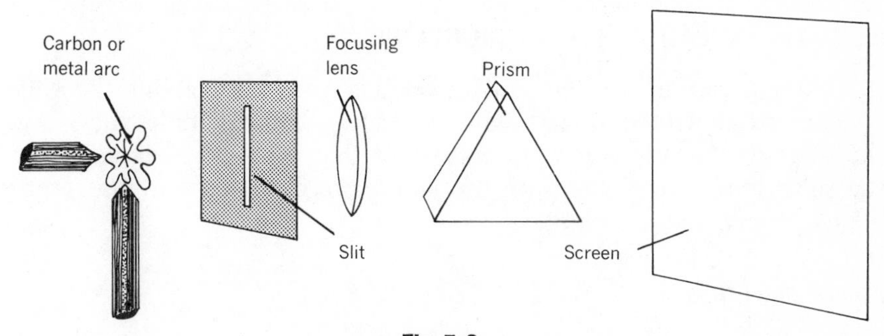

Fig. 7–2.

Strike a carbon arc. Align the slit, focusing lens and prism so that a sharp image appears on the screen.

3. Describe the image.
4. What phenomenon in nature resembles this image?

5. Account for the formation of this image in nature.
6. Why is this image called a continuous spectrum?

D. Strike a copper arc and, as in part B, focus the image on the screen.
7. Describe the image.
8. Why is this image called a discontinuous (bright-line) spectrum?

E. If available, secure a hand-held prism spectroscope or grating spectroscope. Using this spectroscope, examine light coming from the sun or from a carbon-arc lamp.
9. Describe what you observe.

F. Repeat procedure E, but this time observe the light coming from a lighted neon tube (or any other gas tube).
10. Describe what you observe.
11. What determines whether a body will give off a continuous or a discontinuous spectrum?
12. What information does a spectrum reveal to an astronomer?

Introduction

The *solar system* is the region of the universe in which we are located. Our solar system consists of the sun and all the bodies that travel around the sun under the influence of its gravitational attraction. These bodies include the earth, the other *planets* of our solar system, the *satellites* (or moons) of the major planets, *asteroids, comets, meteoroids,* and the dust and gases in the interplanetary space between these bodies.

HOW THE SOLAR SYSTEM ORIGINATED

Although astronomers have discovered a great deal about the solar system and the forces that hold it together, they can only guess how the solar system originated. Two theories that attempt to explain how the solar system originated are the *planetesimal theory* and the *protoplanet theory.*

Planetesimal Theory

According to the once-popular planetesimal (small planet) theory, the solar system came into existence as the result of a near collision between our sun and a passing star (Fig. 7–3). As the star sped past the sun, the gravitational attraction between the star and the sun drew a large mass of hot gases from the sun. The star sped onward, but the gases drawn from the sun did not return. Instead, these gases began

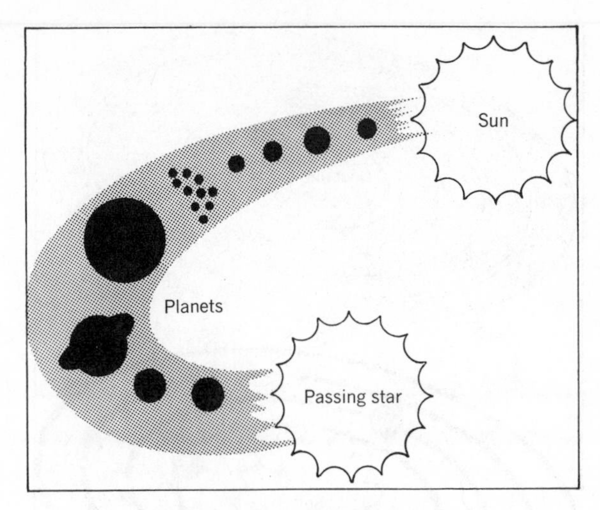

Fig. 7–3. Planetesimal theory.

to circle the sun. In time, they cooled and condensed into the planets that circle the sun today. Few scientists support this theory today.

Protoplanet Theory

The protoplanet theory is more widely accepted. According to the protoplanet theory, our solar system formed from a cloud of dust and gas spinning in space (Fig. 7–4, page 126). The whirling dust and gases in the central region of the cloud condensed, forming the sun. Smaller portions of this cloud of dust and gases condensed into the planets. Astronomers believe that about 99% of the original cloud condensed into the sun; the remaining 1% of the original cloud condensed into the major planets and other solid objects in the solar system.

At first, all of the newly formed planets were surrounded by thick envelopes of gas that had not condensed. Then the sun grew hotter and began to radiate heat and light into space. These radiations swept away all the gases surrounding some planets and some of the gases surrounding other planets.

As the solar system began to assume its present form, other bodies besides the sun and planets came into existence. Among these were the satellites that circle most of the planets, of which our moon is an example, and asteroids, meteors, and comets.

THE SUN

Of all the objects in the universe, the sun is most important to us. Not only does the gravitational attraction between the earth and the

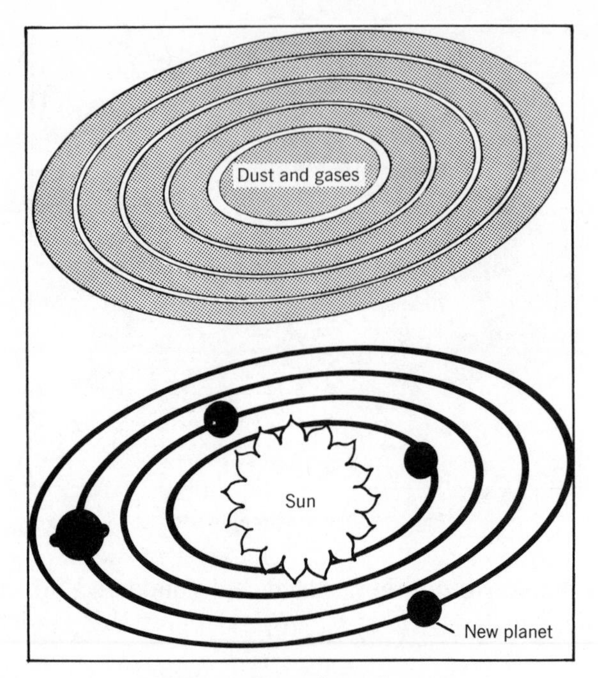

Fig. 7–4. Protoplanet theory.

sun keep the earth in its orbit, but the radiant energy given off by the sun makes possible the existence of life on earth. Plants require sunlight in order to live and grow. The plants produce the food and oxygen that animals need in order to live and grow. In turn, we eat both plants and the meat of animals that we may live and grow. Thus, all of our food and most of our oxygen come indirectly from the sun.

In addition, the radiant energy of the sun evaporates the water from the ocean. The evaporated water forms clouds, from which rain falls to the earth. Rain not only changes the landscape through erosion, but rain also supplies the water that plants and animals require for life. Even the energy stored in coal and oil, which we use to heat our homes and to run our machines, comes from extinct organisms that obtained their energy, either directly or indirectly, from the sun.

Size of the Sun

Although the sun is not very large for a star, it is huge compared to the earth. The diameter of the sun is about 1,400,000 kilometers, over 100 times the diameter of the earth. If the sun were a hollow ball filled with objects the size of the earth, it would take more than a million of these objects to fill the ball completely.

Composition of the Sun

Astronomers study the composition of stars with a *spectroscope*. A common type of spectroscope uses a *prism*, which is a triangle-shaped piece of solid glass. The prism disperses (spreads out) a beam of white light into a band of colors, which, together, make up white light. Such a band, called a *spectrum*, looks like the colors you observe in a rainbow. Recall the spectra you observed in your laboratory experience.

Sunlight (white light) passing through droplets of water in the atmosphere is spread out, as by a prism, into the colors of the spectrum that make up sunlight (Fig. 7–5). The colors of the spectrum are red, orange, yellow, green, blue, indigo, and violet. These colors, representing a *continuous spectrum*, always appear in this order and blend into one another. Under certain conditions, described in Chapter 11, pages 216–217, a spectrum may consist of a series of lines, each line having a specific color. Such a spectrum is called *discontinuous*.

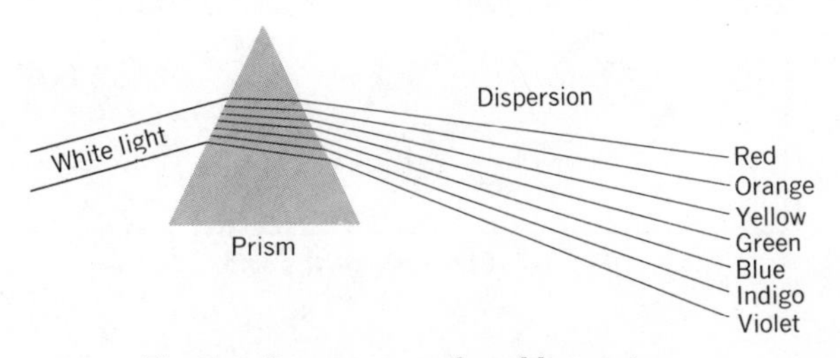

Fig. 7–5. Spectrum produced by a prism.

Studying the sun with a spectroscope, astronomers have discovered that the lines in its spectrum match many of the spectral lines produced by elements here on earth. Minute quantities of about 60 elements found on earth are also present in the sun. Astronomers have also discovered that the sun consists of about 82% hydrogen and about 17% helium.

In fact, through the use of the spectroscope, astronomers discovered helium on the sun before scientists knew it existed on earth. Helium was discovered because astronomers found that certain lines in the sun's spectrum did not match the spectral lines of any element known on earth. Scientists named this strange element helium after *helios*, the Greek word for sun.

Structure of the Sun

At sunset, the sun often appears to the eye as a smooth orange or red disk with a sharply defined edge. Actually, the surface of the sun is a mass of whirling, bubbling gases, which at times flare hundreds of thousands of kilometers upward. The visible part of the sun is its atmosphere, which consists of the *photosphere*, the *chromosphere*, and the *corona* (Fig. 7–6).

The photosphere is the lowest region of the sun's atmosphere. Ordinarily, it appears to us as a dazzling bright yellow disk. The temperature of the photosphere is about 6100°C.

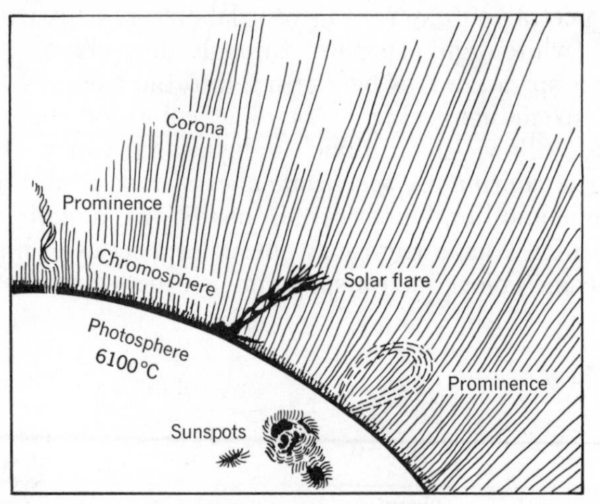

Fig. 7–6. Structure of the sun.

Photographs of the sun taken through special filters show dark spots on the photosphere called *sunspots*. Sunspots appear dark because they are about 1100°C cooler than the photosphere itself. The sunspots constantly appear and disappear on the surface of the sun. Most sunspots last less than a day; a few sunspots last a week or more. The way in which sunspots move over the surface of the sun shows that the sun itself is rotating on an axis, making one complete revolution about every 25 days at its equator and every 33 or more days near its poles.

Sunspots usually occur in groups. An individual sunspot may range from 800 to 80,000 kilometers in diameter. A large group of sunspots may cover an area 300,000 kilometers across. The number of sunspots is changing continually. On the average, the number of sunspots reaches a peak about every 11 years.

An eruption of hot gases called a *solar flare* sometimes occurs in a sunspot. The flare is accompanied by a burst of electrically charged particles (*ions*) and radiations that are ejected from the sun at speeds of thousands of kilometers per hour. When these particles and radiations reach the earth, they produce magnetic and electrical disturbances in the atmosphere that interfere with long-distance telephone communication and that we often hear as static in radio receivers.

The electrically charged particles are also believed to excite, or *ionize*, the very thin gases in our upper atmosphere, causing them to glow with various colors, as described in Chapter 1, page 15. When oxygen atoms in the upper atmosphere are ionized, red, orange, and green rays are produced. Ionized nitrogen gas gives off blue or violet rays.

The chromosphere consists of a layer of gases that extends thousands of kilometers upward from the photosphere. The chromosphere has a red color, caused by the ionized hydrogen gas it contains.

The corona is a thin layer of gases that extends millions of kilometers outward from the chromosphere. It may even extend beyond the earth. During a total eclipse of the sun, the corona may be seen as a halo of weak, silvery light surrounding the sun. At such times also, enormous streamers of hot gases can be seen arching thousands of kilometers into the sun's atmosphere. These streamers are called *prominences*. One prominence reached an altitude of over 1,500,000 kilometers. Prominences do not have the violent effects of solar flares, and they do not disrupt communications on earth.

WHERE THE SUN GETS ITS ENERGY

The violent activity that astronomers can see on the photosphere, when looking at the sun through special telescope attachments, is caused by forces acting deep within the core of the sun.

The sun consists primarily of hydrogen atoms. These atoms are under enormous pressures and temperatures at the center of the sun. These pressures and temperatures are much greater than the pressures and temperatures existing at the center of the earth. For example, the force of gravity on the surface of the sun is 34 times the force of gravity on the earth. The temperature at the center of the sun is estimated to be about 15 million degrees Celsius.

Under conditions such as these, some hydrogen atoms in the core of the sun are converted into helium atoms. This conversion process is called *fusion*. Fusion is the same *thermonuclear reaction* that takes place, on a much smaller scale, in a hydrogen bomb.

During the fusion process, when four hydrogen atoms are converted into one helium atom, some of the mass of the hydrogen atoms is converted into energy (Fig. 7–7, page 130). The conversion of mass to energy takes place according to the famous equation of *Albert Einstein* (1879–1955):

$$E = mc^2$$

In this formula, E stands for energy, m stands for the mass of the atoms that is converted into energy, and c^2 is the speed of light squared.

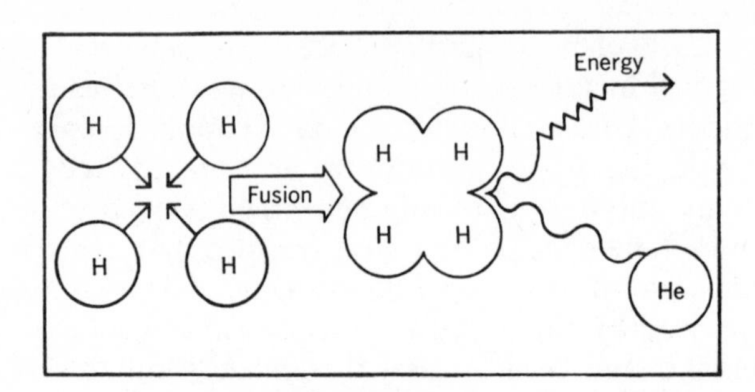

Fig. 7–7. Fusion.

The amount of energy that is released when matter is converted into energy is enormous. For example, if all the matter in three aspirin tablets (which together weigh one gram) could be converted into energy, it would heat all the water in a large swimming pool to the boiling point.

The sun converts about 4,000,000 metric tons of matter into energy every second. Although the sun loses millions of tons of matter every second of its existence, the total mass of the sun is so great that it can continue pouring out energy at its present rate for at least the next 5 billion years.

Only about one two-billionth of the sun's energy output reaches the earth. One third of this energy is absorbed by the earth's atmosphere before the energy reaches the earth's surface. A part of the sun's energy entering the atmosphere consists of ultraviolet radiations. If it were not for the fact that most of the ultraviolet radiations are absorbed by the ozone layer of the atmosphere, these radiations would probably have killed all life on earth billions of years ago.

USING ENERGY FROM THE SUN

As we already know, fuels such as coal and oil are some of the indirect benefits of sunlight. To a very large extent, modern civilization depends on the burning of fuels to produce the energy needed to heat homes, for transportation, and to run machines in factories. Continued use of these fuels, especially fuel oil and gasoline, has produced a fuel shortage—an *energy crisis.* Our supply of fuel is decreasing rapidly and must be carefully conserved. In the future, however, our expanding energy needs may be met by the more direct use of solar energy.

Some scientists and inventors have constructed devices called *solar furnaces* that can concentrate the sun's rays by means of mirrors. The rays are then used as a source of heat and power (Fig. 7–8). The heat produced by the concentrated rays of sunlight can be used to

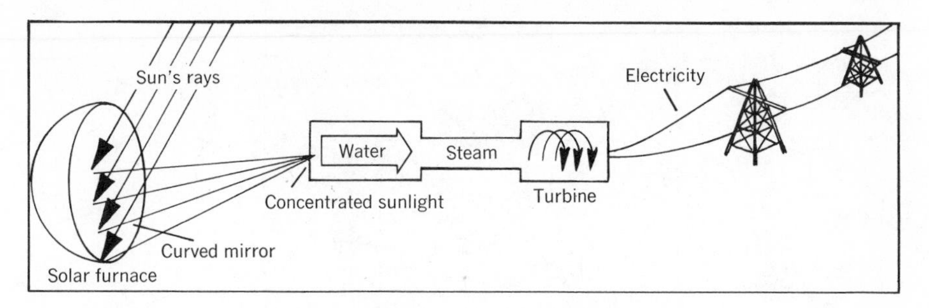

Fig. 7–8. Solar energy changes water into steam.

change water into steam. In turn, the steam is used to turn turbines which generate electricity. Solar energy may be used even more directly to heat homes (Fig. 7–9).

Sunlight has played an important part in powering a number of artificial satellites with electricity. These satellites are equipped with flat plates which are composed of light-sensitive substances. In the presence of sunlight, an electric current is produced within these plates. A large number of such plates connected together is called a *solar battery*. An experimental electrical automobile that uses a solar battery has been designed. The solar battery is on the roof of the car. When the sun shines on the roof, the battery produces electricity that powers the car (Fig. 7–10, page 132). Some of the electricity is led into an ordinary storage battery to be used in the absence of sunlight.

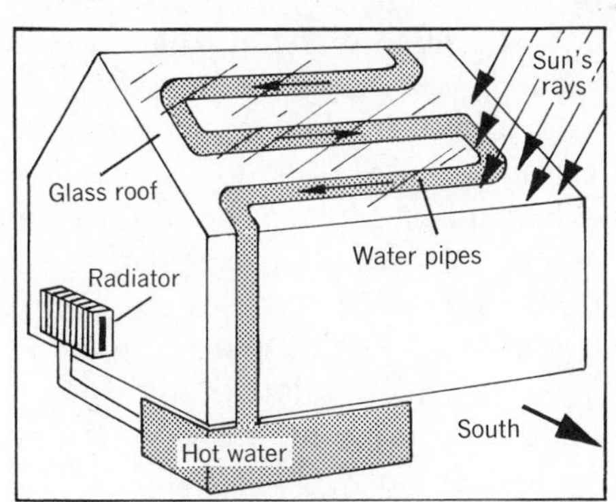

Fig. 7–9. Solar energy heats homes.

Since solar furnaces and solar batteries do not employ the process of burning, they do not discharge harmful pollutants into the atmosphere. Perhaps, when solar furnaces and solar batteries are perfected, they may provide a means both of conserving scarce fuel and of overcoming air pollution.

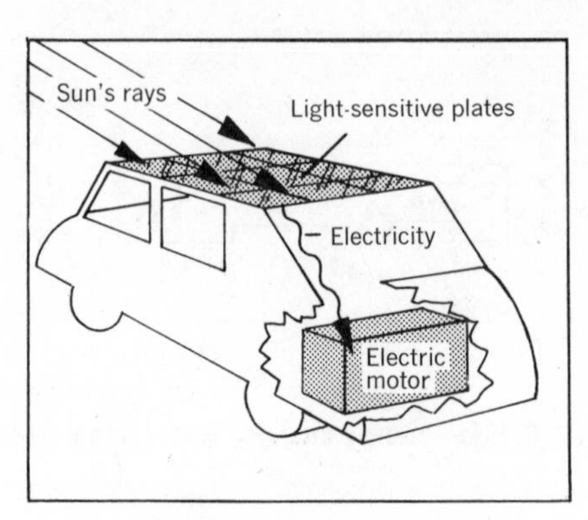

Fig. 7–10. Solar energy powers a car.

THE PLANETS

A planet is a large, solid body that shines by reflected sunlight and revolves in a stable orbit around a star. Early in human history, people noticed that of all the thousands of stars in the heavens, five of them continually changed their positions in relation to the others. These moving stars were called planets by the ancient Greeks, from their word meaning "wanderer."

Motions of the Planets

To observers on earth, planets normally travel through the sky from east to west, in the same direction that the stars, moon, and sun move. Over a period of several weeks, however, a planet appears to slow down, stop, and reverse its direction for a time before continuing in its original direction.

Ancient peoples had many explanations to account for the peculiar motions of the planets. The simplest explanation was that the planets were gods, whose duty it was to move across the sky in this peculiar way so that astrologers could predict the future.

Not everyone believed this explanation. More sensible people attempted to explain the motions of the stars according to what they knew of moving bodies on earth. They believed that the planets were attached to invisible, hollow shells and that the earth was located at the center of all the shells. The motions of the planets were then due to the movements of the shells to which they were attached. The motions of the stars, the sun, and the moon were explained in the same way.

The Greek astronomer *Ptolemy* (2nd century A.D.) offered an explanation for the motions of the planets that satisfied people for over a thousand years. According to Ptolemy, the planets moved in two ways. First, they moved in great circles around the earth, just as the other stars did. Second, for some unknown reason, the planets also moved in smaller circles. It was the motion of these smaller circles that was responsible for the back-and-forth movements of the planets.

It was the Polish astronomer *Nicholas Copernicus* (1473–1543) who first stated that the planets revolved around the sun. But saying something is not the same as proving it. It was not until 1609—66 years after Copernicus first published his theory, and the same year that *Galileo* discovered the moons of Jupiter—that a German astronomer and mathematician, *Johannes Kepler* (1571–1630), finally explained to everyone's satisfaction how the planets move around the sun.

Kepler's Laws of Motion

Kepler's explanation is in the form of three mathematical laws. Simplified, these laws state that:

1. The planets travel in elliptical orbits around the sun (Fig. 7–11) with the sun at one of the foci of the ellipse. (Foci are the two points needed to draw an ellipse.)
2. As a planet comes closer to the sun, its speed increases; as the planet moves farther from the sun, its speed decreases.
3. The time it takes a planet to complete one revolution around the sun depends on the distance between the planet and the sun.

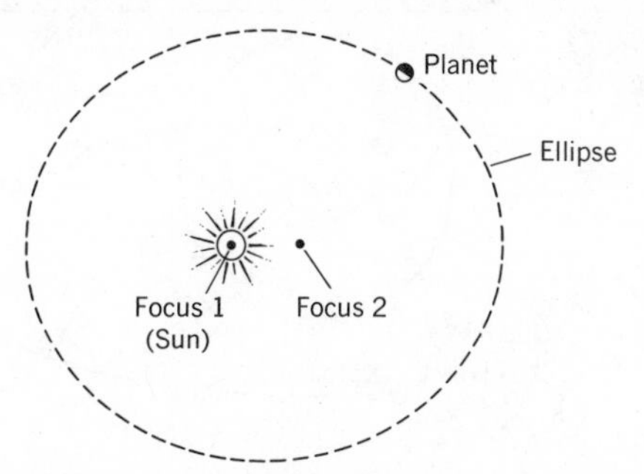

Fig. 7–11. The orbit of a planet is an ellipse.

Rotation and Revolution of the Planets

A planet moves in two ways: It spins on its axis and, at the same time, it moves in an orbit around the sun. *Rotation* is the spinning of a planet on its axis (Fig. 7–12, page 134). The time it takes for one complete spin is called the *period of rotation.* On earth, the period of rotation is close to 24 hours (1 day).

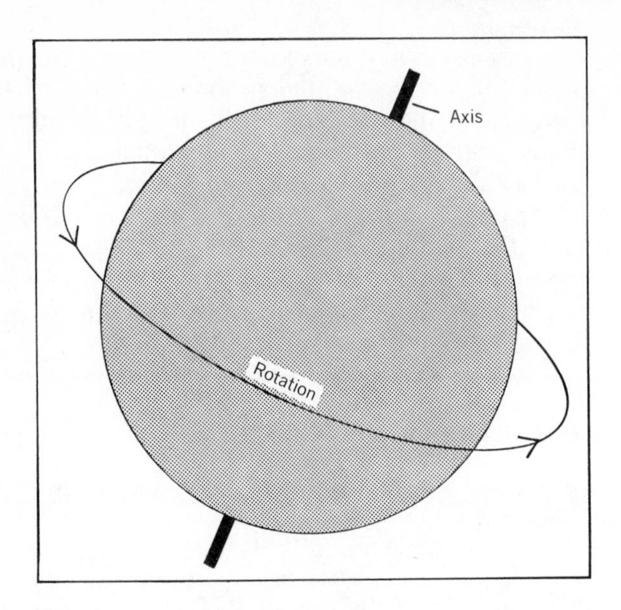

Fig. 7–12. Rotation.

Revolution is the movement of a planet in its orbit around the sun (Fig. 7–13). The earth completes one revolution in its orbit about every 365¼ days.

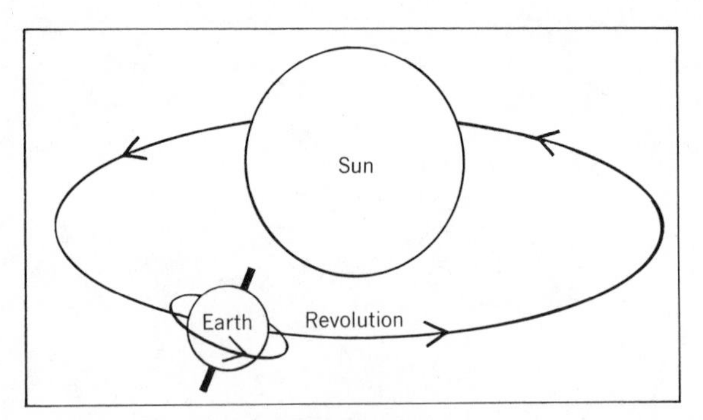

Fig. 7–13. Revolution.

HOW THE PLANETS DIFFER

The planets are often classified into two groups: the *inner planets* and the *outer planets*. Fig. 7–14 shows the positions of these planets. The *inner planets* are the four planets closer to the sun: *Mercury*, *Venus*, *Earth*, and *Mars*. The outer planets are the five planets farther from the sun: *Jupiter*, *Saturn*, *Uranus*, *Neptune*, and *Pluto*.

Inner Planets

The inner planets have several characteristics in common: (1) All appear to consist largely of rock and iron-nickel compounds, just like the earth. (2) The inner planets all have about the same density, which is about four or five times the density of water. (3) The inner planets are all less than 13,000 kilometers in diameter. Mercury, the smallest inner planet, is about 5000 kilometers in diameter; earth, the largest of the inner planets, is about 13,000 kilometers in diameter (Fig. 7–15, page 136).

Mercury is the planet closest to the sun. Mercury is named after the Roman god who was the messenger of the other gods. The name is well chosen, for Mercury travels at a higher speed in its orbit than does any of the other planets.

For many years, Mercury's period of rotation was thought to be 88 days. Recent observations indicate that Mercury's period of rotation is about 59 days.

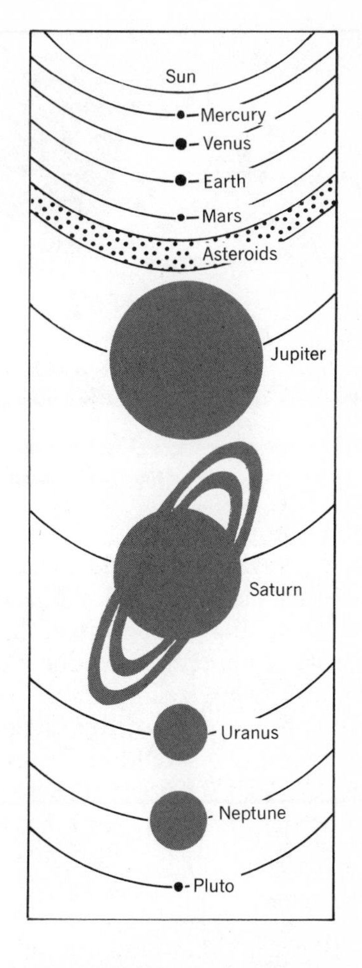

Fig. 7–14. The planets in their orbits.

Venus is named after the Roman goddess of love. Venus is the brightest of all the planets and is also brighter than any of the stars in the night sky. Because Venus is located between the earth and the sun, it can be seen only around the time of sunrise or sunset.

The atmosphere of Venus consists primarily of carbon dioxide, plus small amounts of oxygen and water vapor. The carbon dioxide traps heat radiating from the surface by a greenhouse effect similar to that which causes our atmosphere to retain heat. Because of the trapped heat, the surface temperature of Venus is estimated to be about 425°C.

Earth is the third planet from the sun. The earth's period of rotation is approximately 24 hours, and it makes one revolution about the sun in 365¼ days. The moon is the earth's only natural satellite.

Mars is named after the Roman god of war. Mars is the fourth planet from the sun and our closest neighbor among the planets. Closeup photographs taken by *Mariner* 9 and the Viking landers indicate

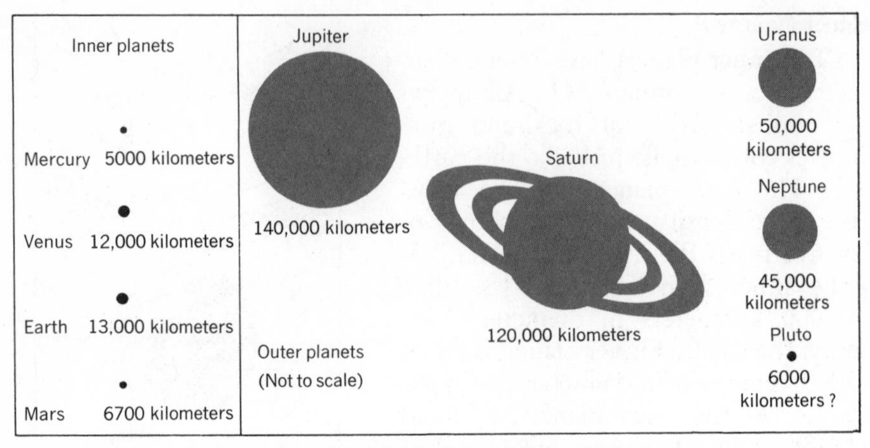

Fig. 7–15. Comparison of sizes of the planets.

that the surface of Mars has features similar to those of the moon. These features include extinct volcanoes, craters, canyons, and long, twisting channels. In addition, there are polar ice caps and light and dark markings that shift with the seasons. The change in color of the markings appears to be due to dust shifted by violent windstorms. The color of Mars, which is red, indicates that its surface is desertlike. Even the desert regions of the earth appear reddish when viewed from space. Mars has two satellites. Reports received from *Viking I* and *Viking II* landers lead scientists to believe that life does not exist on Mars now. Whether life in any form has ever existed there is unknown.

Asteroids

Between Mars and Jupiter, the first of the outer planets, is a belt of thousands of rocky fragments that may be the remains of a shattered planet (see Fig. 7–14, page 135). Astronomers call these fragments *planetoids*, or *asteroids*. The orbits of the larger asteroids have been calculated, and the asteroids have been given names. The largest asteroid is *Ceres*, which is about 770 kilometers in diameter.

Outer Planets

The outer planets have several characteristics in common. (1) The average density of the planets is about the same as water, which means their density is about four times less than the density of the inner planets. (2) Astronomers believe that the outer planets consist chiefly of frozen hydrogen gas and frozen water, which is why their densities are so low. The atmospheres of the outer planets consist of clouds of methane and ammonia gases several thousand kilometers thick. (3) Aside from Pluto, the outer planets are much larger than the inner planets (see Fig. 7–15). For example, the diameter of Jupiter, the largest of all the planets, is about 140,000 kilometers. This is about 11 times the diameter of earth.

Jupiter is named after the chief Roman god. Jupiter is noted for its 12 satellites and a huge red spot on its surface that is about equal in area to the surface of the earth. *Pioneer 10* and *Pioneer 11*, spacecraft that reached the region of Jupiter in 1973 and 1974, have provided us with some information about this planet. The red spot is thought to be a disturbance in Jupiter's atmosphere. The atmosphere is thought to be composed of ammonia crystals, ice crystals, hydrogen, and methane. Winds are present in the atmosphere. They blow east and west and seem to be strongest around the equator.

Saturn is named after the Roman god of agriculture. It is the most distant of the planets that can be seen without a telescope. Viewed through a telescope, Saturn is the most beautiful of all the planets. Saturn's beauty lies in three concentric (one inside the other) rings that encircle the planet at its equator. Astronomers believe these rings consist of tiny particles of frozen gases. Saturn has nine satellites.

Uranus is named after the Greek god of the heavens. Until 1781, Uranus was thought to be a star. In that year, the British astronomer *Sir William Herschel* (1738–1822) noticed that Uranus changed its position among the stars. He concluded, therefore, that Uranus was a planet. Uranus has five large satellites and many smaller ones.

Neptune is named after the Roman god of the sea. The discovery of Neptune came about as the result of careful measurements of the orbit of Uranus. These measurements showed that Uranus did not follow the orbit it should, according to the laws of motion. Astronomers concluded there must be a planet beyond Uranus that was disturbing the orbit of Uranus. After calculating what the position of such a planet should be, astronomers discovered Neptune in 1846. Neptune has two satellites.

Pluto is named after the Roman god of the underworld. Pluto was not discovered until 1930 because it is very small and far away from the earth. Pluto is currently believed to be the most distant planet. Its orbit is such that it will come in closer than Neptune during part of its revolution. Some astronomers believe Pluto may have been a satellite of Neptune originally but, for some unknown reason, Pluto broke out of its orbit around Neptune and began revolving in an independent orbit.

COMETS

Comets are members of our solar system that travel in long elliptical orbits around the sun (Fig. 7–16, page 138). The head of a comet con-

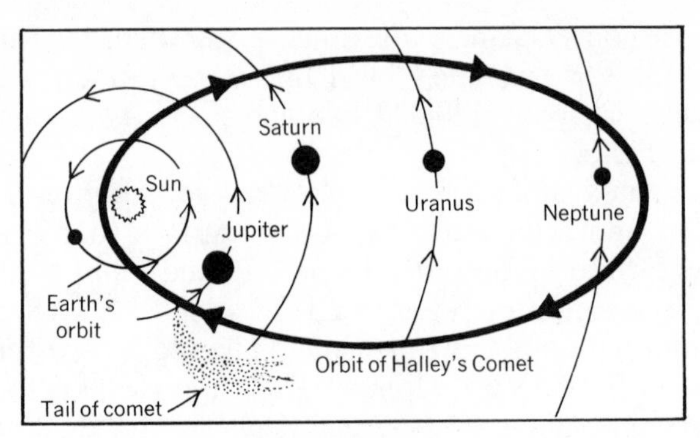

Fig. 7–16. Comets.

sists of a collection of frozen gases and dust particles; it has been called a "dirty snowball." When a comet approaches the sun, the sun's radiations cause the surface of the comet to evaporate and then to glow like an aurora. These glowing gases form the tail of the comet. The pressure of the sun's radiations against these glowing gases pushes the tail away from the head of the comet. For this reason, the head of the comet always appears to point toward the sun as it moves around it.

The most famous of all comets is *Halley's comet,* which swings around the sun about every 76 years. It has appeared in the years 1758, 1835, and 1910. Its next appearance should take place in 1986.

A new comet, called *Comet Kohoutek,* was discovered early in 1973 by Dr. Lubos Kohoutek, a Czechoslovakian astronomer. When this comet was discovered, it was only very faintly visible with powerful telescopes. By Christmas 1973, the comet was so close to the sun that the comet could be seen with the unaided eye. At the present time, Comet Kohoutek is too far away to be seen. It is expected to return in about 80,000 years.

METEOROIDS, METEORS, AND METEORITES

Billions of solid particles of rock and metal are orbiting the sun at average speeds of thousands of kilometers per hour. Most of these particles are smaller than a grain of sand. These particles of solid matter are called meteoroids.

When a meteoroid enters the earth's atmosphere, it strikes the molecules of gas making up the atmosphere. The resulting friction heats up the meteoroid until it glows with light. The burning meteoroid is called a *meteor.* The faster a meteor travels relative to the earth, the greater the friction, and the brighter it burns. (Sometimes the meteoroid and earth meet at a combined speed of 250,000 kilometers per hour.)

Most meteors are entirely consumed high in the atmosphere, long before they can reach the earth. Their fine ashes fall to the ground and into the sea. Sometimes a meteor is so large that it strikes the earth before it is completely consumed. The solid portion of the meteor that strikes the ground is called a *meteorite*.

Rarely, a meteorite strikes the earth with tremendous force. The Barrington crater (or Meteor Crater) in Arizona is an example of such a destructive impact. The crater formed by this impact is a nearly circular depression about 1200 meters wide and 180 meters deep (Fig. 7–17). Many other similar craters also exist. Two giant circular craters, located on the eastern shore of Hudson Bay, Canada, are believed to be meteorite craters. One is 32 kilometers across, and the other is 22 kilometers across.

Fig. 7–17. Meteor crater.

Looking Back

The earth is the third planet from the sun, of the nine planets that travel around the sun in our solar system. In addition to the planets that make up the earth's immediate environment, other members of the solar system include asteroids, satellites, comets, and dust and gases.

Looking Ahead

Just as the earth has the rest of the solar system for its environment, the solar system itself has an environment consisting of millions of stars. We will study this environment in the next chapter.

Multiple-Choice Questions

1. A type of heavenly body that is *not* part of our solar system is
   a. the sun b. a comet c. a meteoroid d. a galaxy
2. Most astronomers believe our solar system was formed from
   a. masses of dust and gas
   b. portions of a condensed star
   c. matter expelled from the sun
   d. the gravitational attraction among meteoroids traveling together in space
3. Of all the mass in our solar system, the sun contains about
   a. 99% b. 75% c. 90% d. 50%
4. The force that prevents the planets from flying off into space is
   a. magnetism b. gravity c. inertia d. momentum
5. The diameter of the sun is about
   a. 14,000 kilometers
   b. 144,000 kilometers
   c. 1,400,000 kilometers
   d. 14,000,000 kilometers
6. The temperature of the sun at its surface is about
   a. 1000° C b. 2000° C c. 6000° C d. 11,000° C
7. Sunspot activity on the sun is directly responsible for
   a. interruptions in radio communications
   b. the number of tornadoes
   c. changes in the weather
   d. meteors
8. Ionized gases glowing in the sun's atmosphere are associated with the sun's
   a. neon-light effect
   b. aurora
   c. corona
   d. chromosphere
9. The lower atmosphere of the sun is called the
   a. chromosphere
   b. troposphere
   c. solar sphere
   d. photosphere
10. In the fusion process that takes place within the sun, hydrogen atoms
    a. split apart to form helium atoms
    b. lose some of their mass
    c. gain mass by joining with helium atoms
    d. burn to produce light
11. Which of the following radiations from the sun are largely blocked by the ozone layer in the earth's atmosphere?
    a. radio waves
    b. X rays
    c. ultraviolet radiations
    d. infrared radiations
12. The mass lost by the sun reappears as
    a. energy b. helium c. oxygen d. magnetism
13. The laws that describe the motions of the planets were first stated by
    a. Copernicus b. Galileo c. Ptolemy d. Kepler
14. The paths that the planets follow around the sun are
    a. ellipses b. perfect circles c. egg-shaped d. epicycles

15. According to the laws of planetary motion, the planets that move the fastest are the
    a. largest planets
    b. smallest planets
    c. planets closest to the sun
    d. planets farthest from the sun
16. A planet that cannot be seen in the midnight sky is
    a. Mars b. Venus c. Jupiter d. Saturn
17. The light given off by a comet is the result of
    a. the reflection of sunlight from the comet
    b. a combination of reflected sunlight and glowing gases
    c. atomic radiations, which cause the comet to glow
    d. its speed through space

Modified True-False Questions

1. The diameter of the sun is almost *10* times larger than the diameter of the earth.
2. *Hydrogen* is the most abundant element in the sun.
3. Sunspots are about 1100°C *hotter* than the surrounding surface of the sun.
4. The glowing layer of gases above the surface of the sun is called the *aurora.*
5. In Einstein's formula $E = mc^2$, the letter c stands for the speed of *light.*
6. The sun loses about 4,000,000 metric tons of mass every *year.*
7. An equivalent of the fusion process that takes place in the sun is the *atomic* bomb.
8. The asteroids orbiting the sun between the planets Mars and Jupiter are believed to come from an exploded *comet.*
9. Most meteoroids burn up in our upper atmosphere and settle to earth in the form of *gases.*

Thought Questions

1. List five different ways in which the sun makes life possible on earth.
2. Explain the importance of plants in making it possible for humans and other mammals to live on the earth.
3. Name three fuels used by humans that were produced by means of solar energy. Explain why these fuels are sources of environmental pollution.
4. Explain how the activity associated with sunspots affects the earth's atmosphere.
5. Explain where the energy of the sun comes from.
6. Account for the fact that the sun continues to shine despite the loss of trillions of tons of its mass every year for the last five billion years.
7. Describe briefly two different ways in which scientists are attempting to harness the energy of sunlight.
8. Describe how the planets move according to the laws of Kepler.
9. List two differences between a comet and a meteor.

CHAPTER 8
WHAT IS THE ENVIRONMENT OF OUR SOLAR SYSTEM?

When you have completed this chapter, you should be able to:

1. *Appreciate* how information is gathered about stars without actually visiting them.
2. *Discuss* the history of astronomy and the major instruments used by astronomers.
3. *Contrast* galaxies, constellations, and stars.
4. *Describe*, in a general way, the size, brightness, temperatures, and composition of heavenly bodies.
5. *Outline* the life history of a star.

In the laboratory experience that follows, you will make and use an astronomical instrument—a simple telescope.

Laboratory Experience

HOW CAN WE CONSTRUCT A TELESCOPE?

A. Of the two lenses at your desk, insert the thinner lens into a holder. Set the holder on a meter stick, as shown in Fig. 8–1*a*. Aim the lens at a source of light (a window or an electric light) that is about 4 or 5 meters away.
   Insert a white card in another holder. Set the holder on the meter stick close to the lens, with the lens between the white card and the source of light. Slowly move the card away from the lens until a sharp image appears on the card.
   1. What is the distance between the card and the lens?

B. Remove the thin lens, and replace it with the thicker lens. Repeat step A with the thick lens.
   2. What is the distance between the card and the lens?
   3. What is the sum of the distances measured in 1 and 2 above?

C. As shown in Fig. 8–1*b*, set the thin lens on the meter stick so that

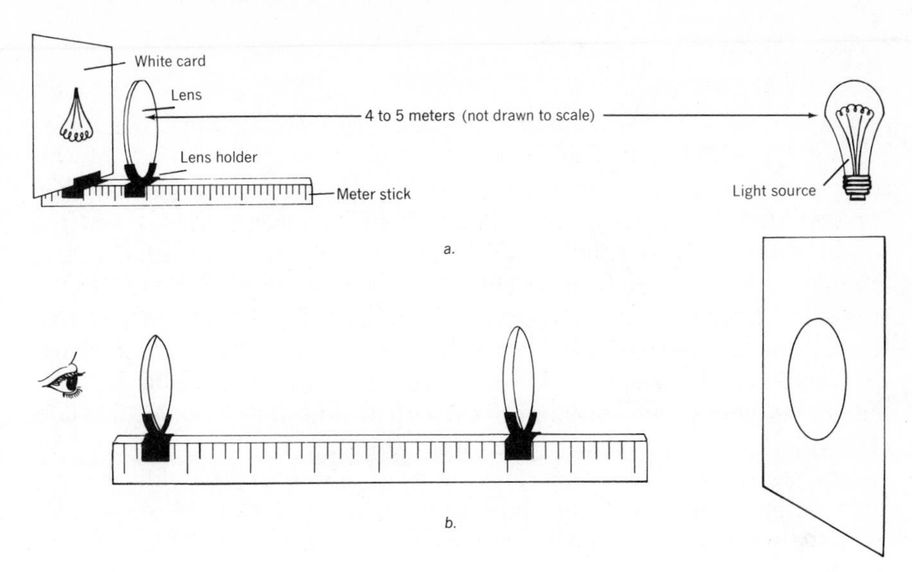

Fig. 8–1.

it is closer to the source of light than the thicker lens. Set the thick lens a distance from the thinner lens equal to the distance you found in 3 above. You have now made a simple telescope, which may need some adjustment.

D. Draw a small circle on the chalkboard. Without disturbing the positions of the lenses, carry the telescope to the opposite end of the room. Place your eye close to the thicker lens, and aim the telescope at the circle you have drawn on the chalkboard. If you cannot see the circle clearly, move either lens slightly toward or away from the other lens. With a little adjustment, the circle will come into focus.

E. Measure the actual size of the small circle on the chalkboard. Note the large measured circle your teacher has already drawn on the chalkboard. Compare the size of the small circle as seen through the telescope with the large circle on the chalkboard.

4. What is the approximate magnifying power of your telescope?

F. Aim your telescope at a sheet of newspaper that has been attached to a wall of the room. Focus the telescope until you get a sharp image.

5. Describe what you see.
6. Explain why the position of a circle seen through a telescope looks different from the position of a letter of the alphabet seen through a telescope.
7. Telescopes make distant objects appear nearer. Explain how a telescope does this.

Introduction

The immediate environment of the earth consists of the other members of the solar system and space. In turn, the environment of the solar system consists of the rest of the universe—the tremendous number of stars and their solar systems and still more space.

The universe is so unimaginably large that our unit of distance, the kilometer, is completely insignificant to use in describing its extent. Instead, astronomers use a special unit called the *light year* to measure the distances between the heavenly bodies. A light year is the distance that light travels in one year. Since light travels at a speed of 300,000 kilometers per second, one light year equals almost 10,000,000,000,000 (10 trillion) kilometers. For example, the sun is about 150,000,000 kilometers distant from the earth, or only about eight *light minutes* away. A great many stars are billions of light years away from us. The light we see when we look at one of these stars is light that left the star billions of years ago and has been traveling through space ever since.

On a clear night, any observer can see thousands of heavenly bodies with the unaided eye. If you observe the heavenly bodies from night to night, you will soon become aware that the bodies move. With the invention of the telescope in 1608, astronomers were able to advance beyond mere observation of the movements of the heavenly bodies.

TELESCOPES

The telescope brought into view thousands of new stars and details of the moon and planets that the early astronomers never dreamed existed. For example, in 1609, using a telescope that he made himself, the great Italian scientist, *Galileo Galilei* (1564–1642), discovered the craters and mountains of the moon. He also discovered that the planet Jupiter had moons that revolved in regular orbits around the planet.

Refracting Telescopes

Recall your laboratory experience in which you made a simple telescope. It was a *refracting telescope*.

The first telescopes used by astronomers were of this type. In such a telescope, the light from a distant object passes through a series of glass lenses in such a way that a distant object appears larger and, therefore, closer.

In a refracting telescope, the light rays from a star first pass through an *object lens*, or *objective*. The object lens concentrates all the rays of light from the star to a single point inside the telescope. This point is called the *focal point*. The astronomer, at the other end of the telescope, looks at the focal point through an *eyepiece lens*, or *eyepiece*, which acts as a magnifying glass. When the eyepiece is focused correctly on the concentrated rays of light at the focal point, the astronomer sees a very bright, sharp image of the star. If he is looking at the moon or a planet through the telescope, the moon or planet also appears much larger.

The basic construction of a refracting telescope used by astronomers is shown in Fig. 8–2. The maximum diameter of the object lens in a refracting telescope is limited because if the object lens is too large, the weight of the glass would cause it to sag. This, in turn, would result in a distorted image. The world's largest refracting telescope is located at the Yerkes Observatory in Wisconsin. This telescope has an object lens with a diameter of 100 centimeters.

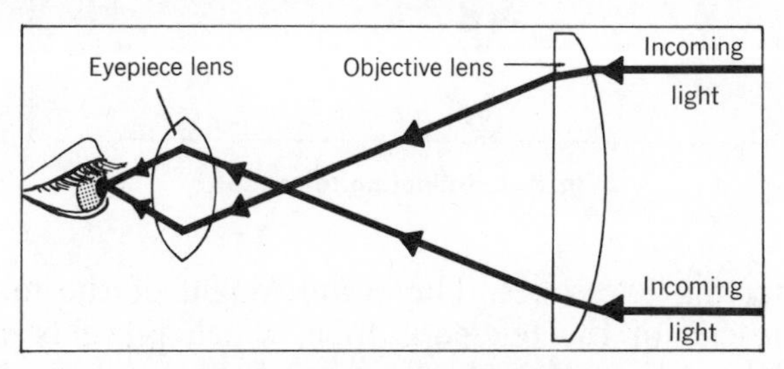

Fig. 8–2. Refracting telescope.

Reflecting Telescopes

The first refracting telescopes had many defects, which led to the invention of *reflecting telescopes* by the famous English scientist, *Sir Isaac Newton* (1642–1727). In a reflecting telescope, the light from a distant object is reflected from a curved mirror into a lens in such a way that the distant object appears larger and closer.

In a reflecting telescope, the light rays from a star are reflected by a curved (concave) mirror at the far end of the telescope tube. The mirror is curved in such a way that all the rays of incoming light are reflected to the same focal point. A small, flat (plane) mirror inside the telescope then reflects the concentrated rays of light to the side of the telescope where an eyepiece is mounted (Fig. 8–3, page 146).

In other types of reflecting telescopes, the rays of light reflected from the curved mirror strike a flat mirror and are reflected through a hole in the very center of the curved mirror. In this type of reflecting telescope, the eyepiece is located behind the mirror.

Reflecting telescopes are much more practical to build in large sizes

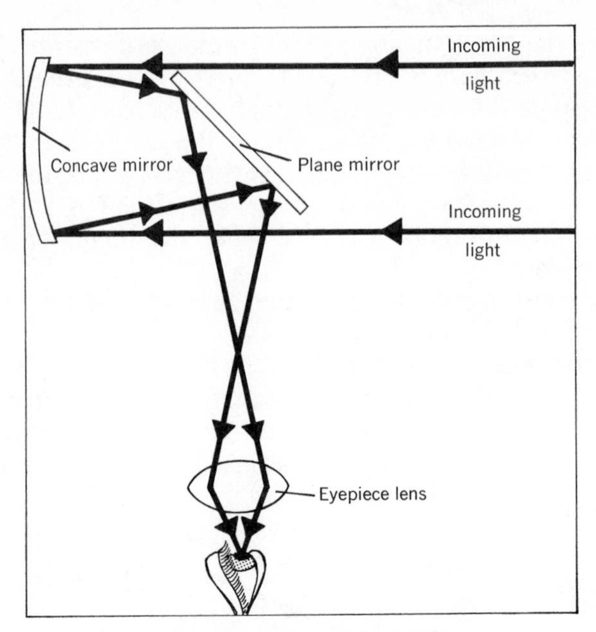

Fig. 8–3. Reflecting telescope.

than are refracting telescopes. The entire weight of the mirror is supported by the end of the telescope tube, which prevents sagging and distortion of the mirror. It is also easier and cheaper to make a curved mirror than it is to cast and grind a very large piece of glass into a large lens.

One of the world's largest reflecting telescopes is the Hale telescope located on Mount Palomar, California. The mirror in the Hale telescope has a diameter of 500 centimeters. A Russian reflecting telescope has a mirror that is 650 centimeters in diameter.

Telescope Attachments

By making distant objects appear closer and, more important, by making them appear brighter, telescopes led to a great many important discoveries about the universe. However, it was not until astronomers recorded what they saw with cameras and other devices attached to their telescopes that they were able to make the tremendous discoveries that form the basis of modern astronomy.

Today, astronomers rarely look at the stars directly through a telescope. Instruments attached to the eyepiece of a telescope can collect much more data, and collect it more accurately, than can the human eye. For example, a camera filled with special film can take photographs of stars in which the exposures last several hours. When the film is developed, the negative will show much more detail than an astronomer will ever see by himself.

Probably the most useful telescope attachment used by astronomers is the spectroscope. As we noted in Chapter 7, a common type of spectroscope uses a triangular glass prism which spreads out a beam of white light into a spectrum, or the colors making up the light. Astronomers use a spectroscope to study the spectrum of planets and stars. The appearance of the spectrum depends on the chemical elements present in the planet or star and on the temperature of the body. Each chemical element present has a spectrum that is different from the spectrum of other elements.

Since a star is a glowing body that gives off light, a spectroscope placed at the eyepiece of a telescope spreads the light from the star into a spectrum. By comparing the spectra of the stars with the spectra of elements known on earth, astronomers have discovered what elements are present in the stars and how hot the stars are.

Radio Telescopes

Earlier (Chapter 3, pages 38–39), we noted that the sun gives off visible radiations, which we call light, and invisible radiations, including radio signals.

A radio telescope is a specially designed radio receiver that can pick up radio signals from the sun and other stars. Many radio telescopes have huge collecting antennas shaped like saucers, as shown in Fig. 8–4, page 148. They perform the same function as the curved mirrors in reflecting telescopes. That is, the antennas concentrate the incoming radio signals to a common focal point, where special radio-detecting equipment can pick up the signals and magnify them. Special electronic equipment then changes these signals into a picture on an oscilloscope tube (which resembles a television screen) or inked lines on a sheet of graph paper. By studying these graphs, astronomers have discovered much more about the universe than they could learn by using refracting and reflecting telescopes.

Radio telescopes have certain advantages over optical (eye) telescopes. First, radio signals can penetrate the dust and gases in outer space and the clouds in our atmosphere. These substances will block light waves. Second, radio telescopes can receive signals from the stars in the daytime as well as at night, whereas optical telescopes cannot ordinarily be used during the day because of the glare caused by sunlight. Third, the largest optical telescopes can detect stars and galaxies a little more than two billion light years distant. Radio telescopes can detect objects billions of light years farther away.

The largest radio telescope that has been built so far is located in

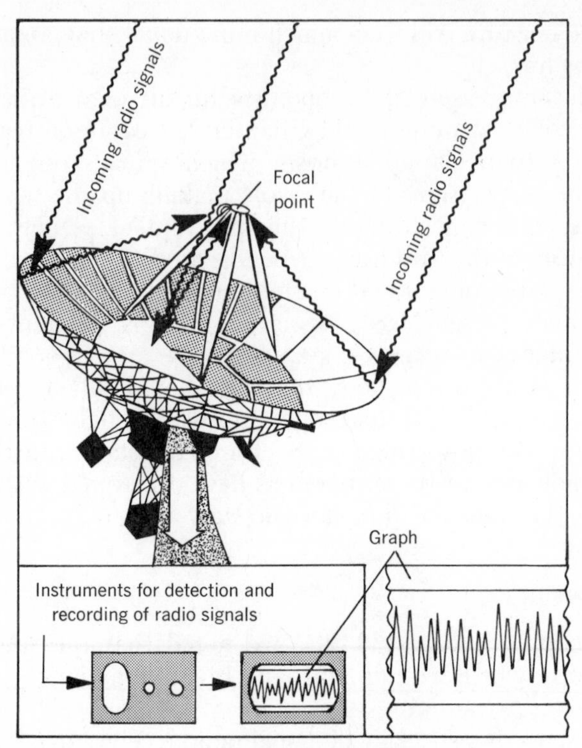

Fig. 8–4. Radio telescope.

a mountain valley in Arecibo, Puerto Rico. The antenna of this telescope is 300 meters in diameter. Another large radio telescope is located at Jodrell Bank, England. Its antenna, which is 75 meters in diameter, is mounted on massive machinery that can turn and aim the antenna at different parts of the sky. The Jodrell Bank telescope has played an important part in tracking spacecraft traveling to the moon and to some of the planets.

The United States has launched several telescopes into space. These telescopes can observe the stars from far above the dust, smoke, clouds, and haze that interfere with observations on earth. Observations made by such instruments in space are sent back to earth by means of radio and television transmitters.

HEAVENLY BODIES OUTSIDE THE SOLAR SYSTEM

In the 300 years that have passed since Galileo explored the skies with his telescope, astronomers have learned a great deal about the universe. Before the invention of the telescope, astronomers could see only those heavenly bodies that were visible to the unaided eye. Only about 2000 stars could be seen at one time. With a telescope, millions of stars can be seen.

Even before the invention of the telescope, astronomers noticed hazy-looking stars. They called these stars *nebulae* (singular, *nebula*), which means mist or clouds. Through their telescopes, however, astronomers discovered that many of these hazy-looking stars are actually enormous collections of millions and billions of stars. Today, astronomers call such a collection of stars a *galaxy*. Nebula now means a collection of dust and gas in space, which sometimes glows by reflected starlight. The galaxies closest to the earth (outside our own galaxy) are the "Great Magellanic Clouds," which are about 100,000 light years away, and the "Great Nebula" in Andromeda, which is about 2,000,000 light years away. It is possible that many stars in our galaxy and other galaxies have planets revolving around them as has our sun.

OUR GALAXY: THE MILKY WAY

Our sun is a star that belongs to the galaxy called the *Milky Way*. This galaxy consists of billions of stars arranged in the form of a flattened spiral (Fig. 8–5*a*). If we could see the Milky Way from another galaxy, the stars in our galaxy would appear as a huge disk that bulged in the center (Fig. 8–5*b*). From the center, long and wispy arms spiral outward. The Milky Way is about 80,000 light years in diameter and about 10,000 light years thick.

Within our galaxy, the distances between the stars are fantastic. A spaceship launched from earth would have to travel through space at the speed of light for about 300 years to reach the North Star, which is one of the closer stars to the earth.

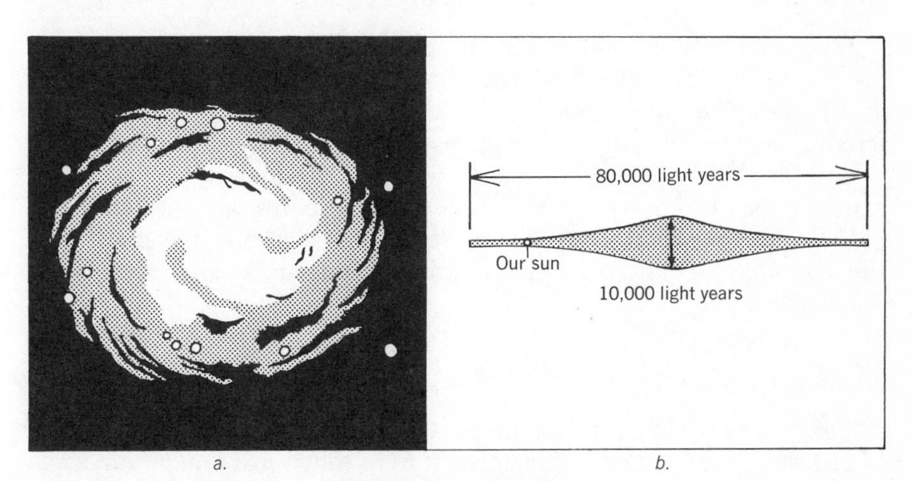

Fig. 8–5. The Milky Way.

The space between galaxies and between individual stars is not entirely empty. It contains dust and gases such as hydrogen. However, the individual particles of dust and gas are so far apart that space is, in fact, an almost perfect vacuum.

GROUPS OF STARS

When ancient peoples looked at the night sky, they imagined that groups of stars formed the outlines of animal and human figures. They gave names to these imaginary figures, such as the swan, the bear, the queen, and the hunter. We still use these names today. Each of these groups of stars is called a *constellation.*

The constellations most familiar to people living in the Northern Hemisphere are the Big Dipper and the Little Dipper. Astronomers refer to the Big Dipper as *Ursa Major* (big bear) and to the Little Dipper as *Ursa Minor* (little bear). These two constellations are also called *circumpolar constellations* because they are visible all year round and appear to revolve around the North Star, which is almost exactly over the North Pole. Other common circumpolar constellations are *Draco* (the dragon) and *Cassiopeia,* named after a mythical queen (Fig. 8–6).

CHARACTERISTICS OF STARS

To most people, the stars look pretty much alike. However, stars differ in many ways, such as size, brightness, color, composition, and age.

Size of Stars

Stars range from about 16,000 kilometers in diameter to about 3,000,000,000 kilometers in diameter. The smallest stars are called *dwarfs,* and the largest stars are called *supergiants.* An important difference between dwarfs and supergiants is their density. The matter in a dwarf star is packed so closely together that only about 16 cubic centimeters of the star would weigh a metric ton. In contrast, the particles of matter in a giant star are so far apart that the density of the star may be less than the density of the air at the top of our atmosphere.

Brightness of Stars

The ancient Greek astronomers classified stars according to how bright they looked. The brightest stars were called *first-magnitude stars*; the dimmest stars that could be seen by the naked eye were called

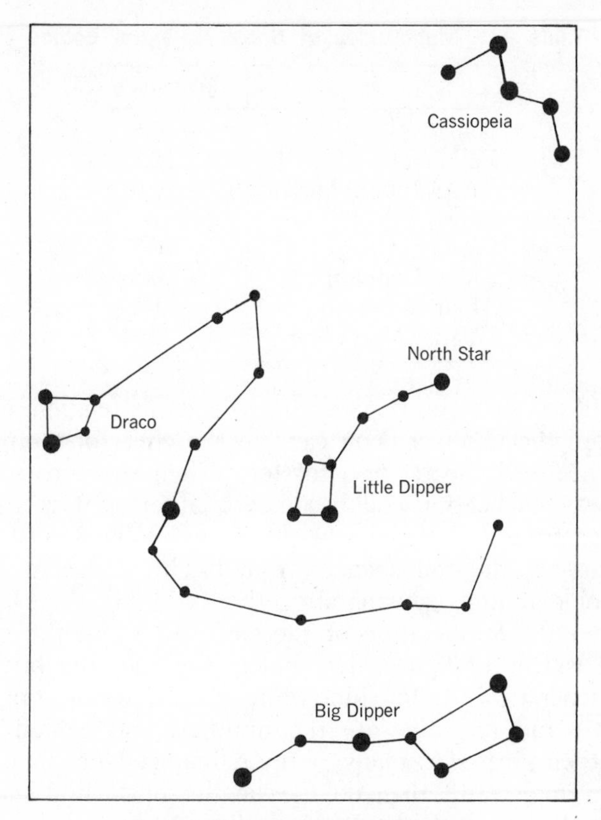

Fig. 8–6. Circumpolar constellations.

sixth-magnitude stars. All other stars were classified according to their apparent brightness between the first- and sixth-magnitude stars.

The magnitude system depends on the *apparent* brightness of stars, that is, their brightness as measured by the eye or by a light-sensitive device. To the eye, a typical first-magnitude star appears to be 100 times as bright as a typical sixth-magnitude star.

The 500-centimeter Hale telescope can enable us to see stars having a magnitude of $23\frac{1}{2}$, which is about 1 million times dimmer than a first-magnitude star.

Stars or other heavenly objects that appear brighter than first-magnitude stars have magnitudes smaller than 1. For example, the magnitude of the star *Altair* is 1, the magnitude of the brighter star *Sirius* is −1.5, and the magnitude of the sun is −26.5. The magnitudes of some celestial bodies are given in Table 8–1, page 152. Remember, these magnitudes tell us how bright the stars appear to us and not how bright they actually are.

Table 8–1. Magnitudes of Some Celestial Bodies

Body	*Magnitude*
Sun	−26.5
Full moon	−12.5
Venus (at brightest)	− 4.0
Sirius	− 1.5
Canopus	− 0.7
Alpha Centauri	− 0.3
Altair	1.0
Polaris (North Star)	2.0

The brightness of a star depends on its size, its temperature, and its distance from the observer. You can see the effect of temperature by observing an electric heater or a toaster. When you turn on either of these devices, the heating coil becomes brighter as it gets hotter. Its color changes from dull red to a bright orange. When you turn off the heater or toaster, the coil changes from bright orange to a dull red, and, as it cools, it stops glowing altogether.

The higher the temperature of the coil, the brighter it glows. The same thing is true of a star. The hotter the star, the brighter is its color. In general, white or blue-white stars are the brightest and hottest stars, and red stars are the dimmest and coolest. However, because of their great size, many of the red supergiants appear brighter to an observer on earth than do the smaller blue-white stars.

The star closest to the earth, our sun, is so bright that it completely lights up the side of the earth facing it, even though it is about 150 million kilometers away. Of the estimated 100 billion stars in the Milky Way, billions of them shine more brightly than the sun. The sun looks bright to us because it is so much closer to the earth than any of the other stars. In fact, if our sun were ten light years away from the earth instead of being only about eight light minutes away, it would look just like an ordinary star in the night sky.

Temperature of Stars

The color of a heated object is related to its temperature. Just as the color of a heating coil or a toaster, when properly connected, tells us something about its temperature, so does the color of a star tell us something about its surface temperature. If you look at the stars on a clear night, you will notice that some stars appear red, others yellow, and still others, blue-white. A dull red star has a surface temperature of about 1600°C; a blue-white star has a surface temperature of about 40,000°C. Yellow stars like our sun have surface temperatures of about 6000°C.

Composition of Stars

The spectroscope has revealed that many of the chemical elements on earth are also present in the stars. Most stars consist chiefly of hydrogen and helium. The sun, for example, consists of 82% hydrogen, 17% helium, and 1% of other chemical elements such as carbon, oxygen, and calcium.

THE LIFE HISTORY OF STARS

Stars are believed to arise from clouds of dust and gases scattered in space. The particles making up a cloud exert a gravitational pull on one another and, in time, the particles draw closer together. The cloud of dust and gas grows warmer as it draws together. As the gravitational attraction among the particles increases, the cloud becomes smaller and hotter. Eventually, when the mass of dust and gas has been compressed enough, the mass becomes hot enough to glow.

After a star begins to glow, it goes through several stages. Newly formed stars are still relatively cool. Consequently, they are dull red in color. The forces acting upon the particles that make up a young star, as it continues to contract, cause the star to become even hotter. Its color changes from dull red to bright red, to orange, and then to yellow. When the internal temperature of the star reaches many millions of degrees, the hydrogen atoms within the star begin being converted into helium by a fusion reaction (see Chapter 7, pages 129–130). Our sun is in this stage now.

After a star reaches its hottest stage, the star stops contracting. Eventually, however, the supply of hydrogen becomes insufficient to continue the fusion reaction. When this stage is reached, the core of the star contracts, giving off tremendous quantities of heat in the process. The heat causes the star to expand outward by millions of kilometers. The star is now in the red giant stage.

Eventually the star collapses and becomes a white dwarf. At this stage of its history, temperatures within the star may reach billions of degrees. The helium in the core of the star is converted into elements such as iron and carbon. Subsequently, the star begins to cool. In time, the star no longer glows, and it ends its life, becoming a dark mass in space.

The life history of a star probably takes 10 billion years from beginning to end. Our sun is believed to be about halfway through its life. It is expected to continue sending heat and light to the earth at its present rate for at least another five billion years. Afterwards, the sun will become a red giant, then contract into a dwarf, and finally stop shining altogether.

Looking Back

Unit II teaches us that our environment extends far beyond the surface of the earth and the atmosphere around it. That is, the environment extends into space, the solar system, and the bodies beyond the solar system. Most of the energy we receive on earth comes from the sun; a little comes from other heavenly bodies.

Looking Ahead

Energy is a vital part of our environment. In the next unit, we will study the various forms of energy.

Multiple-Choice Questions

1. The branch of science that studies the universe as a whole is called
   a. astrology c. geology
   b. astronomy d. space exploration
2. The light year is equal to a distance of about
   a. 300,000 kilometers c. 10 billion kilometers
   b. 150 million kilometers d. 10 trillion kilometers
3. The telescope was invented about the year
   a. 850 b. 1554 c. 1608 d. 1654
4. The first person to see the craters of the moon through a telescope was
   a. Newton b. Ptolemy c. Galileo d. Copernicus
5. Telescopes that use glass lenses to gather the incoming light are called
   a. refracting telescopes c. radio telescopes
   b. reflecting telescopes d. spectroscopes
6. The largest refracting telescope in the United States is located at the
   a. U.S. Naval Observatory in Washington, D.C.
   b. Mt. Kitt Observatory in Arizona
   c. University of California
   d. Yerkes Observatory in Wisconsin
7. The world's largest refracting telescope is only 100 centimeters in diameter because a larger lens would
   a. be too heavy to move c. sag and produce distorted images
   b. be too difficult to keep steady d. be too expensive to build
8. The Jodrell Bank telescope gathers
   a. weakly colored light c. ultraviolet radiations
   b. infrared radiations d. radio waves
9. The instrument that makes use of a glass prism to study the stars is the
   a. range finder c. beam splitter
   b. infrared telescope d. spectroscope

10. The greatest number of stars that can be seen by one person at one time with the naked eye is about
    a. 1000 b. 2000 c. 6000 d. 200
11. The stars in a galaxy can be numbered in the
    a. hundreds b. thousands c. billions d. trillions
12. The galaxy that is closest to our galaxy is at a distance
    a. of 100,000 light years
    b. of 4.3 light years
    c. of 10 light years
    d. that is too far to measure
13. The name of our galaxy is
    a. the Milky Way
    b. Andromeda
    c. Draco
    d. Cassiopeia
14. The polar constellations are those constellations that
    a. point to the North Star
    b. appear to revolve around the North Star
    c. are directly over the North Pole
    d. are the brightest stars in the heavens
15. Giant stars are
    a. the hottest stars
    b. blue-white stars
    c. collections of densely packed particles
    d. very thin collections of particles
16. Radio telescopes *cannot* be used to
    a. study the stars in the daytime
    b. study the stars during cloudy weather
    c. take photographs of the stars
    d. detect stars beyond the range of optical telescopes
17. When seen through a telescope, the color of the hottest type of star is
    a. dull red b. yellow c. bright red d. blue-white
18. The magnitude of the full moon is about
    a. 1.0 b. −1.0 c. 6.0 d. −12.5
19. The two most abundant elements in the stars are
    a. hydrogen and helium
    b. hydrogen and iron
    c. hydrogen and calcium
    d. helium and iron
20. The color of a young star is usually
    a. red b. yellow c. white d. blue-white
21. The sun is believed to be about
    a. 5 million years old
    b. 600 million years old
    c. 5 billion years old
    d. 10 billion years old

Modified True-False Questions

1. One light year is equal to a distance of about *300,000* kilometers.
2. The two principal types of optical telescopes are the reflecting telescope and the *radio* telescope.
3. The largest optical telescope in the United States is the *500-centimeter* Hale telescope on Mt. Palomar.

4. The radio telescope at Arecibo, Puerto Rico, has a diameter of about *100* meters.
5. The *spectroscope* is the instrument used by astronomers to determine the composition of the stars.
6. The hazy patches of light that can be seen on a clear night are the types of stars called *meteors*.
7. Our galaxy consists of about *100,000* stars.
8. Some supergiant stars have diameters of about *3,000,000,000 kilometers*.
9. Sixth-magnitude stars are *100* times as dim as first-magnitude stars.
10. The fusion reaction that takes place within a star involves the conversion of hydrogen atoms into *helium* atoms.

Matching Questions

Column A	Column B
1. refractor	a. star systems composed of millions or billions of stars
2. spectroscope	b. telescope that gathers light by means of lenses
3. galaxy	c. telescope that uses mirrors
4. constellation	d. instrument used to determine the composition of the stars
	e. small groups of stars that have been named for their resemblance to animals or human figures

Thought Questions

1. How would you account for the possibility that a star you see in the sky no longer exists?
2. Name the three main types of telescopes and, in a few words, describe the principle of each.
3. Give three reasons why astronomers may attach a camera to a telescope.
4. Explain how a spectroscope works. What information does a spectroscope gather about the stars?
5. Describe the difference between a galaxy and a constellation.
6. List five different ways in which stars may differ from each other.
7. Describe the changes in size and color that a star undergoes from its birth to its death.

UNIT III
Energy on Our Planet

Overview

Energy exists in many forms: chemical, electrical, mechanical, heat, light, and sound. All the forms of energy, just like the different kinds of matter, represent a very important factor in our environment. Without energy from some source, no work of any kind could be done. Our homes would be cold, factories still, radios silent, television screens blank, and our means of transportation halted. Without energy, everything in the universe would soon become motionless and cold. Life would cease to exist everywhere.

Recall that energy, like matter, can be neither created nor destroyed, but can be changed from one form to another. This idea has been stated as the law of conservation of energy.

Whenever we use some form of energy, some of the energy is changed to another form. Often, some energy is wasted in this process. Thus, when we burn oil, we may use chemical energy to produce electricity. Some of the energy in the oil is wasted in the form of heat. When we use electricity to produce light, some of the electrical energy is wasted in the form of heat also. The detailed study of energy in this unit may help us understand and control energy so that we waste as little of it as possible.

CHAPTER 9
HOW DOES THE HEAT ENERGY OF THE ENVIRONMENT AFFECT US?

When you have completed this chapter, you should be able to:

1. *State* one theory of the nature of heat energy, and explain how this theory accounts for energy transformation.
2. *Describe* the effects of heat on solids, liquids, and gases and some problems that arise from these effects.
3. *Distinguish* between (*a*) thermometer, thermostat, and thermograph (*b*) temperature and heat.
4. *Explain* the construction and operation of a gas thermometer, solid thermometer, and liquid thermometer.
5. *Compare* the Fahrenheit, Celsius, and Kelvin temperature scales.
6. *Calculate* the amount of heat gained or lost by a substance.

In the laboratory experience that follows, you will investigate the effect of heat on each of the three states of matter.

Laboratory Experience

HOW DOES MATTER BEHAVE WHEN HEATED?

A. Using the ball and ring apparatus provided by your teacher, push the ball into and out of the ring several times.

Holding the ball by its insulated handle, heat the ball in a flame for a few minutes. Now try to push the ball through the ring.

1. Describe what happens.

Cool the ball by plunging it in a container of cold water. Try to push the ball through the ring now.

2. Describe what happens.
3. What effect does heat have on the ball?

B. Push the ball through the ring and keep it there. Heat the ball in a flame. Try to pull the ball through the ring.

4. Describe what happens.

5. How can you remove the ball without first cooling it?
6. Try the procedure you have suggested. What is the result?

C. Fill an Erlenmeyer flask with colored water. Insert a one-hole stopper into the neck of the flask. The stopper should be fitted with a length of glass tubing as shown in Fig. 9–1. Set the flask on a circle of wire gauze mounted on a tripod. Heat the flask. Observe the glass tube.

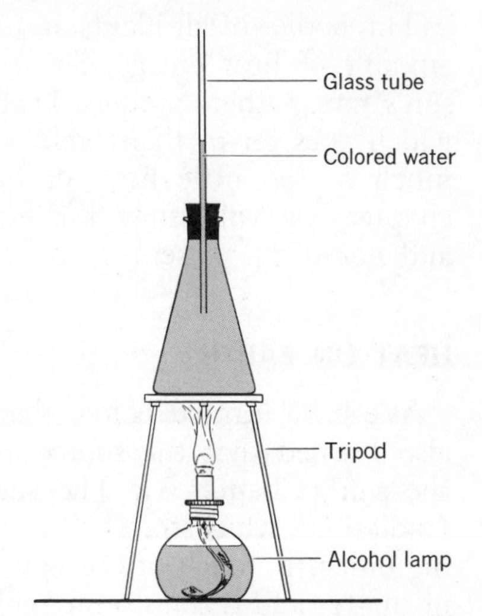

Fig. 9–1.

7. What happens to the water in the glass tubing as the water in the flask is heated? Explain.

Allow the Erlenmeyer flask to cool.

8. What happens to the water in the glass tubing as the water in the flask cools? Explain.

D. Pour the water out of the Erlenmeyer flask. Attach a rubber balloon to the open end of the glass tubing. Use a rubber band to make a tight fit around the tubing, as shown in Fig. 9–2. Gently warm the flask over a flame.

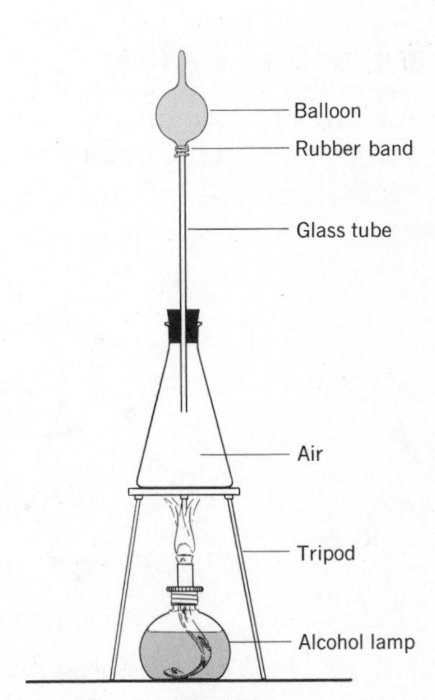

Fig. 9–2.

9. What substance is inside the flask?
10. What happens to the balloon as the flask gets warmer?
11. How do you explain the change in the balloon?
12. What effect does heat have on all the substances you experimented with in this laboratory experience?
13. Would you expect that heat would have the same effect on other substances? Explain.

Introduction

The bodies of all plants and animals must obtain and keep a certain amount of heat energy. Some organisms are warmed directly by the sun's rays. Others produce heat as a result of the process of oxidation which goes on in their bodies. When plants and animals receive too much or too little heat, or lose heat too rapidly, they die. In this chapter, we will study the effect of heat upon matter, both living and nonliving, present on earth.

HEAT ON EARTH

We have learned before that heat is one form of energy. We have also learned that the source of almost all the earth's heat energy is the sun (Chapter 3). The sun gives off energy in the form of rays (radiation) which travel through space before reaching us. Upon arriving on earth, much of the radiant energy is absorbed by different kinds of matter and is transformed into heat that we can feel (sensible heat). Thus, when you sit in the sun for a period of time on a clear spring day, you may find that your clothing and other objects around you become warm. Similarly, when you walk barefoot across a beach on a summer day, you may find the sand so hot that it burns your feet. In both cases, radiant energy from the sun has been absorbed by matter and has been converted into heat that you can feel.

THE NATURE OF HEAT

Have you ever tried to drill a hole through a piece of metal? Both the drill and the metal become very hot, as shown in Fig. 9–3.

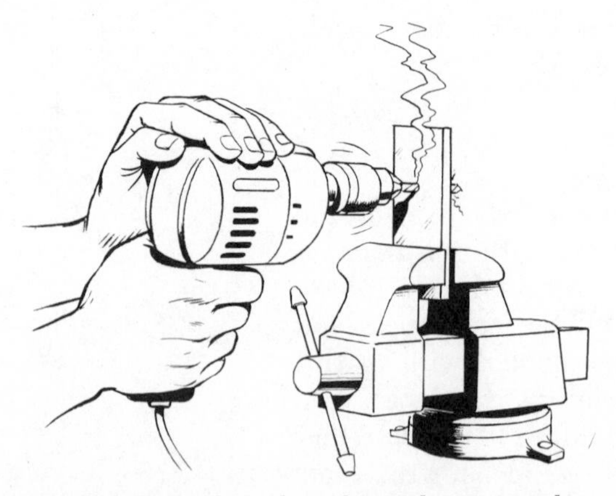

Fig. 9–3. Drilling a hole through metal generates heat.

Around 1800, an English scientist named *Count Rumford* noted that when a drill was used to bore a cannon, both the bit (cutting point) of the drill and the walls of the cannon became very hot. To keep the metals cool, he placed a cylinder of water around the end of the cannon. As the boring continued, the water became warmer and eventually boiled. Since the bit of the drill and the cannon were cold at the start, Rumford concluded that the heat produced probably came from the friction created by the particles of the metal of the drill bit rubbing against the particles of the metal of the cannon. Further, he theorized that the motions of the particles (atoms or molecules) in the metals themselves generated the heat.

Recall that one form of energy can be converted into another form. When electrical energy passes through a thin wire, as in a toaster, the wire becomes hot (electrical energy is changed to heat energy). When you rub your hands together, heat is produced from the friction between the rubbed surfaces (mechanical energy is changed to heat energy). In general, when any form of energy is absorbed by matter, the energy is changed to heat.

The Kinetic-Molecular Theory of Heat

The conversion of absorbed energy to heat energy may be explained by the *kinetic-molecular theory*. This theory states that molecules of all forms of matter are in constant motion. When the molecules absorb energy, they become excited—that is, the molecules move faster than before. As a result of their faster movement, the molecules collide more frequently. As more collisions take place, more and more heat is produced. Thus, heat is really the result of the motions of molecules. Not only is heat an effect of the motions of molecules, but the opposite is also true. The motions of molecules are affected by heat.

Effect of Heat on Molecules

The effect of heat energy on the motions of molecules can be demonstrated by using a sealed tube containing a little mercury and some glass beads (Fig. 9–4, page 162). At ordinary temperatures, the glass beads merely float on the surface of the mercury. However, when the tube of mercury is heated, the glass beads begin to bounce up and down violently in all directions. As still more heat is supplied to the sealed tube, particles of mercury begin to move more swiftly. The glass beads are repeatedly struck by many mercury particles at the same time, so that the glass beads move even more violently in all directions.

According to the kinetic-molecular theory, heat energy acquired by a body is transformed into increased kinetic energy (energy associated

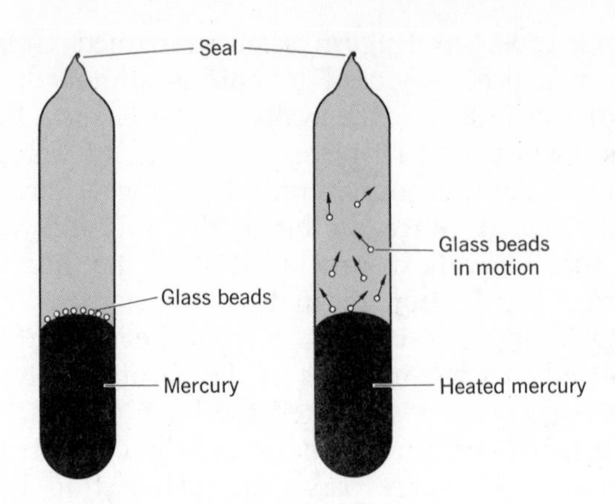

Fig. 9–4. Heat causes molecules to move.

with motion) of the molecules of the body. We observe this increased kinetic energy whenever we heat a solid, a liquid, or a gas. When we supply a great deal of heat to a solid, the molecules of the solid acquire more kinetic energy. Soon, the solid melts. Similarly, an increase in kinetic energy causes the particles of a liquid to separate enough to evaporate (become a gas).

You know that when an ice cube (a solid) is heated, it melts and becomes liquid water. When the water is heated, it vaporizes and becomes gaseous water (water vapor). According to the kinetic-molecular theory, as increasing amounts of heat are supplied to a piece of ice, the water molecules move more rapidly until they gain sufficient energy to overcome the attractive forces holding them together. This permits the ice to liquefy and become water. Similarly, as still more energy is received, the water molecules move at even greater speeds. The attractive forces in the liquid are weakened, and the water is converted into water vapor.

EFFECT OF HEAT ON SOLIDS

Your laboratory experience with the ball-and-ring apparatus indicates that heat causes the solid ball to *expand,* or to increase in volume. This increase in size is not due to an increase in the size of the molecules that make up the solid ball, but rather to an increase in the average distance between the molecules. When an object is heated, its molecules move faster, collide more violently, and consequently move farther apart, thereby increasing the volume of the object.

When the object is cooled, the opposite change occurs, and the volume of the object decreases. This decrease in volume is called *contraction.* As you saw in the laboratory, when the heated brass ball is cooled, the ball contracts and once more can be pushed through the ring.

Problems Resulting From Expansion and Contraction of Solids

The expansion of solids by heating may cause serious practical problems. For example, the expansion of railroad tracks, bridges, or the concrete in a roadbed can create dangerous situations. When rails are laid, gaps between the ends of the rails provide for expansion. If this were not done, consider what would happen to the railroad tracks on a very hot day. The metal would expand, making the tracks bend and buckle, which might cause an oncoming train to be derailed. In bridge construction, expansion joints allow for changes in the length of the bridge. Concrete roadbeds are built with spaces between the sections of concrete to allow for expansion.

The contraction of solids, by cooling, may also present problems. Thus, telephone and electrical wires are strung loosely to prevent their snapping as contraction takes place during the colder times of the year.

Using Expansion and Contraction of Solids

Through extensive studies, scientists have found that different metals, when heated, expand at different rates. For example, when a strip of iron and a strip of aluminum of equal size are heated together, the aluminum expands more than twice as much as the iron. When two such strips of different metals are fastened together, they form a *compound bar*, or *bimetallic strip* (Fig. 9–5). Strips of two different

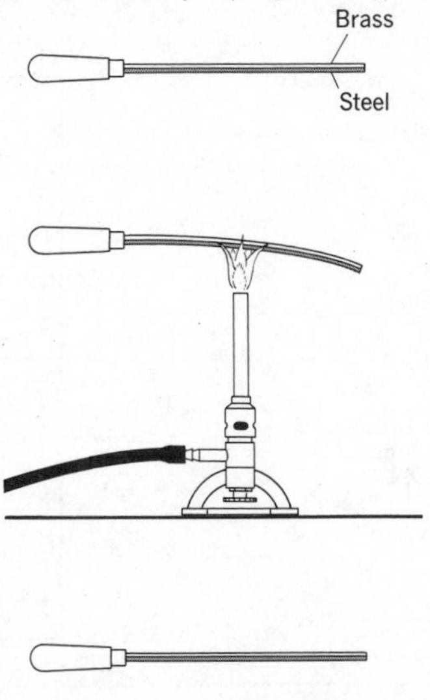

Fig. 9–5. A compound bar.

metals, usually brass and steel, are welded together to form a compound bar. When the bar is heated, the brass expands more than the steel and becomes longer than the steel. Because of the unequal expansion of the metals, the bar bends, with the brass strip on the outside of the bend. When the bar cools, it returns to its original shape. Bimetallic strips are employed in such useful devices as *thermostats, metallic thermometers,* and *thermographs.*

The thermostat is a device containing a compound bar that regulates the heating systems of our homes. When the temperature in the house falls below the setting on the thermostat, the compound bar, which contracts as it cools, closes an electrical circuit and turns on the heat. As the room is warmed, the compound bar in the thermostat expands, bends, and thereby breaks the circuit, shutting off the heat.

The bimetallic thermometer is often used as an oven thermometer to indicate the temperature within an oven, or within a piece of meat that is cooking. We will describe the bimetallic thermometer more fully later in this chapter when we discuss different kinds of thermometers.

In the thermograph (Fig. 9–6), a bimetallic strip is coiled like a watch spring. As the temperature changes, the metals in the strip change length at different rates. This causes the bimetallic strip either to coil more or to uncoil. A pen attached to the bimetallic strip by levers moves up and down on a chart as the temperature changes. The chart is attached to a drum (cylinder) which is rotated by a clockwork device. Thus, a written record of the temperature (an ink trace) is made continuously.

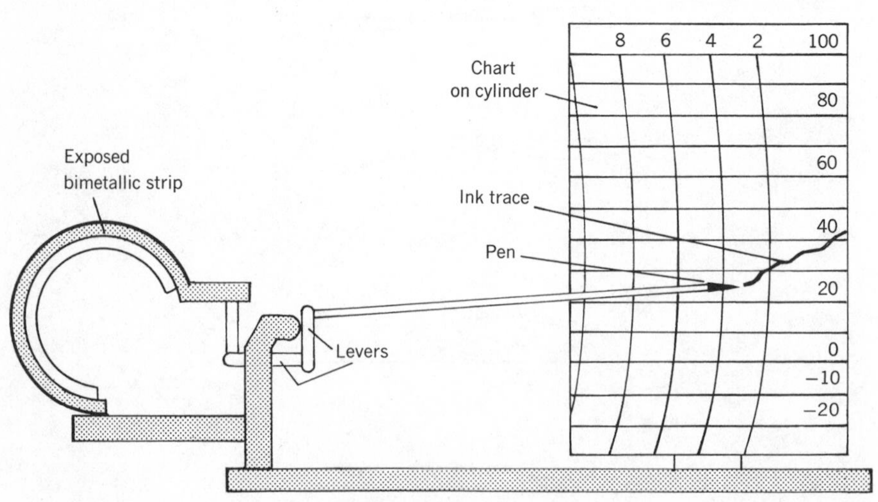

Fig. 9–6. A thermograph.

EFFECT OF HEAT ON LIQUIDS

Liquids, like solids, expand when heated. In the apparatus you used in your laboratory experience (see Fig. 9–1, page 159), the colored water rises in the glass tube as the flask is gently heated with an alcohol lamp. The water level drops down as the flask cools. Thus, we can see that when water is heated, it expands. When the same water is cooled to its original temperature, the water contracts to its original volume. Many other liquids, such as alcohol and mercury, behave in the same way.

At lower temperatures, however, the behavior of water is an exception to this rule. As water is cooled from 100°C to 4°C, the water—like other liquids—contracts. However, when water is cooled below 4°C, the water—unlike other liquids—*expands*. Water continues to expand until it reaches 0°C, its freezing point.

It has been found that the spaces between the water molecules in ice are larger than the spaces between the water molecules in liquid water (Fig. 9–7). The increased space between molecules, caused by expansion just before freezing, means that the volume of a piece of ice is greater than the volume of the water from which the ice was formed. Thus, the density (weight per volume) of ice is less than the density of water. This is why ice floats on water. This unusual behavior of water explains why water in rivers and lakes freezes from the top down, allowing fish and other underwater life to survive.

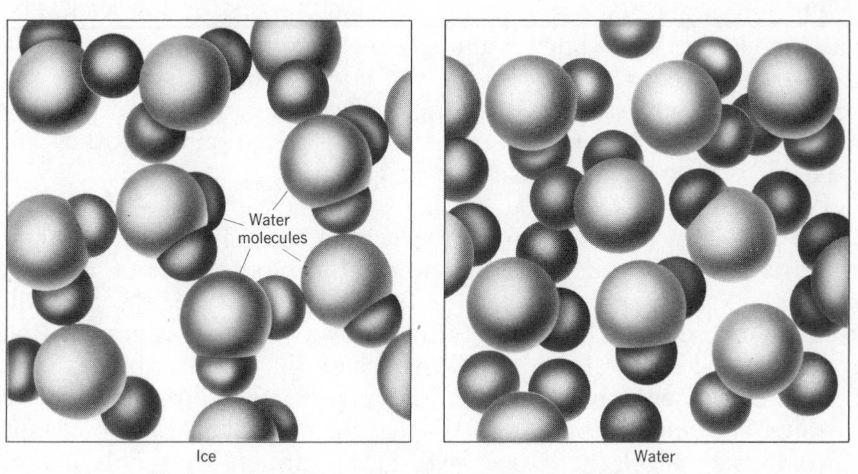

Fig. 9–7. Spacing of molecules in ice and in liquid water.

Problems Resulting From the Expansion of Liquids

In a hot-water heating system, allowances must be made for the expansion of heated water. As the furnace heats the water in the heating system, the water expands. If the expansion continued, pressure would build up in the pipes and could damage the entire system. To avoid this difficulty, an expansion tank is provided. Excess heated water enters the expansion tank and thereby reduces the pressure in the system.

Using Expansion and Contraction of Liquids

Like solids, different liquids expand at different rates. The expansion and contraction of liquids is used in alcohol and mercury thermometers. We will discuss the use of liquids in thermometers later in this chapter.

EFFECT OF HEAT ON GASES

Gases, like solids and liquids, expand when heated. In the apparatus you used in your laboratory experience (see Fig. 9–2, page 159), the balloon becomes inflated as the flask is gently heated. This indicates that, as air is warmed, it expands, moves into the balloon, and inflates it. Similar observations with other gases indicate that gases confined in an elastic container expand when heated and contract when cooled.

Problems Resulting From the Expansion of Gases

The expansion of gases produces many problems. For example, automobile tires could burst if allowed to remain in the sun indefinitely. This fact has been considered by tire manufacturers, who make the walls of tires very strong. A less serious hazard caused by expanding gases is that bottles of soda may crack or even explode if they are exposed to heat for a considerable length of time.

Products such as whipped cream, shaving cream, deodorants, and insect repellents are now supplied in aerosol cans. These cans contain the product itself and a gas that forces the product out of the can when the valve is open. When the product is used up, the can still contains unused gas. If such a can is thrown into an incinerator, the gas becomes heated, expands, and may cause the can to explode. Such aerosol cans should be discarded in a manner that does not involve heating. We noted before (page 43) that the propellants in aerosol cans can adversely affect the ozone layer of the atmosphere. This hazard and the explosive nature of aerosol cans should guide us to less harmful methods of forcing useful products out of cans.

Using Expansion and Contraction of Gases

The fact that gases expand when heated and contract when cooled suggests that gases, like solids and liquids, might also be used in devices such as thermometers. However, gases are less reliable for ordinary purposes, as we shall see.

HEAT AND TEMPERATURE

Heat and temperature are two terms that are often confused. We know that the temperature of the water in a pot of boiling water is considerably higher than the temperature of the water in the ocean. However, the total amount of heat in the water in the pot is much less than the total amount of heat in the water of the ocean. Let us see why this is so.

Suppose we place on a stove a small pot holding one cup of water and another pot holding four cups of water. If we heat both pots at the same time, using flames of the same size, the single cup of water will boil sooner than will the four cups of water. The reason for the difference is simple: One cup of water requires less heat to set its molecules into the violent motion we call boiling than do four cups of water. Thus, by the time four cups of water boil, the water has absorbed more heat (four times as much) than has one cup of water. However, when both pots of water boil, both are at the same temperature—100°C. Note that although both quantities of water are at the same *temperature,* the larger quantity of water has more *heat* in it.

A thermometer measures how hot a mass of matter is—its temperature. However, the thermometer cannot tell us how much heat is present in the matter. The quantity of heat present in a given mass of matter is measured by means of a different instrument, which we will study later in this chapter.

MEASURING TEMPERATURE

Instruments designed to measure temperature are called thermometers. Most thermometers work on the principle that matter expands when heated and contracts when cooled. In general, matter expands and contracts regularly. This means that the amount of expansion or contraction in length is generally the same for the same increase or decrease in temperature. This regular expansion and contraction of certain materials has made it possible to construct three different types of thermometers: gas (air) thermometers, liquid (mercury and alcohol) thermometers, and solid (bimetallic) thermometers.

The Air Thermometer

An air thermometer can be constructed as shown in Fig. 9–8. In this thermometer, the glass bulb contains air. When the bulb is warmed, the air in the bulb expands and forces some of the colored water out of the tube. This changes the level of the liquid in the tube. By placing a suitable scale alongside the tube, we can measure temperature changes. Air thermometers of this type, while interesting, are not very accurate because the volume of a gas is also influenced by the air pressure around it. (Note that the flask also contains a tube open at both ends. Why?)

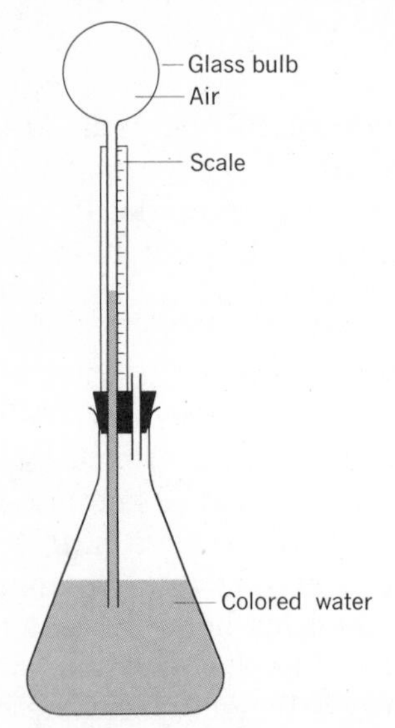

Fig. 9–8. An air thermometer.

Liquid Thermometers

Thermometers containing liquids such as mercury and alcohol are useful and accurate because these liquids usually expand and contract uniformly (regularly).

A mercury thermometer is made by filling a thin glass tube with mercury at a temperature greater than the maximum to be measured. The tube is then cut and sealed at the top. When the mercury cools, it contracts, leaving a partial vacuum above the mercury. (Liquids expand and contract to a much greater extent than do solids. Thus, in the given temperature range, the glass tube is scarcely affected by the temperature change.) The partial vacuum eliminates the effect of air resistance to the expansion of the mercury. The scale of the thermometer is generally fixed by locating the boiling and freezing points of water on the scale. The distance between the boiling and freezing points is then divided into the units of the temperature scale being used. Different temperature scales will be discussed later in this chapter.

Since mercury freezes at −39°C, it cannot be used to measure very low temperatures. However, mercury boils at 357°C, which means that a mercury thermometer can be used to measure temperatures above the boiling point of water. On the other hand, alcohol freezes at −114°C. Accordingly, alcohol thermometers are used to measure low temperatures. However, since alcohol boils at 78°C, alcohol thermometers cannot be used to measure high temperatures.

Bimetallic Thermometers

Recall that a bimetallic strip (Fig. 9–5, page 163) behaves as it does because different metals expand at different rates. Because most metals melt only at very high temperatures, a thermometer that uses a bimetallic strip can measure temperatures as high as 1000°C. The *dial thermometer*, used in most homes as an oven thermometer, is an example of a bimetallic thermometer. A curved bimetallic strip, with the faster-expanding metal on the outside of the bend, is attached to a pointer. Upon heating, the bimetallic strip moves, causing the pointer to indicate the temperature on a circular scale.

TEMPERATURE SCALES

Temperature markings on thermometers are indicated in Fahrenheit degrees or in Celsius degrees. For some scientific purposes, a third temperature scale, the Kelvin scale, is used.

The Fahrenheit and Celsius Scales

The Fahrenheit and Celsius scales are named after their originators, *Gabriel Fahrenheit* and *Anders Celsius.* (The Celsius scale is also called the centigrade, or "hundred grade," scale.) The Fahrenheit scale is used in the customary system of measurement and the Celsius scale in the metric system.

Both Fahrenheit and Celsius scales are calibrated (marked in degrees) by using the boiling and freezing points of water (Fig. 9–9, page 170). In the Fahrenheit scale, the freezing point of water is 32°F, and the boiling point of water is 212°F. The remainder of the scale between these two points is marked off into 180 equal divisions ($212 - 32 = 180$). In the Celsius scale, the freezing point of water is 0°C, and the boiling point of water is 100°C. The remainder of the scale between these points is divided into 100 equal divisions ($100 - 0 = 100$).

Note that there are 180 divisions between the freezing and boiling points of water in the Fahrenheit scale and 100 divisions between these points in the Celsius scale. Thus, each Celsius division (degree) is $\frac{180}{100}$ or $\frac{9}{5}$ as large as a Fahrenheit division (degree). This relationship, together with the fact that there are 32 Fahrenheit divisions (degrees) between 0°F and 32°F, makes it possible to convert one scale into the other by using the following formulas:

$$\text{degrees C} = \frac{5}{9} \times (\text{degrees F} - 32 \text{ degrees})$$

$$\text{degrees F} = (\frac{9}{5} \times \text{degrees C}) + 32 \text{ degrees}$$

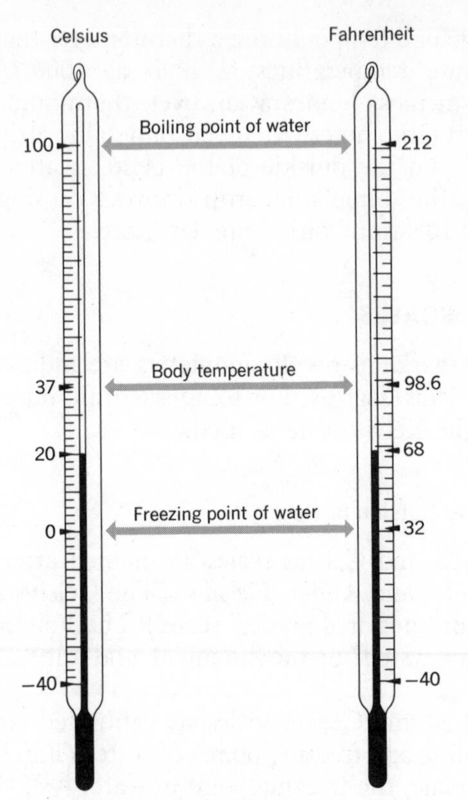

Fig. 9–9. The Celsius and Fahrenheit scales.

These formulas may be written as

$$°C = \frac{5}{9}(°F - 32°) \qquad (1)$$

$$°F = \frac{9}{5}°C + 32° \qquad (2)$$

For example, to convert 40°C to degrees Fahrenheit, we substitute this number in formula (2):

$$°F = \frac{9}{5}°C + 32°$$

$$°F = \frac{9}{\not{5}} \times \overset{8}{\not{40}} + 32$$

$$°F = 72 + 32$$

$$°F = 104$$

Thus, 40°C is equivalent to 104°F.

The Kelvin Scale

Confined gases, like most solids and liquids, expand and contract uniformly. For this statement to be true, however, a gas must be heated or cooled in such a way that the pressure remains constant. (Recall that the air thermometer is inaccurate because it is affected by surrounding air pressure.)

If we start at 0°C, we find that, for every Celsius degree rise in temperature, the volume of a gas increases $\frac{1}{273}$ of its original volume (provided the pressure does not change). Similarly, if we again start from 0°C, we find that for every Celsius degree drop in temperature, the volume decreases $\frac{1}{273}$ of its original volume. At −273°C, the volume of a gas would shrink to zero and all molecular motion would cease. This, in turn, means that the gas would contain no heat. (Actually, gases generally liquefy before this temperature is reached.) Scientists refer to −273°C as *absolute zero*, a temperature that has never been attained, although some scientists have come very close to this point.

Absolute zero, −273°C, is also called 0° Kelvin (0°K) or 0° absolute (0°A). The Kelvin scale, named after its originator, *Lord Kelvin*, is based on absolute temperatures. Since the Kelvin scale begins with absolute zero (−273°C), we use the following formula to convert the Celsius scale to the Kelvin scale:

$$\text{degrees Kelvin} = \text{degrees Celsius} + 273 \text{ degrees}$$

This formula may be written as

$$^\circ K = {}^\circ C + 273^\circ$$

Let us find the freezing point of water (0°C) in the Kelvin scale:

$$^\circ K = {}^\circ C + 273^\circ$$
$$^\circ K = 0 + 273$$
$$^\circ K = 273$$

Thus, 0°C is equivalent to 273°K.

Now, let us find the boiling point of water:

$$°K = °C + 273°$$
$$°K = 100 + 273$$
$$°K = 373$$

Thus, 100°C is equivalent to 373°K.

MEASURING HEAT

We learned (page 167) that temperature measures how hot a substance is, but not how much heat it contains. We also learned that a large quantity and a small quantity of water at the same temperature possess different quantities of heat.

In the metric system, we measure the quantity of heat by means of a unit called the *calorie.* The calorie is the amount of heat needed to raise the temperature of 1 gram of water 1 Celsius degree.

The Calorimeter

The amount of heat energy present in a substance cannot be measured directly with simple measuring devices. Instead, the amount of heat energy is measured by observing its effect on a given quantity of water in a device called a *calorimeter.* One type of calorimeter, shown in Fig. 9–10, consists of two polished metal cups surrounded by air, a poor conductor of heat. An insulating cover, holding a thermometer,

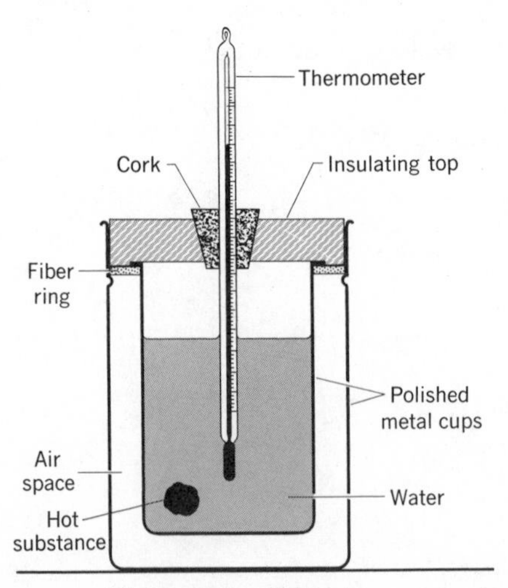

Fig. 9–10. A calorimeter.

makes up the top of the calorimeter. The polished cups reflect heat, thus maintaining the temperature of the liquid in the container.

To determine the amount of heat energy absorbed (or lost) by a given quantity of water, we multiply the weight of the water in grams by the change in temperature of the water in Celsius degrees. Thus:

$$\underset{\text{(calories)}}{\text{amount of heat}} = \underset{\text{(grams)}}{\text{weight of water}} \times \underset{\text{(Celsius degrees)}}{\text{change in temperature}}$$

In a calorimeter, when 20 grams of water at 20°C are heated to a temperature of 30°C, how much heat is absorbed?

$$\underset{\text{(calories)}}{\text{amount of heat}} = \underset{\text{(grams)}}{\text{weight of water}} \times \underset{\text{(Celsius degrees)}}{\text{change in temperature}}$$

The change in temperature is found by subtracting the initial temperature from the final temperature. Thus, 30°C − 20°C = 10 Celsius degrees, the change in temperature. Substituting,

$$\text{amount of heat} = 20 \text{ grams} \times 10\ \text{C}^\circ = 200 \text{ calories}$$

We conclude that 200 calories have been absorbed. (We assume that no heat has escaped from the calorimeter.)

Calculating an Exchange of Heat

In some cases, we may wish to know how much heat is lost or gained when we mix two substances having different temperatures. Keep in mind that heat energy cannot be created or destroyed, though it may be "lost" or changed to another form of energy. Thus, if two substances are mixed, the amount of heat lost by the "hot" substance is equal to the amount of heat gained by the "cold" substance.

Suppose we mix 100 grams of water at 90°C with 100 grams of water at 40°C and find that the final temperature of the mixture is 65°C. Let us calculate the number of calories lost by the hot water and gained by the cold water.

The temperature of the hot water dropped from 90°C to 65°C, a decrease of 25 Celsius degrees. Since we began with 100 grams of hot water that underwent a temperature change of 25 C°, we determine the amount of heat lost:

$$\underset{\text{(calories)}}{\text{amount of heat}} = \underset{\text{(grams)}}{\text{weight of water}} \times \underset{\text{(Celsius degrees)}}{\text{change in temperature}}$$

$$\text{amount of heat} = 100 \text{ grams} \times 25\ \text{C}^\circ$$

$$\text{amount of heat} = 2500 \text{ calories}$$

Note: To avoid possible confusion, scientists often indicate a loss of heat with a minus sign. Using this method, the above equation would be solved as follows:

amount of heat = weight of water × change in temperature

amount of heat = 100 grams × (−25 C°)

amount of heat = −2500 calories

The minus sign in the answer indicates that 2500 calories of heat have been *lost.*

The temperature of the cold water increased from 40°C to 65°C, an increase of 25 Celsius degrees. Since we began with 100 grams of cold water that underwent a temperature change of 25 C°, we determine the amount of heat gained:

amount of heat = weight of water × change in temperature
(calories) (grams) (Celsius degrees)

amount of heat = 100 grams × 25 C°

amount of heat = 2500 calories

Note that the amount of heat lost by the hot water (2500 calories) is the same as the amount of heat gained by the cold water (2500 calories). We assume that the heat exchange was "perfect"; that is, no heat escaped from the calorimeter.

The quantity of heat needed to raise the temperature of 1 gram of a substance 1 Celsius degree is called the *specific heat* of the substance. For water, the specific heat is 1. This means that 1 calorie of heat will raise the temperature of 1 gram of water 1 C°. Water is the only substance for which this is true. Other substances vary in the quantity of heat needed to raise 1 gram of the substance 1 Celsius degree. Consequently, the formula

amount of heat = weight of water × change in temperature

applies only to water since the right side of the equation is being multiplied by 1.

Calories and Food

Your body requires energy in order to perform its daily tasks. Most of this energy comes from energy-rich food compounds such as carbohydrates and fats. This energy is released when the body oxidizes these compounds. Using special calorimeters, scientists have measured the energy content, or the number of calories present, in given quantities of certain foods. For example, a slice of white bread contains about 60,000 calories; a typical chocolate bar may contain about 300,000 calories.

Nutritionists use a special kind of notation when discussing the calorie content of foods. They define a food Calorie (written with a capital letter) as 1000 calories. On a calorie table, therefore, we would read that a slice of white bread contains about 60 Calories and that a chocolate bar contains about 300 Calories.

Calorie tables have been prepared to enable people to determine the diet best suited to their bodies and to their work. The problem of underweight and overweight is dependent upon a person's calorie intake as well as upon the proper selection of foods.

Looking Back

Heat energy is required for the continued existence of all living things. Heat energy is also necessary for the operation of many devices that are useful in homes and in industry. The addition of heat to solids, liquids, and gases causes them to expand, and the removal of heat causes them to contract. The temperature of a substance is measured in degrees. The amount of heat in a substance is measured in calories.

Looking Ahead

Light energy, like heat energy, is important for life. We will study how light energy affects us in the next chapter.

Multiple-Choice Questions

1. On a sunny day, your clothing becomes hot because
   a. light is absorbed and changed to heat
   b. heat and light are reflected
   c. heat and light are transmitted
   d. heat is transmitted and light is reflected
2. The scientist who proposed that heat results from the motion of molecules was
   a. Celsius b. Fahrenheit c. Rumford d. Newton

3. When heat is absorbed,
   a. molecules move more slowly
   b. molecules move more rapidly
   c. there is no change in molecular motion
   d. temperature remains unchanged
4. When heat energy is absorbed by a body, it is transformed to
   a. potential energy
   b. light energy
   c. electrical energy
   d. kinetic energy
5. As heat energy is absorbed by a liquid, the attractive forces holding the molecules together are
   a. not affected b. weakened c. strengthened d. eliminated
6. When a brass ball is heated in a flame, it
   a. remains unchanged b. expands c. contracts d. melts
7. Expansion is due to
   a. an increase in the size of molecules
   b. a decrease in the size of molecules
   c. a decrease in the distance between molecules
   d. an increase in the distance between molecules
8. Studies of the expansion of metals show that different metals expand
   a. at different rates when heated
   b. at different rates when cooled
   c. at the same rates when heated
   d. at the same rates when cooled
9. A thermostat contains a
   a. compound bar
   b. bar of silver
   c. bar of iron
   d. bar of steel
10. As water is cooled from a temperature above 4°C to temperatures approaching 0°C, it
    a. expands, then contracts
    b. contracts
    c. expands
    d. contracts, then expands
11. Liquids, when heated,
    a. do not expand
    b. expand at the same rate
    c. expand at different rates
    d. contract but do not expand
12. To avoid excess pressure in a hot-water heating system, engineers make use of
    a. an expansion tank b. a boiler c. a circulator d. an oil tank
13. If an aerosol can is placed in an incinerator, it probably will
    a. contract b. melt c. not be affected d. explode
14. In a mercury thermometer, the amount of expansion of the mercury for each degree increase in temperature
    a. increases
    b. decreases
    c. is the same
    d. is different
15. A mercury thermometer is constructed at
    a. room temperature
    b. a temperature higher than the maximum of the thermometer
    c. a temperature lower than the minimum of the thermometer
    d. 0° Kelvin

16. Of the following thermometers, the one best suited to measure temperatures far below the freezing point of water contains
    a. dry ice b. alcohol c. mercury d. water
17. In the Fahrenheit scale, the number of equal divisions between the freezing and boiling points of water is
    a. 100 b. 160 c. 212 d. 180
18. Each Celsius degree is
    a. $\frac{5}{9}$ of a Fahrenheit degree b. $\frac{9}{5}$ of a Fahrenheit degree
    c. twice as large as a Fahrenheit degree
    d. half as large as a Fahrenheit degree
19. For each one-degree rise in Celsius temperature, the volume of a gas increases its original volume by
    a. $\frac{1}{273}$ b. $\frac{1}{200}$ c. $\frac{1}{2}$ d. $\frac{1}{3}$
20. The Celsius equivalent for absolute zero is
    a. 0°C b. −273°F c. −459.7°C d. −273°C

Modified True-False Questions

1. The decrease in the volume of an object as it cools is called *compression*.
2. When two strips of different metals are fastened together, they form *a bimetallic strip*.
3. As the air in a balloon is heated, the balloon *deflates*.
4. An instrument used to measure temperature is known as *a thermostat*.
5. Alcohol boils at a temperature of *seventy-eight degrees C*.
6. A temperature of −273°C is known as *the freezing point*.
7. In the metric system, the amount of heat needed to raise the temperature of 1 gram of water 1 C° is called *a degree*.
8. The amount of heat in an object can be measured with *a thermostat*.

Thought Questions

1. Contrast each of the following pairs of terms:
   a. expansion and contraction
   b. heat and temperature
   c. one Celsius degree and one Fahrenheit degree
2. a. Change 77°F to the comparable Celsius temperature.
   b. Change 212°F to the comparable Celsius temperature.
   c. Change 20°C to the comparable Fahrenheit temperature.
   d. Change 5°C to the comparable Fahrenheit temperature.
3. Convert the following Celsius temperatures to the Kelvin scale:
   a. 16°C b. 30°C c. 100°C d. 70°C e. 44°C
4. Find the quantity of heat (in calories) in water when:
   a. 100 grams of water at 20°C are heated to a temperature of 70°C.
   b. 60 grams of water are heated until their temperature changes by 10°C.

CHAPTER 10
WHAT IS THE NATURE OF LIGHT ENERGY IN OUR ENVIRONMENT?

When you have completed this chapter, you should be able to:

1. *Discuss* some of the major theories of the nature of light.
2. *Explain* how the speed of light was first measured.
3. *Demonstrate* that light travels in straight lines.
4. *Distinguish* between (*a*) luminous and illuminated bodies (*b*) umbra and penumbra (*c*) transparent, translucent, and opaque bodies.
5. *State* and *illustrate* the law of reflection.
6. *Compare* light waves with sound waves.

In the laboratory experience that follows, you will investigate the properties of an image formed by reflection.

Laboratory Experience

WHAT ARE THE PROPERTIES OF AN IMAGE FORMED IN A PLANE MIRROR?

A. Make a copy of Fig. 10–1 on a piece of white paper, and secure the paper to a drawing board with either tape or tacks.

B. Using a rubber band, attach a plane (flat) mirror to a block of wood, and stand the mirror upright on line *EF*. Stick a pin in the paper at point A.

C. Move a little to the right of the pin to point C. Sight the image of the pin in the mirror by placing a ruler at point C, looking along the edge of the ruler to the image of the pin in the mirror. Draw a line from point C to line *EF* to indicate this sighting. *N* is the point where the line touches the mirror.

   1. With respect to the mirror, where does the image of the pin appear to be?

D. Move to the left of the pin to point *D*, and again sight the image

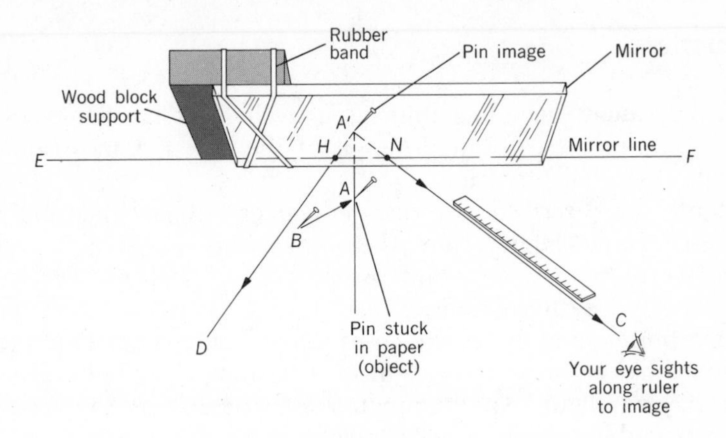

Fig. 10–1.

of the pin along a ruler between point *D* and the mirror. Draw a line to indicate this sighting by connecting point *D* with line *EF*. *H* is the point where the line touches the mirror.

E. Remove the mirror, and extend line *CN* behind the mirror using a dotted line. Extend line *DH* behind the mirror by a dotted line also. *A′* is the point where line *CN* crosses line *DH*. This is the apparent position of the image.

F. Move the pin from point A to point B. Repeat procedures C, D, and E for the image of the pin at point B. *B′* is the point behind the mirror where the dotted lines meet. Connect points *A′* and *B′* with a dotted line. This represents the image of an object, line AB.

G. Make the following measurements, and record them in your notebook on separate lines.

   a. Length of *object* AB

   b. Length of *image* A′B′

   c. Distance point A to mirror line

   d. Distance point *A′* to mirror line

   e. Distance point *B* to mirror line

   f. Distance point *B′* to mirror line

2. How does the size of the object *AB* compare with the size of the image *A′B′*?
3. What conclusion can you draw concerning the distance of the object to the mirror and the distance of the image to the mirror?
4. What does the mirror appear to do to the position of the image *A′B′* as compared to the position of the object *AB*?

Introduction

All living things, including humans as well as green plants, obtain energy for life processes from the light of the sun. For most animals, light is also essential for vision.

Light may be described as either *natural* or *artificial*. Natural light is light that comes largely from the sun. Artificial light is a product of human invention; it is usually associated with burning, electricity, or other energy transformations.

Lighted objects may be described as either *luminous* or *illuminated*. A luminous object, such as the sun or a burning light bulb, gives off (emits) its own light. An illuminated object, such as the moon or a mirror, is visible because it reflects light.

When a nonluminous object receives more energy than it naturally possesses, the object may begin to glow and emit light energy. For example, when you heat a piece of iron in a hot flame, the iron soon glows red. As the heating continues, the iron glows white, and finally, if the source of heat is strong enough, the iron glows blue. When you remove the source of heat, the iron continues to glow for a while until it cools and returns to its original state.

Thus, the introduction of energy (such as heat) into an object can apparently cause the emission of radiant energy. It is thought that the emitted energy results from disturbances within the atoms of the object. The emitted energy sometimes takes the form of visible light. At other times, the energy emitted may be in the form of ultraviolet light or X rays, which are invisible to the human eye. Disturbances in the atoms of elements present in the sun are thought to be responsible for the sun's heat and light.

Unlike luminous objects, which give off their own light, illuminated objects give off light that reaches them from other sources, that is, by *reflection* (rebounding). Examples of illuminated objects, in addition to the moon and the planets, include clouds, the pages of this book, and all other objects that we see but which do not emit their own light.

THEORIES ABOUT THE NATURE OF LIGHT

Light, like heat, is a form of energy. Although everyone is familiar with light energy, scientists still puzzle over just what it is. Investigations to determine the nature of light started in the seventeenth century and are still continuing. The major theories that have been proposed to explain the nature of light are the *corpuscular theory*, the *wave theory*, the *electromagnetic theory*, and the *quantum theory*.

Newton's Corpuscular Theory

The corpuscular theory of light was first proposed in the seventeenth century by the English scientist *Sir Isaac Newton*. According to this theory, the light emitted by luminous bodies consists of tiny particles of matter, or *corpuscles*. These emitted corpuscles are propelled outward in all directions, traveling in succession much like bullets from a machine gun. Newton thought that when corpuscles strike a surface, each particle is reflected in much the same manner that a handball bounces off a wall. From his studies in gravitation, Newton predicted that light traveling from air into water would increase its speed. Since water is denser than air, he reasoned, the corpuscles of light, on entering water, would be attracted more to the water and hence the speed of the corpuscles would increase.

Huygens' Wave Theory

Christian Huygens, a Dutch scientist, proposed his wave theory of light at about the same time that Newton proposed his corpuscular theory. Huygens believed that light is emitted as a series of waves that spread out from the light source in all directions. These waves are much like the ripples formed when a pebble is dropped into water. These waves, unlike corpuscles, are not affected by gravity. Disagreeing with Newton, Huygens predicted that light, on entering water from air, would decrease in speed. When the speed of light through different substances (air, glass, or water) was determined two centuries later, Huygens' prediction was found to be correct.

Maxwell's Electromagnetic Theory

The wave theory of light, as developed by Huygens, assumes that light waves must travel through (be transmitted by) some substance, or *medium*.

Toward the end of the nineteenth century, *James Clerk Maxwell*, a Scottish physicist, proposed that light waves do not require a medium for transmission. According to Maxwell, light waves possess electrical and magnetic properties and can travel through a vacuum. Later experiments by Maxwell and other scientists showed that light waves are a part of a larger family of electromagnetic waves, which make up the *electromagnetic spectrum* (Fig. 10–2, page 182).

According to the electromagnetic theory of light, different electromagnetic waves are produced by disturbances of atomic particles by various forms of energy. Only a small portion of these waves (or rays, as they are sometimes called) can be seen by the eye. These are the familiar colors of the visible spectrum, which we mentioned before in Chapters 3 and 7. We will study the visible spectrum in more detail in Chapter 11. The other waves are invisible and can be detected only with special devices.

Each type of wave in the electromagnetic spectrum possesses a particular *wavelength* and a particular *frequency* (vibrations per second, or vps). Thus, a radio wave that is 1000 meters long has a frequency of 300,000 vibrations per second. A visible light ray that is five ten-millionths of a meter long has a frequency of 600,000,000,000,000 vibrations per second. An X ray that is one ten-billionth of a meter long has a frequency of about 3,000,000,000,000,000,000 vibrations per second. The shorter the wavelength, the greater the frequency, as shown in Fig. 10–2.

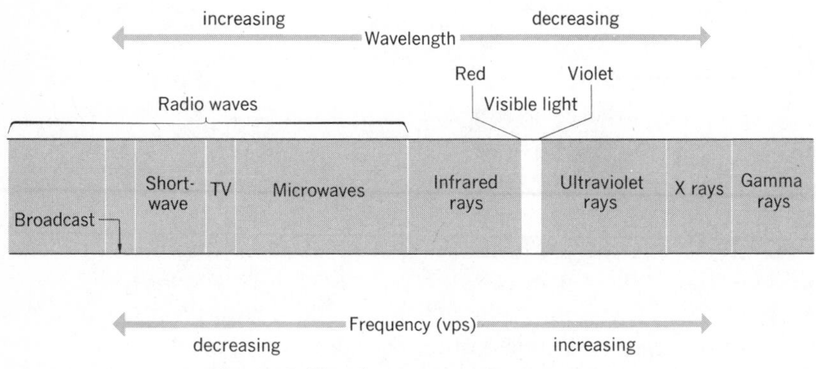

Fig. 10–2. The electromagnetic spectrum.

Electromagnetic waves somewhat longer than those of red light are called infrared rays (see Chapter 3, page 39). Infrared rays are invisible to the human eye but can affect a special type of photographic film. Electromagnetic waves longer than infrared are radio waves.

Electromagnetic waves somewhat shorter than those of violet light are called ultraviolet rays (see Chapter 3, page 38). Ultraviolet rays are also invisible to the human eye and can affect photographic film. These rays tan the skin, stimulate the production of vitamin D, and kill bacteria in the air. Electromagnetic waves shorter than ultraviolet are X rays, gamma rays, and cosmic rays. The shorter the wavelength, the more penetrating is the ray. Thus, great caution must be exercised in using rays of short wavelength.

Planck's Quantum Theory

By the end of the nineteenth century, experiments had shown that electromagnetic waves possess energy and that each wave possesses a different quantity of energy from the others. In 1900, the German scientist *Max Planck* proposed the theory that light waves travel as separate packets of energy called *quanta* (singular, *quantum*) or *photons*. In some respects, Planck's photons resemble the corpuscles of Newton's theory. However, instead of considering the photons to be particles of matter, they are considered to be bundles of energy.

In recent years, it has become evident that, in some respects, light seems to behave as corpuscles; in others, light behaves as visible and invisible waves; and in still others, light behaves as bundles of energy. Since the quantum theory merges the ideas of the three theories that preceded it, this theory explains the nature and behavior of light more satisfactorily than does any other theory.

MEASURING THE SPEED OF LIGHT

We see a flash of lightning long before we hear the sound of the thunder caused by the lightning. It is therefore apparent that the speed of light is much greater than the speed of sound.

As long ago as 1676, *Olaus Roemer*, a Danish scientist, devised a method to accomplish the difficult task of finding the speed of light. Through a telescope, he observed the motions of the planet Jupiter and one of its satellites (moons). Roemer found that, at one time of the year, the satellite revolved around Jupiter once every 42½ hours. This observation was made when the earth was in position A in Fig. 10–3, page 184. This revolution could be accurately timed because, at some point in its orbit, the satellite passed behind Jupiter and was eclipsed. Whenever this eclipse occurred, a revolution of the satellite was completed. Six months later, the earth had traveled halfway around the sun and was as far from its original location as possible. At this location, *B* in Fig. 10–3, page 184, the earth was about 300,000,000 kilometers farther away from Jupiter than it had been in position A. This distance, which is the diameter of the earth's orbit, had been previously calculated by astronomers.

Since Jupiter takes about 12 years to circle the sun, it had moved only about 15° along its orbit during the six months. This relatively small movement does not affect its distance from the earth. When the earth reached position *B*, Roemer found that the time between two successive eclipses of Jupiter's satellite was about 1000 seconds longer than the observed 42½ hours. He reasoned that the increase in time was due to the greater distance that the light had to travel to reach the earth from Jupiter. He divided the increased distance, 300,000,000 kilometers, by the increase in time, 1000 seconds, and found the speed of light to be

$$\frac{300{,}000{,}000 \text{ kilometers}}{1000 \text{ seconds}} \text{ or } 300{,}000 \text{ kilometers per second.}$$

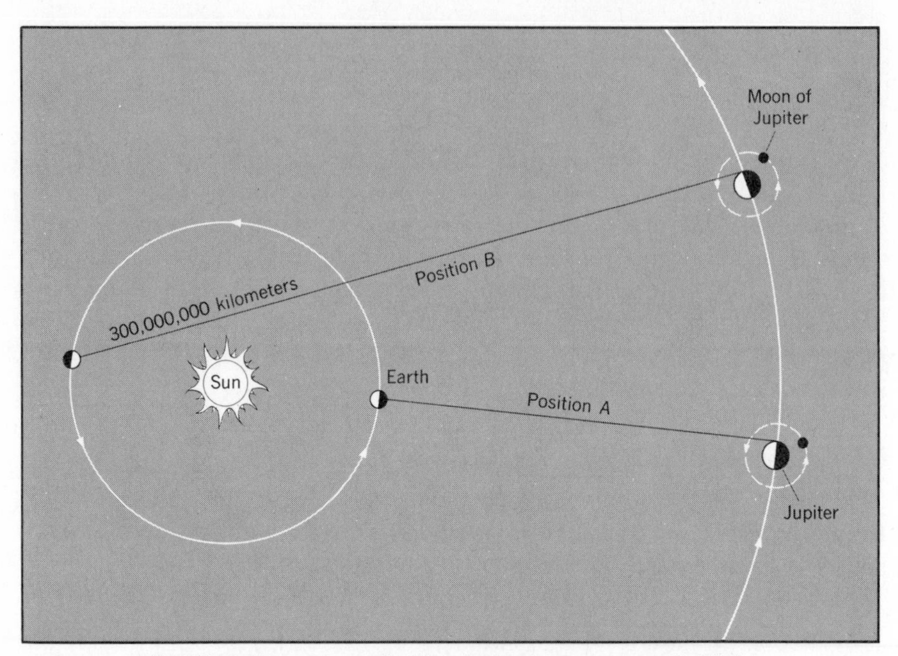

Fig. 10–3. Roemer's method for determining the speed of light.

Modern experimenters have checked Roemer's determination of the speed of light. Among these was *Albert A. Michelson,* who in 1926 used rotating mirrors to measure the time required for light to make one round trip from Mt. Wilson to Mt. San Antonio in California, a distance of about 70 kilometers. He checked his results by measuring the time it took light to travel through a specially constructed tunnel that was one mile long. From his precise experiments, Michelson calculated the speed of light to be 299,796 kilometers per second. For most purposes, however, we use the approximate figure of 300,000 kilometers per second.

While the speed of an electromagnetic wave is unaffected by temperature changes, it is affected by the medium through which it travels. The value for the speed of light is about the same in air as it is in a vacuum. However, the speed of light does decrease as light passes through liquids and solids. We will deal with some of these effects in the next chapter.

LIGHT TRAVELS IN STRAIGHT LINES

Punch a small hole in the center of each of four large square cards. Attach each card to a separate block of wood. Light a candle and arrange the cards, as in Fig. 10–4, so that the candle flame can be

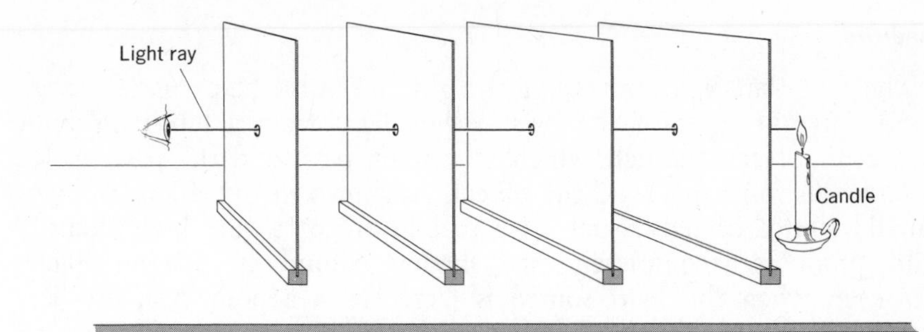

Fig. 10–4. Light travels in a straight line.

seen when all four holes are in line. If you thread a piece of string through the holes, while keeping the card arrangement undisturbed, you will find that the string makes a straight line. Since light rays from the candle can reach your eye only by traveling along the path of the string, it is reasonable to conclude that light travels in straight lines.

Pinhole Camera

The fact that light travels in straight lines helps us understand how a pinhole camera (Fig. 10–5) forms an image of an object viewed through it. You can make such a camera by using a pin to pierce the center of one side of an opaque box. Cut out the opposite side of the box, and replace it with a screen made of ground glass or waxed paper.

When an object is viewed through the pinhole, its image is seen on the screen in an inverted (upside-down) position. The inversion occurs because light rays from each part of the object must pass through the pinhole to reach the screen. As shown in Fig. 10–5, light rays from the top of the object and light rays from the bottom of the object, in passing through the pinhole, must cross each other's path. After crossing, the lower rays reach the upper part of the screen and the upper rays reach the lower part of the screen, thereby producing the inverted image.

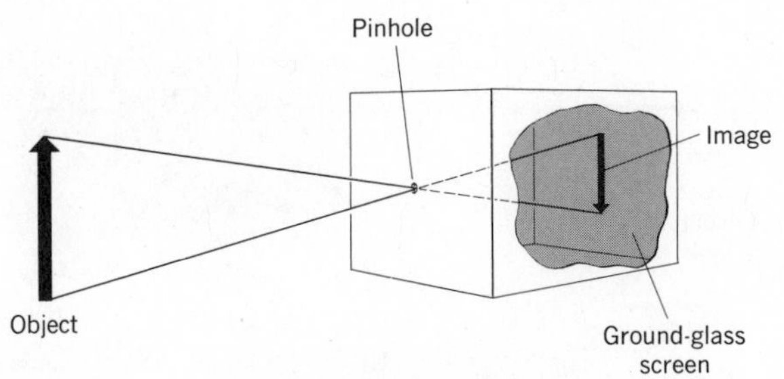

Fig. 10–5. A pinhole camera.

Shadows

The fact that light travels in straight lines also helps us to understand different types of shadows. When light from a luminous body strikes an object through which it cannot pass, a dark space called a *shadow* is formed behind the object. As shown in Fig. 10–6*a*, a point (small) source of light, such as a carbon arc or a tiny high-intensity bulb, produces a completely dark shadow behind the opaque object. However, when the light source is larger than a point (an ordinary light bulb, for example), the shadow formed is often seen to consist of two parts, an *umbra* and a *penumbra* (Fig. 10–6*b*). The umbra is the darker central portion of the shadow that receives no light from the source. The penumbra is the lighter shadow that surrounds the umbra. The penumbra is lighter because it receives some light from the outer edges of the light source. As the rays in the diagram show, shadows would not form unless light travels in straight lines.

LIGHT IS AFFECTED BY MATTER

All of us are aware that light energy is transmitted to the earth across many millions of miles of space from the sun and other stars.

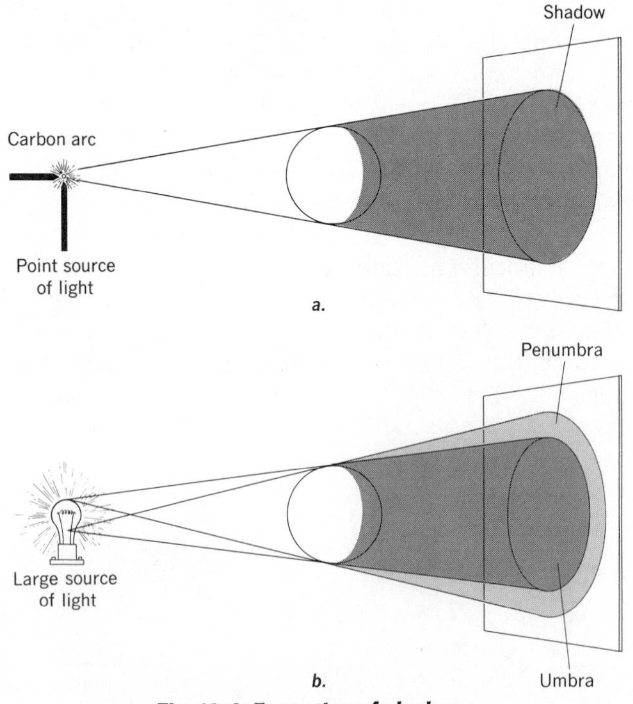

Fig. 10–6. Formation of shadows.

Since outer space is an almost perfect vacuum, it is apparent that light can travel through a vacuum.

Light waves easily pass through a vacuum, undergoing little change. When light waves come in contact with matter, however, they slow down and may change in other ways. In traveling through matter, light may be blocked (or absorbed), either partially or completely; it may be distorted (twisted out of position); or it may pass through with little change.

Objects that completely block light and through which we cannot see are called *opaque* objects. Examples include wood, stone, and steel. Objects that readily transmit light and through which we can see clearly are called *transparent* objects. Plate glass, air, and clear plastics are examples of transparent objects. Objects that allow light to pass through partially or that distort the light so that we cannot see through them are called *translucent* objects. Frosted glass, cloth window shades, and oiled paper are examples of translucent objects.

REFLECTION OF LIGHT

When light strikes opaque objects, it is generally absorbed. If the object is dark in color, as we have learned before, the light energy is transformed into heat energy. When light strikes transparent or translucent objects, it passes through them and continues on its path. However, when light strikes certain surfaces, it is reflected. That is, the light bounces off the surface in much the same manner as a handball bounces off a wall.

Law of Reflection

When we play handball, we return a ball best when we place ourselves in the spot where we expect the ball to be after it rebounds from the wall. We learn to predict which way the ball will bounce off the wall. This is possible because, in general, the ball rebounds from the wall at the same angle that it struck the wall.

Light rebounds from an object in much the same way as a ball rebounds from a wall. When a ray of light strikes a smooth, shiny surface, the ray is reflected (Fig. 10–7, page 188). The light ray that strikes the surface is called the *incident ray*; the light ray that bounces off the surface is called the *reflected ray*. The line drawn at right angles (perpendicular) to the surface is called the *normal*. When a light ray strikes a surface such as a plane (flat) mirror along the normal, the light ray rebounds from the mirror along the same line. When a light ray strikes the mirror at an angle to the normal, it is reflected from the mirror at an angle equal to the original angle. The angle between

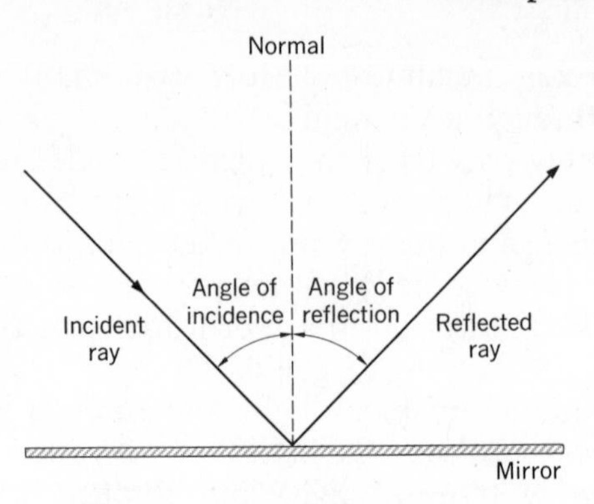

Fig. 10–7. Law of reflection.

the incident ray and the normal is called the *angle of incidence;* the angle between the reflected ray and the normal is called the *angle of reflection.* Thus, when light strikes a mirror at an angle, the angle of incidence is equal to the angle of reflection. This relationship is called the *law of reflection.*

The law of reflection is readily demonstrated by a device called an *optical disk* (Fig. 10–8). The mirror of this device is lined up so that the normal to the mirror crosses the zero point of the scale. When an incident ray strikes the mirror at an angle of 50° from the normal, the beam of light is reflected and crosses the scale at the 50° mark on the other side of the normal. You can test the law of reflection by using as many different angles for the incident ray as you like.

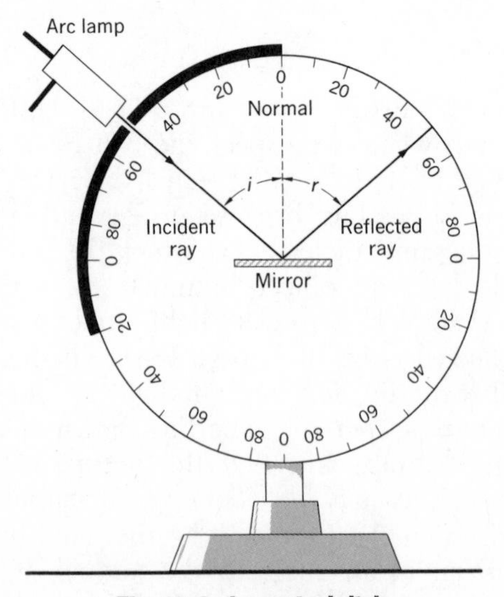

Fig. 10–8. An optical disk.

When a single ray of light is reflected from a smooth shiny surface, it behaves according to the law of reflection. However, when a *beam* of light, which is composed of many parallel light rays, strikes a given surface, the manner in which the beam is reflected depends on the nature of the surface.

Regular Reflection

Reflection that occurs from a smooth flat surface, such as a mirror or a quiet pool of water, is called *regular reflection*. In this type of reflection, when many parallel rays of light strike the surface at some angle from the normal, all of the rays remain parallel and are reflected from the surface in the same direction and at the same angle of reflection (Fig. 10–9).

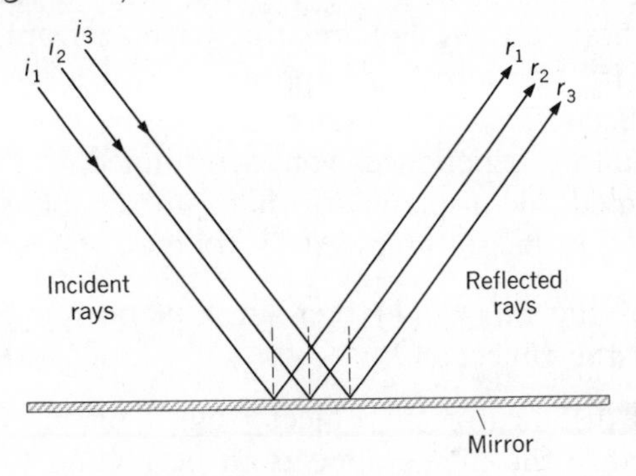

Fig. 10–9. Regular reflection.

Diffuse Reflection

Reflection from a rough surface is called *diffuse reflection*. When a beam of light composed of many parallel light rays strikes a rough surface, each individual light ray obeys the law of reflection according to the position of each portion, or facet, of the surface (Fig. 10–10). Since the surface is not smooth, the reflected rays that leave it are no longer parallel. Thus, the reflected rays bounce off the surface in

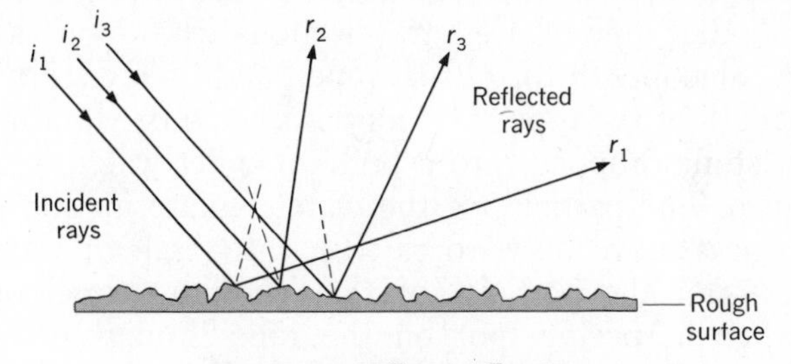

Fig. 10–10. Diffuse reflection.

all directions. Diffuse reflection is the type of reflection by which we see many illuminated objects. For example, you see the paper of this page because of the diffuse reflection of light from the individual fibers of which the paper is made.

Reflected Images

You observe a familiar example of regular reflection every time you look into an ordinary mirror. If you stand 2 meters from a full-length mirror and examine your image, it will appear to be 2 meters behind the mirror. Your image will also appear to be as tall as you are. Furthermore, you will find your image to be reversed laterally (sideways), that is, from left to right. This means that your left hand appears in the image as your right hand, and so forth. The reversal of position is best seen by holding this page in front of a mirror and trying to read it. The letters all appear to be backward; the image of the print has been reversed laterally.

In the laboratory experience, you determined the characteristics of an image formed by a plane, or flat, mirror (Fig. 10–11). These characteristics may be summarized as follows.

1. The size of the image (I) seen in a plane mirror is the same as the size of the object (O).
2. The actual distance of the object from a plane mirror is the same as the distance the image appears to be behind the mirror.
3. The image seen in a plane mirror is reversed laterally when compared to the object.

WAVE MOTION OF LIGHT

Although we are familiar with the fact that light waves travel in straight lines, many of us have difficulty conceiving that a wave can move in a straight line.

Fasten one end of a rope to a fixed support. As you shake the free end of the rope, waves travel along the rope, as shown in Fig. 10–12. Shaking disturbs the rope, and the disturbances travel along the length of the rope. The rope is said to be vibrating. Similarly, a pebble or stone dropped into a body of quiet water acts as a center of disturbance. The particles in the water vibrate up and down, while the disturbances move outward as waves. In each of these cases, the disturbances—not the particles of the medium—travel outward. For example, when a specific spot on the rope is marked and the rope is shaken, the spot moves up and down in the same position, whereas

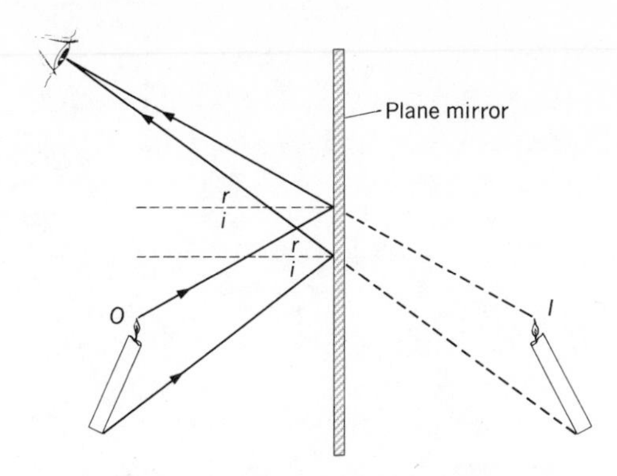

Fig. 10–11. Image formed by a plane mirror.

the disturbances travel along the rope. Similarly, a piece of wood floating on the surface of a quiet, windless pond bobs up and down in the same position as waves pass by it.

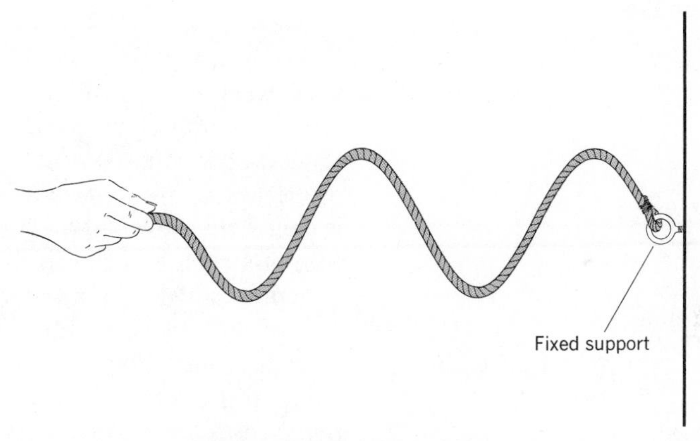

Fig. 10–12. A vibrating rope.

Types of Waves

The direction of the disturbances (waves) compared to the direction of motion of the vibrating particles determines the type of wave. Two common wave types are recognized:

1. *Transverse waves.* The particles vibrate at right angles to the direction of the wave (Fig. 10–13*a*). The vibrating rope and water waves are examples of transverse waves.

2. *Longitudinal waves.* The particles vibrate back and forth, parallel to the direction the wave travels (Fig. 10–13*b*). Sound waves travel in this way. We shall study sound waves in detail in Chapter 12.

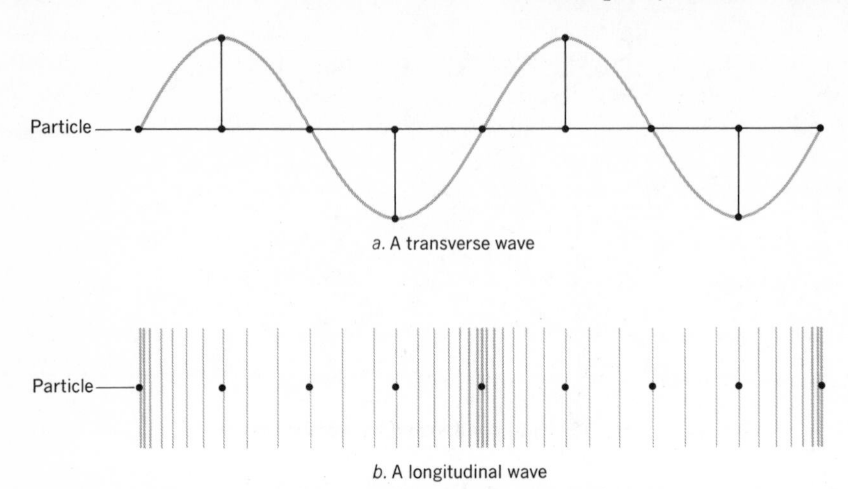

Fig. 10–13. Types of wave motion.

Transverse Waves

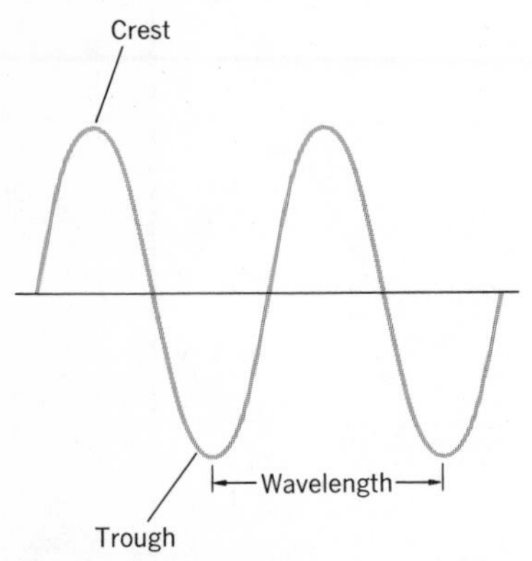

Fig. 10–14. Properties of a transverse wave.

As shown in Fig. 10–14, a transverse wave has high points, or *crests*, and low points, or *troughs*. The distance between two successive crests, or between two successive troughs, is called the *wavelength*. A combination of a crest and the corresponding trough is called a complete *vibration*, or *cycle*. Two complete vibrations, or cycles, are shown in Fig. 10–14. The number of vibrations, or cycles, per second the wave makes is called the *frequency*.

Refer to Fig. 10–2 (page 182), and note that there is a specific relationship between the wavelength and frequency of the waves of the electromagnetic spectrum. Long wavelengths are associated with low frequencies, and shorter wavelengths are associated with higher frequencies. When the wavelength is multiplied by the frequency, the product gives the velocity (speed) of the particular wave. This relationship is expressed by the equation:

$$\text{wavelength} \times \text{frequency} = \text{velocity}$$

$$l \times f = v$$

Recall that visible light, which appears white, actually consists of seven basic colors—red, orange, yellow, green, blue, indigo, and violet. Each color has a characteristic wavelength and frequency. Of the visible light rays, red rays have the longest wavelength and lowest frequency; violet rays have the shortest wavelength and the highest frequency.

DIRECTION OF VIBRATION OF LIGHT WAVES

A light source, such as the sun or a lamp, emits waves that vibrate vertically, horizontally, and in all directions. Because the wave is transverse, the vibrations are at right angles to the plane in which the waves travel. A ray of light composed of light waves vibrating in all directions is said to be *unpolarized.* We can picture unpolarized light waves by attaching one end of a rope to a support and then gently shaking the other end of the rope. Waves in the rope can be produced in any direction by rotating the hand.

Suppose we place the free end of the rope through a piece of wood that contains a grate and again shake the rope, producing waves (Fig. 10–15). If the plane of the grate is parallel to the plane of the vibrating rope, the waves pass through the grate. If the grate is rotated while the plane of the vibrating rope remains unchanged, fewer and fewer waves can pass through. When the plane of the grate is at right angles to the plane of the vibrating rope, no waves pass through.

We can see this effect most clearly by passing the free end of the

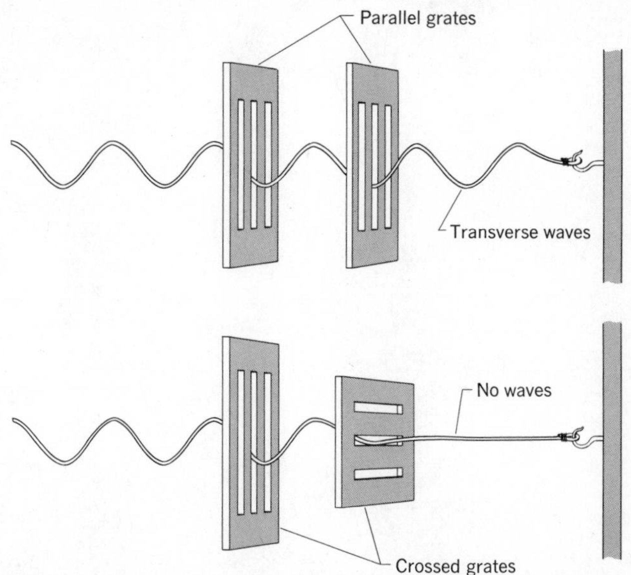

Fig. 10–15. Passage of transverse waves through parallel grates.

rope through two pieces of wood, each containing a grate, as shown in Fig. 10–15. Gently shake the rope up and down. If the planes of both grates are parallel to the plane of the vibrating rope, waves pass through both grates. However, suppose the grate nearer the rope support is rotated, as the rope is shaken vertically. When the two grates are at right angles to one another (crossed), no waves pass through to the support.

Polarized Light

In certain naturally occurring crystals, the atoms in the crystals are arranged in rows. The space between any two rows of atoms resembles the grate discussed previously. Not all the vibrations associated with a light wave can pass through these crystals. Only those vibrations that are parallel to the rows of atoms will pass through. The light that emerges consists of waves that vibrate in a single plane and is called *polarized* light. Note that we have explained the polarization of light by assuming that light is a transverse wave. The corpuscular theory cannot account for this behavior.

The crystal that produces polarized light is called a *polarizer*. The plastic known as *Polaroid* acts as a polarizer. Two sheets of Polaroid, set on one another so that their axes are at right angles, will not permit any light to pass through them (Fig. 10–16). When both

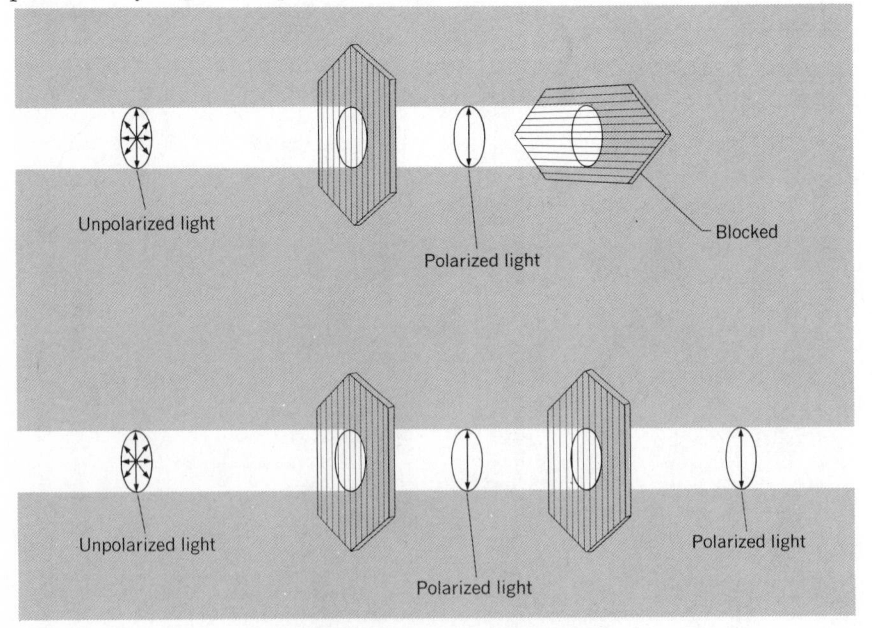

Fig. 10–16. Polarization of light.

sheets of Polaroid are arranged so that their axes are parallel, polarized light passes through both sheets.

Uses of Polarized Light

Polarized light has many applications. Polarizing lenses in eyeglasses or cameras help to reduce glare. Polarized light is used by engineers to locate points of stress in automobiles and machinery. As a research tool, polarized light is extremely useful. Since different crystals polarize light differently, the identities of these crystals can be determined.

Looking Back

Directly, light energy enables us to see and, thereby, adjust to our environment. Indirectly, light energy, acting on green plants, is the source of our food. Light energy is also the indirect source of most of the energy needed to run our machinery.

Investigations reveal that light travels as transverse waves in straight lines at about 300,000 kilometers per second. When these waves come in contact with matter, the matter may absorb, reflect, transmit, or polarize the waves.

Looking Ahead

When light enters a transparent material at certain angles, the light bends. Such bending of light has proved valuable in devices we use in daily living and in studying our environment. Some of these devices are described in the next chapter.

Multiple-Choice Questions

1. An object that emits light is said to be
   a. luminous b. illuminated c. opaque d. transparent
2. Light is believed to be produced by the sun by
   a. chemical changes c. atomic disturbances
   b. physical changes d. explosions
3. The corpuscular theory of light was proposed by
   a. Maxwell b. Huygens c. Planck d. Newton
4. The theory of light proposed by Christian Huygens is known as the
   a. corpuscular theory c. quantum theory
   b. wave theory d. electromagnetic theory

5. James Maxwell proposed that light
   a. has electrical and magnetic properties
   b. travels as particles
   c. is composed of quanta
   d. travels in waves
6. According to the quantum theory of light, the separate packets of energy by which light waves travel are called
   a. molecules b. photons c. corpuscles d. atoms
7. The theory of light most universally accepted today is the
   a. corpuscular theory c. wave theory
   b. electromagnetic theory d. quantum theory
8. Objects that block all light are said to be
   a. transparent b. luminous c. opaque d. translucent
9. An example of a translucent substance is a
   a. windowpane b. frosted glass c. book d. movie screen
10. Light travels in
   a. a circular path c. straight lines
   b. an elliptical path d. straight or circular paths
11. In a pinhole camera, the image formed on the film is
   a. right side up c. inverted
   b. reversed laterally d. polarized
12. The blocking of light produces
   a. shadows c. interference
   b. streaks of light d. dark and light lines
13. The lighter fringe of a shadow is called the
   a. filter b. penumbra c. polarized light d. umbra
14. When light strikes an opaque object, it is generally
   a. absorbed c. polarized
   b. transmitted d. changed to chemical energy
15. When light is absorbed by a dark object, it is generally changed to
   a. mechanical energy c. heat energy
   b. potential energy d. chemical energy
16. A light ray that strikes a reflecting surface is called
   a. a reflected ray c. an absorbed ray
   b. a normal ray d. an incident ray
17. Reflection from a rough surface is said to be
   a. diffuse b. irregular c. regular d. translucent
18. Compared to the object, the image produced by the object in a plane mirror is
   a. larger b. smaller c. the same size d. distorted
19. If you stand at a distance of 1 meter from a full-length mirror, your image in the mirror appears to be
   a. $\frac{1}{2}$ meter behind the mirror c. 2 meters behind the mirror
   b. 1 meter behind the mirror d. 3 meters in front of the mirror
20. Light travels as a
   a. longitudinal wave c. polarized wave
   b. transverse wave d. compressional wave

21. The scientist who first measured the speed of light was
    a. Huygens b. Planck c. Maxwell d. Roemer
22. The speed of light is approximately
    a. 3000 kilometers per second
    b. 30,000 kilometers per second
    c. 300,000 kilometers per second
    d. 300,000,000 kilometers per second
23. The dark inner part of a shadow is known as the
    a. umbra b. crest c. penumbra d. trough

Modified True-False Questions

1. An object that reflects light from another source is said to be *luminous.*
2. According to the corpuscular theory of light, the corpuscles are tiny particles of *energy.*
3. Light waves are a part of a family of electromagnetic waves called the *electromagnetic spectrum.*
4. The quantum theory of light was proposed by *Max Planck.*
5. Objects which allow light to pass through them and through which we can see are said to be *opaque.*
6. A line drawn at right angles to a reflecting surface is called the *normal.*
7. That the angle of incidence is equal to the angle of reflection is stated in the *law of angles.*
8. A device used to demonstrate that the angles of incidence and reflection are equal is the *optical disk.*
9. Reflection from a smooth flat surface is called *diffuse reflection.*
10. The high point of a transverse wave is called the *trough.*

Thought Questions

1. Define each of the following terms, and give an example of each:
    a. luminous c. transparent e. opaque
    b. illuminated d. translucent
2. Explain the difference between regular reflection and diffuse reflection.
3. Compare the image of an object in a plane mirror with the object itself with respect to each of the following:
    a. size
    b. distance from the mirror
    c. position
4. Explain the properties of a light wave.
5. Describe how special filters can polarize light.
6. Describe how Roemer determined the speed at which light travels. Would you expect his method to provide an exact value or an approximate value? Explain.

CHAPTER 11
HOW DO WE USE LIGHT ENERGY?

When you have completed this chapter, you should be able to:

1. *Discuss* and illustrate the law of refraction.
2. *Distinguish* between (*a*) convex and concave lenses (*b*) real and virtual images.
3. *Relate* (*a*) the properties of convex lenses placed at different distances from objects to the uses of convex lenses (*b*) the properties of concave lenses placed at different distances from objects to the uses of concave lenses.
4. *Compare* the properties of convex and concave lenses with those of convex and concave mirrors.
5. *Describe* the dispersion of white light, including the formation and uses of the spectrum.

In the laboratory experience that follows, you will study the refraction and dispersion of white light.

Laboratory Experience

WHAT CAUSES LIGHT RAYS TO BEND?

A. Place a coin in the center of a shallow metal tray. Lower your head and view the coin until the coin just disappears behind the rim of the tray, as shown in Fig. 11–1. Remain in this position while someone else slowly and carefully fills the tray with water.

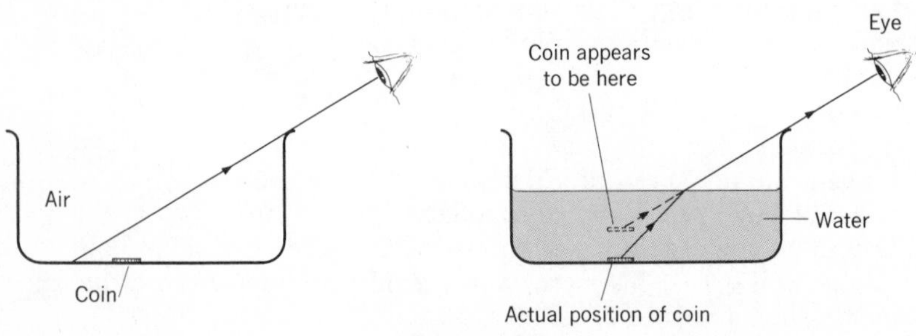

Fig. 11–1.

1. What do you observe as the water fills the tray? Explain.

B. Fill a battery jar about three-quarters full of water. Place a ruler in the water so that it stands up straight. Lower your head so that your eye is at the level of the water, and observe the appearance of the side of the ruler. Draw what you see.

C. Tip the ruler so that it is resting at an angle in the battery jar. Again lower your head so that your eye is at the level of the water, and observe the appearance of the side of the ruler. Draw what you see.

2. Describe any differences in the appearance of the ruler as you moved it in the jar from an erect to a tilted position.
3. Since light travels in straight lines, how do you account for your observations?

D. Observe the light that illuminates your room.

4. Describe the color of light.

Observe the light through a spectroscope.

5. Describe what you see.
6. Suggest an explanation for your observation.

E. Your teacher will project light of different colors on a screen. The colors will first be projected separately, then together.

7. List the colors that are projected separately.
8. What happens when these colors are projected together on the same spot?
9. From the results of parts D and E, what can you conclude about the nature of white light?

Introduction

Everything we see and almost everything we use in our environment depends upon the reflection of light by opaque objects. However, the usefulness of many devices, such as cameras, windows, eyeglasses, and even the human eye itself, also depends on how light waves are affected by transparent materials. We will study these effects in this chapter.

LIGHT CAN BE BENT BY TRANSPARENT MATERIALS

In your laboratory experiment with the coin and the tray of water, you observed what happens to light (reflected from the coin) as it passes from one transparent material (water) into another (air). Without water in the tray, the light from the coin is blocked from reaching your eyes by the rim of the tray. After water is poured into the tray, the coin appears to be at a higher level than it really is. The ray of light from the coin is bent, or broken, on its way to the eye.

In the same way, a slanting ruler sticking out of a jar of water appears broken at the spot where the ruler comes out of the water.

These types of optical illusions are caused by the *refraction* of light. Refraction is the bending of light rays as they pass at an angle from one material, or medium, such as water, into another medium, such as air. Study the direction of the light rays coming from the coin in the tray of water as shown in Fig. 11–1 (page 198). The blocked coin becomes visible as water fills the tray because the light rays from the coin slow down in the water and appear bent. When the tray is empty, the light is not bent and thus cannot reach the eye by refraction. Objects in water, on being viewed from above, appear closer to the surface of the water than they really are.

The refraction of light rays occurs only when light rays enter a new medium at an oblique angle. (An oblique angle is any angle that is neither a right angle nor a straight angle.) As you observed in your laboratory experience, when you place a ruler in a jar of water at right angles to the surface of the water (Fig. 11–2*a*), the portion of the ruler below the surface seems to be magnified and appears to be a straight-line extension of the portion of the ruler above the surface. When the ruler is slanted at an oblique angle to the surface of the water (Fig. 11–2*b*), the ruler again appears magnified, but this time the ruler appears to be broken at the surface. The magnification of the ruler and the apparent break in it are both due to the refraction, or bending, of the light rays.

EXPLAINING THE BENDING OF LIGHT

When light travels through a medium such as water or glass, its speed is less than 300,000 kilometers per second. In water, the speed

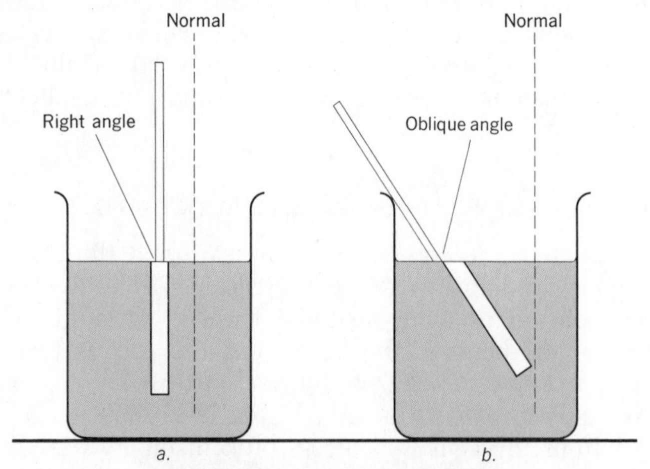

Fig. 11–2. Observing a ruler in water.

of light is roughly three-quarters of its speed in air. In glass, the speed of light decreases to about two-thirds of its speed in air. This decrease in the speed of light occurs because the molecules in water and the molecules in glass are packed more tightly than are the molecules in air. The closeness of the molecules, called *optical density*, acts as a barrier to the passage of light. Consequently, when we see an object through both air and water, as in Fig. 11–2, we are viewing light rays from the same object coming to our eyes at different speeds.

Law of Refraction

Many experiments have shown that, when a ray of light passes at an oblique angle from one medium to another, the ray behaves according to the *law of refraction*. This law states that when a ray passes from a less dense medium into a more dense medium, the ray bends *toward the normal*. The normal, you will recall, is the line drawn at right angles to the surface of the medium. However, when a ray passes at an oblique angle from a more dense medium into one that is less dense, the ray bends *away from the normal*. Reviewing the coin and ruler experiments will show you that the light rays in both cases behave according to this law.

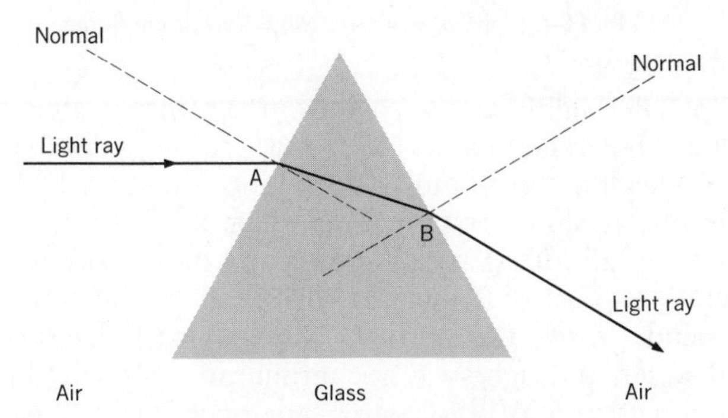

Fig. 11–3. The law of refraction.

Another example of the law of refraction is shown in Fig. 11–3, using a triangular piece of glass, or prism. When a ray of light passes from air into a triangular piece of glass (a medium of greater density than air) at point A, the ray bends toward the normal. When the light ray reaches the end of the glass at point B and reenters the air (a medium of lesser density than glass), it bends away from the normal. As a result of these two refractions, the horizontal light ray entering at point A is bent downward as it emerges from point B. In order to see the light entering at the left side, therefore, the observer's eye would have to be in line with the light ray emerging from point B.

Why Refraction Occurs

Fig. 11–4 represents a series, or train, of light waves coming from a source. A, B, C, or D are called wavefronts—similar points on crests and troughs that have been connected. Perpendiculars drawn to these wavefronts are light rays. In the discussion that follows, for the sake of simplicity, wavefronts are designated as light waves.

When parallel light waves (wavefronts) *A*, *B*, *C*, and *D* in Fig. 11–4 in a beam of light pass from air into water along the normal (at right angles to the surface), all the waves are slowed down. Since all the waves travel at the same speed, the beam does not bend. Consequently, the beam continues in the same direction (Fig. 11–4*a*).

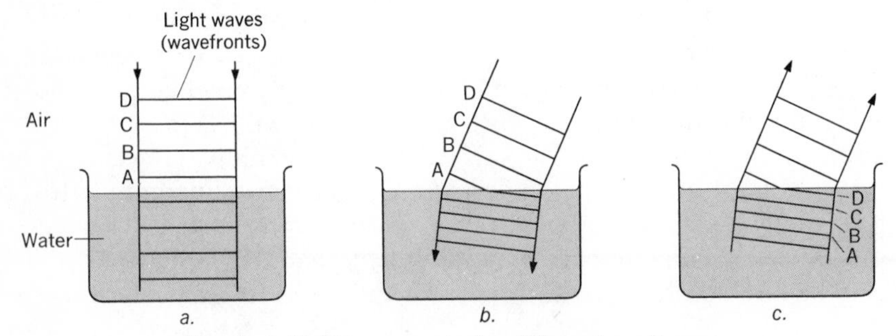

Fig. 11–4. Light waves entering different mediums.

When parallel light waves pass from air into water at an angle (Fig. 11–4*b*), however, not all of the waves are slowed down at the same time. They are forced out of step. Since the wave labeled A enters the water first, it slows down sooner than does the wave labeled *B*. Accordingly, as all the waves continue to move forward, the waves pivot around A. This difference in the speed of the waves causes the beam to bend toward the normal. After all parts of the light beam are in the water, the light waves continue in a straight line in a new direction because all of the waves are once again traveling at the same speed.

When a beam of light passes from water to air, as shown in Fig. 11–4*c*, the opposite effect occurs—the light beam bends away from the normal. The light wave labeled *D* enters the air first and increases in speed. The succeeding waves pivot around *D*. Thus, the direction of the beam is changed. When all parts of the beam have reentered the air, the light waves continue in a straight line in a new direction because they again travel at the same speed.

You can better understand this bending of a light beam by considering what happens to a group of people running at an angle from one type of ground surface into another. Assume that you are watching a group of five of your friends, holding hands, running at the same speed from the beach into the water at an angle (Fig. 11–5). Friend A enters the water first, but he cannot run as fast in water as on land. The other four friends (*B*, *C*, *D*, and *E*) continue at the original speed until each, in turn, enters the water and slows down. You would then observe that *B*, *C*, *D*, and *E* would swing around A, changing the direction of the group toward the normal.

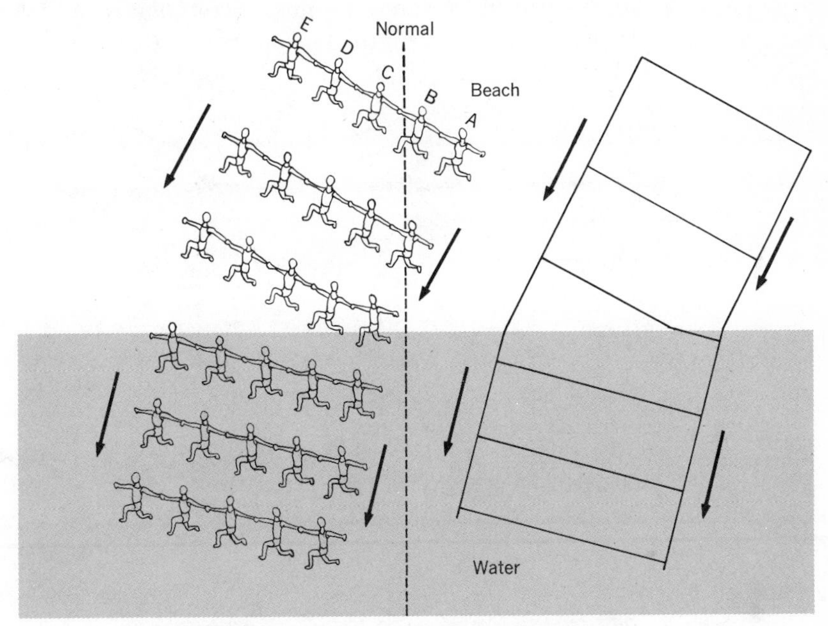

Fig. 11–5. Running from the beach into water.

How We Use Refraction

Whenever we use our eyes and devices such as telescopes, spectroscopes, microscopes, eyeglasses, cameras, projectors, and binoculars, we make use of the law of refraction. The heart of each of these consists of one or more lenses and sometimes a triangular glass prism. A lens, as you know, is a thin disk of transparent material, such as glass, whose opposite sides are smooth, curved surfaces. There are two general types of lenses, convex and concave. A *convex lens* is a lens that is thicker in the middle than at the edges. A *concave lens* is a lens that is thicker at the edges than in the middle.

EFFECTS OF CONVEX LENSES

When parallel rays of light pass through a convex lens (Fig. 11–6, page 204), they are refracted and are brought together, or *converged*, at a point called the *principal focus,* or *F*. The distance measured from the center of the lens to the principal focus is called the *focal length.* The *principal axis* is a line, normal to the curved surface, that passes through the center of the lens. Note that a ray of light passing along this line is not refracted.

Since a convex lens can converge parallel rays of light, it is often called a *converging lens.* In general, the greater the curvature of a convex lens, the shorter the focal length. Thus, a completely spherical convex lens has the shortest focal length possible for a convex lens.

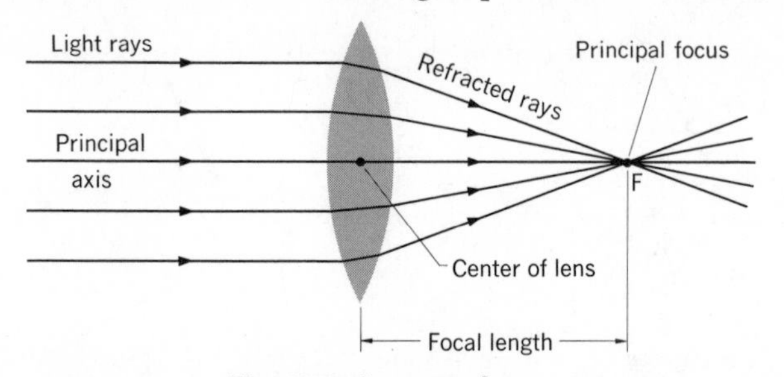

Fig. 11–6. A convex lens.

IMAGES FORMED BY CONVEX LENSES

The images formed by convex lenses are of two general types, known as *real images* and *virtual images.*

Real Images

A real image is an image formed by actual rays of light. The image produced by a "magic lantern," a device for projecting opaque pictures onto a screen, is an example of a real image.

Fig. 11–7 is the ray diagram of a magic lantern. Notice that the

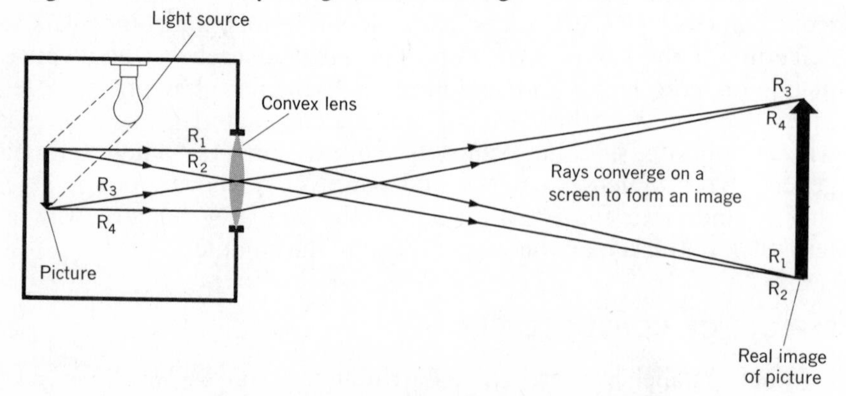

Fig. 11–7. A real image formed by a convex lens.

rays of light converge to form the image (R_1 and R_2 meet; R_3 and R_4 meet; these two points fall in the same plane). Also, by following the rays in the diagram, you will discover that the image is inverted. (R_1 and R_2 come from the top of the picture, but these rays form the bottom of the image; R_3 and R_4 come from the bottom of the picture, but these rays form the top of the image.)

As we shall see, all real images have the following characteristics: (1) A real image is formed by actual rays of light. (2) A real image can be projected onto a screen. (3) A real image is always inverted.

Virtual Images

A virtual image is an image that only *seems* to be formed by rays of light. When we examine a postage stamp through a magnifying glass, for example, the stamp seems to be larger. While we know that the stamp really remains the same size, the virtual image that we see in the lens creates the illusion we call magnification.

Fig. 11–8 shows the ray diagram of a magnifying glass being used to examine a stamp. Notice that the actual rays of light (indicated by solid lines) do not converge to form an image. Since we see an image in the lens, however, we know that an image is formed. To explain this, study the ray diagram. Note that by extending the rays downward (as indicated by the dashed lines), a virtual image (shown

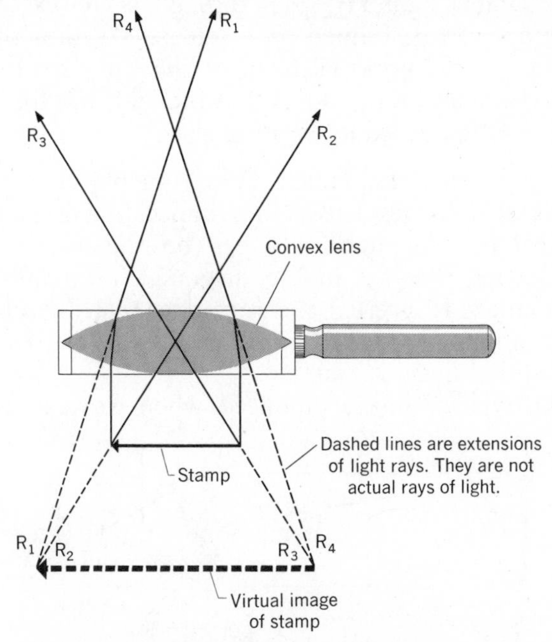

Fig. 11–8. A virtual image formed by a convex lens.

by a heavier dashed line) is formed. By following the rays in the diagram, you will discover that R_1 and R_2 come from the left side of the stamp and R_3 and R_4 come from the right side. The image, therefore, has not been reversed. The image of the stamp is also larger than the stamp itself. Note that the virtual image is not formed by actual rays of light—it is imaginary. However, since the word "imaginary" suggests something that cannot be seen, scientists use the word "virtual" to describe such an image.

All virtual images have the following characteristics: (1) A virtual image is formed by *extensions* of light rays (that is, the image is not formed by actual rays of light). (2) A virtual image cannot be projected onto a screen. (3) A virtual image is always erect, that is, right side up.

Types of Images

The type of image produced by a convex lens depends on the distance of the object from the lens with respect to *F*, the principal focus, and 2*F*, which is twice that distance. Different devices employ objects at various distances from the lens to produce different types of images.

1. A *tiny, real image.* An object is said to be at infinity when the object is very far away. Light rays from an object at infinity are parallel. When such parallel light rays pass through a convex lens, an image the size of a dot can be formed on a screen. To form this image, the screen is placed at the principal focus of the lens (see Fig. 11–6, page 204). When the image of the sun is thus brought into focus by a convex lens, the lens is often called a "burning glass."

2. A *small, inverted real image.* When an object is placed on the principal axis of a convex lens at a distance that is greater than 2*F*, the image can be formed on a screen on the opposite side of the lens. By following the rays in the diagram shown in Fig. 11–9, we find that the image is inverted and is smaller than the object. Furthermore, since the image is formed by actual rays of light from the object, we know that the image is real.

This is the type of image produced when we take a picture with

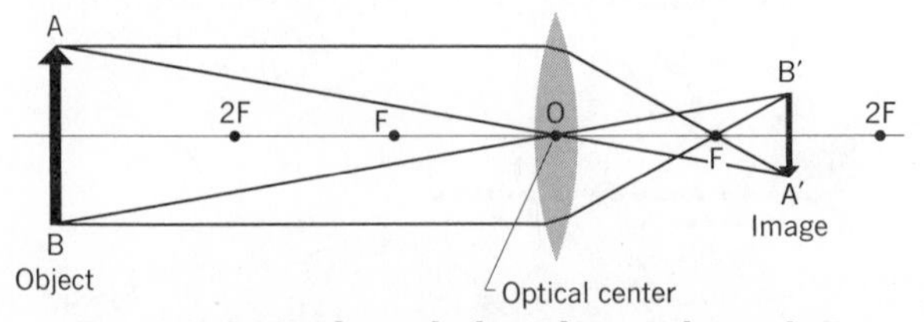

Fig. 11–9. Image formed when object is beyond 2F.

a camera. The object photographed is large; the image formed on the film is small and inverted (Fig. 11–10).

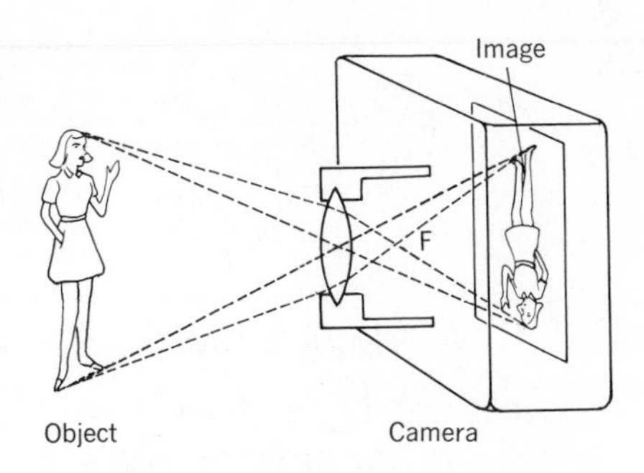

Fig. 11–10. Image formed in a camera.

The image formed in the eye is formed in the same way. Light from an object is converged by the convex lens (Fig. 11–11). The image formed on the screen, called the retina, is very small and inverted. This image starts signals in the retina that reach the brain by way of the optic nerve. The brain interprets the image and we "see" that the object is right side up. (See Chapter 19 for details of vision.)

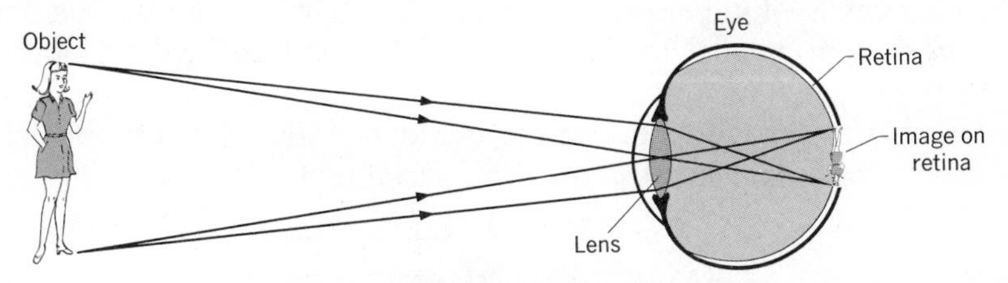

Fig. 11–11. Image formed in the eye.

3. *An inverted, real image of the same size as the object.* When an object on the principal axis is exactly on 2*F*, an image can be formed on a screen at the 2*F* point on the opposite side of the lens. As shown in Fig. 11–12, the image is real, inverted, and the same size as the object. This is the arrangement used when copying a small object or a small picture with a camera. The lens of the camera is moved so that it is twice its focal distance away from the screen. The object to be photographed is then placed at the same distance in front of the camera lens.

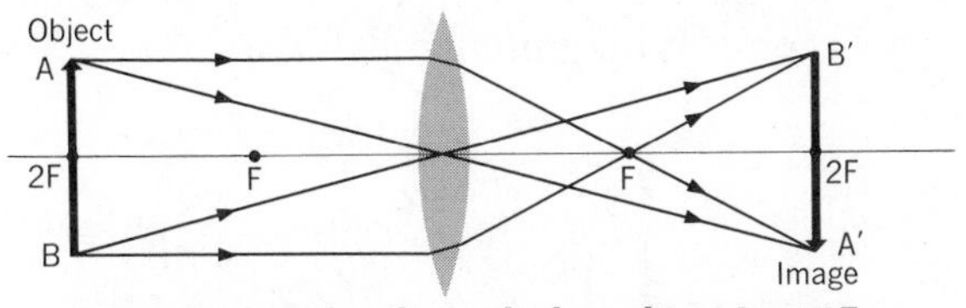

Fig. 11–12. Image formed when object is at 2F.

4. *An enlarged, inverted, real image.* When an object lies between *F* and 2*F*, an image can be formed on a screen at a point beyond 2*F* on the opposite side of the lens. As shown in Fig. 11–13, page 208, the

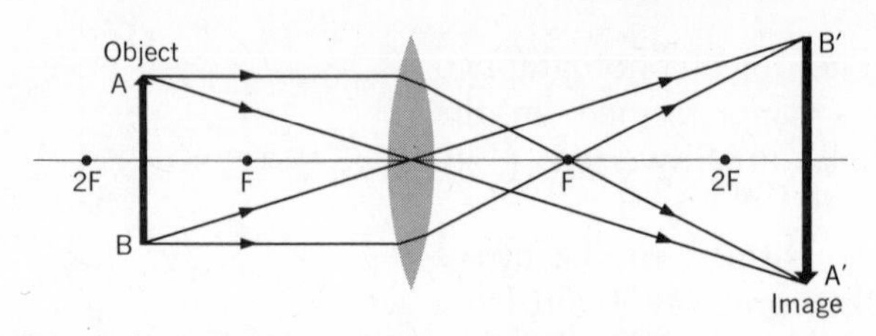

Fig. 11–13. Image formed when object is between F and 2F.

image is real, inverted, and larger than the object. Convex lenses are used in this manner in motion-picture projectors and similar types of projectors. In these, the object is a small film placed in an inverted position close to the principal focus of the lens. The image formed on the screen is then far from the lens and is upright.

5. *No image, but a spot.* When an object is placed exactly at the principal focus of the lens, the rays emerging from the opposite side of the lens are parallel to each other. (This is essentially the opposite of the situation shown in Fig. 11–6, page 204.) When projected onto a screen no image is formed—only a bright disk of light is visible (Fig. 11–14). This arrangement is used for a spotlight.

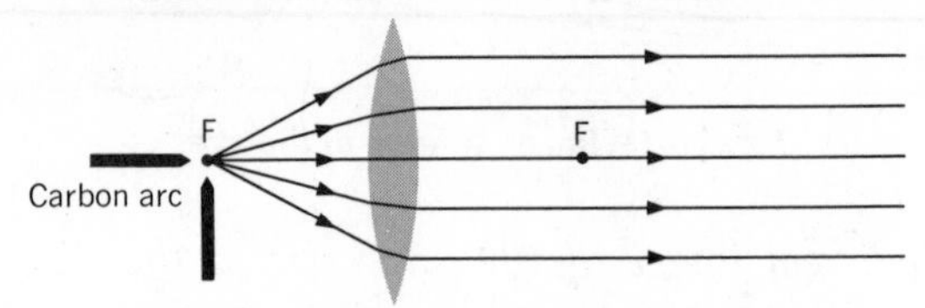

Fig. 11–14. A spotlight.

6. *Enlarged, erect, virtual image.* When an object is placed between the principal focus and the lens, an image cannot be formed on a screen. As shown in Fig. 11–15, the actual rays from the object do not form an image. However, by extending the diverging rays backward through the lens until their extensions meet at a point, a virtual image (heavy dashed line) is formed. Thus, if you look through the lens at the object, you see an enlarged, erect, virtual image. A convex lens used in this way becomes a magnifying glass (see pages 205–206).

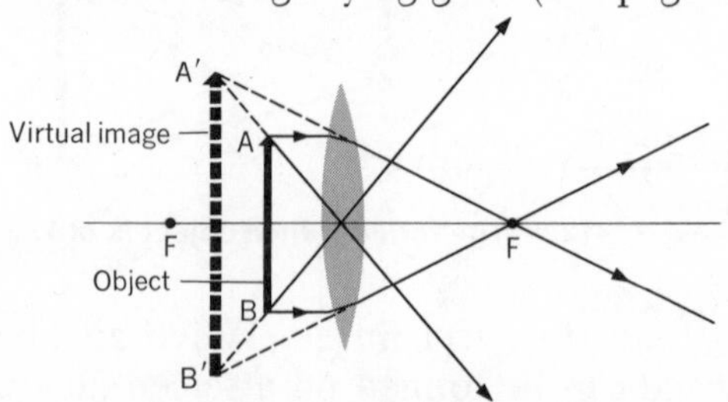

Fig. 11–15. Image formed when object is at less than F.

SOME COMMON USES OF CONVEX LENSES

Some types of eyeglasses, as well as the telescope and the microscope, employ convex lenses.

Eyeglasses

Convex lenses are used in eyeglasses to correct the vision of farsighted people, as shown in Fig. 11–16. In farsightedness, a sharp image would fall behind the retina because the lens of the eye is not convex enough. As a result, the image on the retina appears blurred. Placing a convex lens in front of the lens of the eye brings the image forward enough to fall on the retina and appear sharp.

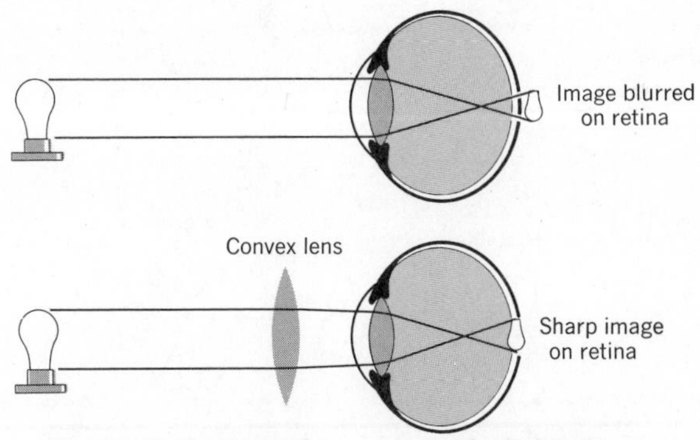

Fig. 11–16. A convex lens corrects farsightedness.

The Telescope

A combination of at least two convex lenses is used in a refracting telescope (see Chapter 8). In such a telescope (Fig. 11–17), the lens that is pointed toward a star (objective lens) has a long focal length. This lens produces a real, smaller, inverted image of the star (object). This small image is then viewed through a convex eyepiece lens which enlarges the image. The final magnified image is a virtual image.

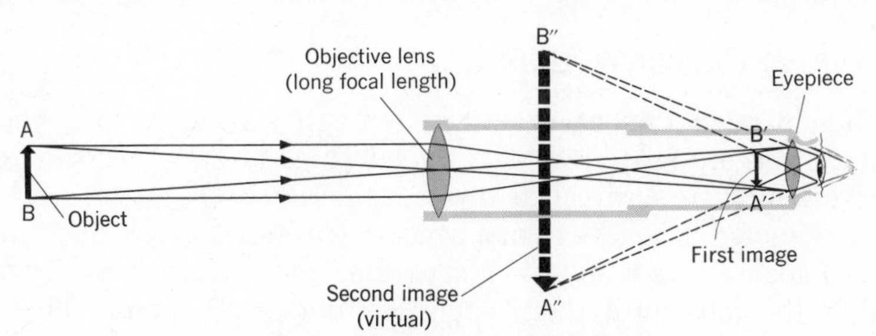

Fig. 11–17. A refracting telescope.

The Microscope

Like the refracting telescope, a microscope has an objective lens and an eyepiece lens (Fig. 11–18). The specimen (object) is placed on the stage a little beyond the principal focus of the convex objective lens. Since the specimen is more than one focal length from the lens, the image produced by this lens is real, larger, and inverted. This image falls within one focal length of the convex eyepiece lens. The eyepiece lens then forms a second image that the eye observes. The second image is virtual, larger than the first image, and erect. (A concave mirror, to be discussed in a later section, gathers the necessary light to illuminate the specimen.)

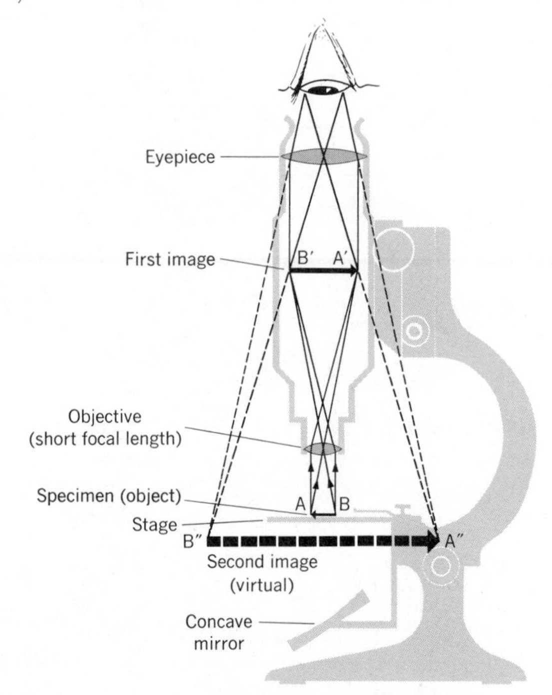

Fig. 11–18. A microscope.

EFFECTS OF CONCAVE LENSES

When parallel rays of light pass through a concave lens, they are refracted and are separated, or *diverged* (Fig. 11–19). For this reason, concave lenses are also called *diverging lenses.*

The refracted light rays from a concave lens never meet. The principal focus of such a lens is found by extending the diverging rays backward through the lens until their extensions meet at a point. This point is called a *virtual focus* because the light rays do not actually meet here.

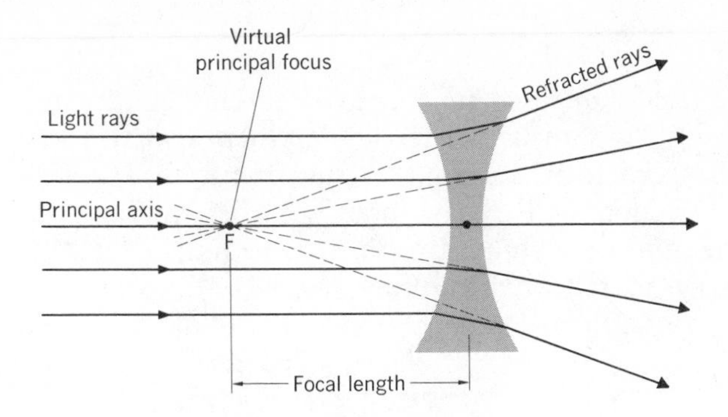

Fig. 11–19. A concave lens.

The focal length of this lens is found by measuring the distance from the center of the lens to the point where the extensions of the diverging rays meet.

IMAGES FORMED BY CONCAVE LENSES

Unlike the images formed by convex lenses, the images produced by concave lenses are always virtual, erect, and smaller than the object. The properties of these images are the same no matter where the object is placed with regard to the principal focus of a concave lens.

Study Fig. 11–20 and note that, except for the light ray that travels along the principal axis, all other rays are refracted away from the center of the lens. As a result of the diverging rays, no image can form on a screen on the side of the lens opposite that of the object. However, a virtual image can be seen (but cannot be formed on a screen) on the same side of the lens as the object.

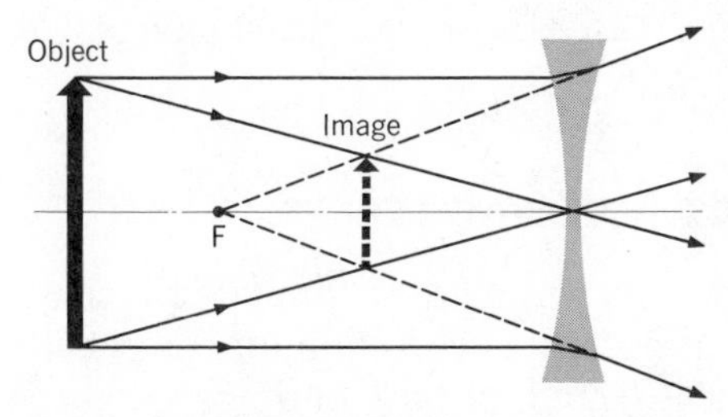

Fig. 11–20. Image formed by a concave lens.

SOME COMMON USES OF CONCAVE LENSES

Some types of eyeglasses and certain types of opera glasses employ concave lenses.

Eyeglasses

Concave lenses are used in eyeglasses to correct the vision of nearsighted people, as shown in Fig. 11–21. In nearsightedness, an image comes to a sharp focus in front of the retina. By the time the light rays reach the retina, they are not in focus. When a concave lens is placed in front of such an eye, this lens diverges the rays and allows a sharp image to fall on the retina.

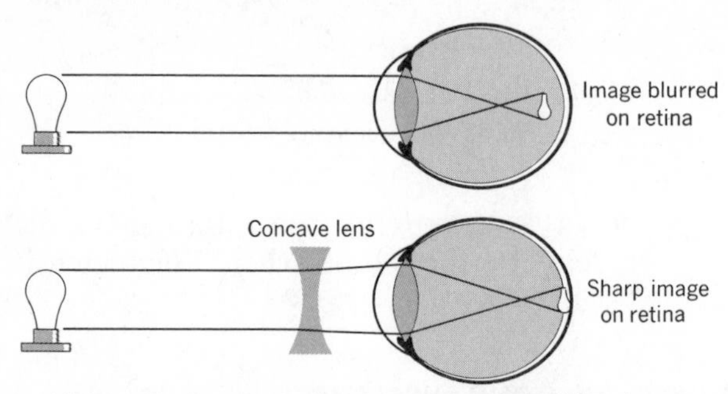

Fig. 11–21. A concave lens corrects nearsightedness.

Opera Glasses

Concave lenses, in combination with convex lenses, are used in such devices as opera glasses. The opera glass is a kind of telescope containing an eyepiece that is a concave lens. The focal length of this lens matches the focal length of the convex lens of the eye. Since a concave lens diverges light, while a convex lens converges light, the net effect of a concave eyepiece is to neutralize the convex lens of the eye. This means that the convex *objective* lens of the opera glass forms the image on the retina. This image is real and is between three and six times larger than the image would be if the opera glass was not used.

CURVED MIRRORS RESEMBLE LENSES

Curved mirrors have properties similar to those of convex and concave lenses. A mirror that curves inward is called a *concave mirror* (Fig. 11–22). The silvered surface converges light rays by reflection and can be used in much the same way as a convex lens.

Used in combination with a convex lens and an ordinary, flat mirror, a concave mirror makes a reflecting telescope (see Chapter 8). The function of the concave mirror in the reflecting telescope is to gather light. The function of the flat mirror is to reflect the gathered light to

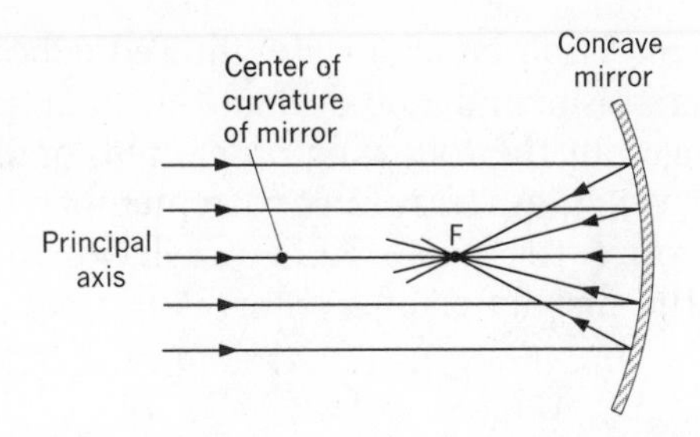

Fig. 11–22. A concave mirror converges light rays.

the eye. The larger the concave mirror, the greater is the light-gathering power. As the objective lens in the refracting telescope (see Fig. 11–17, page 209) is made larger, the lens also gathers more light. However, it is easier to make a larger mirror than a larger lens. Thus, reflecting telescopes, some with mirrors over 5 meters in diameter, are more widely used than are refracting telescopes.

A mirror that curves outward is called a *convex mirror* (Fig. 11–23). This type of mirror diverges light rays by reflection. Like a concave lens, a convex mirror forms only small, virtual images. Such mirrors are used as rear-view mirrors, in which a large area can be viewed in a small space.

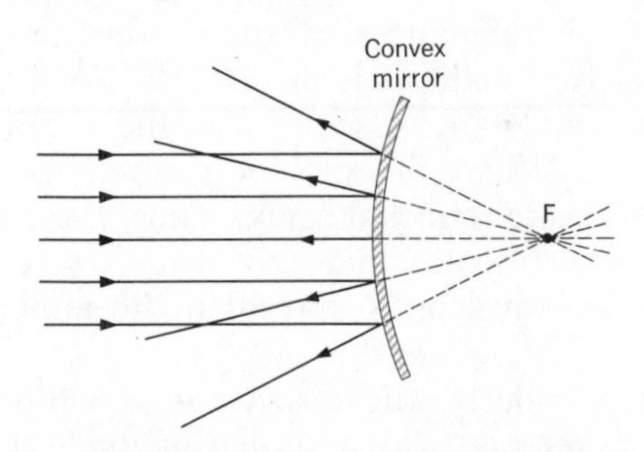

Fig. 11–23. A convex mirror diverges light rays.

EFFECTS OF PRISMS

A beam of white light entering a triangular glass prism is refracted as it enters the prism and again when it emerges from the prism (see Fig. 11–3, page 201). The emerging light splits into a series of colors—an artificial rainbow (see Fig. 7–5, page 127). A natural rainbow is produced in the same manner, by the refraction of light through droplets of water. The splitting of white light into colors is called *dispersion*.

That white light is composed of a mixture of colors was first demonstrated by Sir Isaac Newton. He allowed a beam of white light to pass through a prism and noted that the light is broken up into seven colors arranged in the following order: red, orange, yellow, green, blue, indigo, and violet. An easy way to remember the order of these colors is to memorize the name ROY G. BIV. In this name, each letter represents the first letter of a color:

R	O	Y	G	B	I	V
red	orange	yellow	green	blue	indigo	violet

To prove that white light is composed of separate colors, Newton allowed these seven colored rays of light to pass through a second, inverted prism. He showed that the seven colors recombined and produced a beam of white light.

EXPLAINING THE DISPERSION OF LIGHT

Recall that when a light beam enters a more dense medium (such as the glass of the prism) at an oblique angle, the speed of the light is decreased, and the beam is refracted. Upon entering the prism, however, the red rays of the white light are slowed down the least, whereas the violet rays of the white light are slowed down the most. As a result of these differences in speed, the rays are refracted to different degrees. Red light, which has the longest wavelength, is refracted the least; violet light, which has the shortest wavelength, is refracted the most. When the rays of colored light reenter the air from the prism, they are refracted again. Thus, these rays cannot rejoin to form white light. Instead, they are seen as seven separate colors, each having its own wavelength, spread in the rainbow-like band, the visible spectrum.

As mentioned previously, the dispersion of white light to form a natural rainbow takes place in a similar manner. During or after a rain, tiny water droplets present in the air act in much the same manner as does the prism. The water droplets cause the white light passing through them to undergo dispersion, producing a spectrum.

COLOR AND WAVELENGTH

As we learned in Chapter 10, visible light is only a part of the total electromagnetic spectrum. The wavelengths of the various rays of the electromagnetic spectrum differ. Within the visible light range, each of the seven colors has a different wavelength. These wavelengths range from about one forty-millionth of a centimeter (red) to one seventy-millionth of a centimeter (violet).

EXPLAINING THE COLORS OF OBJECTS

The objects in our environment are of various colors. The colors we see depend on the nature of the objects and their effect on light waves.

The Color of Transparent Objects

The color of a transparent object is the color of the light that the object transmits. Ordinary window glass transmits all colors equally well and, therefore, appears to be colorless in white light. However, when white light strikes a piece of red glass, the glass absorbs orange, yellow, green, blue, indigo, and violet light. Since this glass transmits only red light to our eyes, the glass appears red. Similarly, blue glass transmits only blue light and absorbs the remaining colors; green glass transmits green light and absorbs the remaining colors.

When a beam of red light shines on a piece of blue glass, no light is transmitted because the blue glass absorbs all of the red light. In such a case, the blue glass may appear black, which is the absence of color. Light is transmitted by a transparent object only when light waves of the same color as that of the transparent object are present in the beam that reaches the object.

The Color of Opaque Objects

The color of an opaque object is the color of the light reflected by the object. A piece of white paper appears white because the paper reflects all of the colors in a beam of white light. When white light falls upon a piece of red paper, the paper appears red because the coloring material in the paper reflects red rays and absorbs all the other colors. When white paper is viewed in red light, the white paper appears red because only red light is reflected from it. The same holds true for light rays of all other single colors. Thus, in blue light the paper appears blue; in green light the paper appears green.

An object that reflects no light, but absorbs all light rays that fall upon it, appears black. When white light falls upon a black shoe, the shoe appears black because the coloring matter of the shoe absorbs all the colored rays that strike it. As a result, the eye sees no color; that is, the eye sees black. When blue cloth is viewed in red light, the cloth appears black because the blue dye in it absorbs the red rays and reflects no light at all.

In general, an object appears white (or colorless) when it either reflects or transmits all colors of light at the same time. On the other hand, an object appears black when it absorbs the light reaching it and neither reflects nor transmits any light.

HOW SPECTRA ARE USED BY SCIENTISTS

In Chapter 10, we learned that whenever an object is heated sufficiently, it glows and emits light. We have also learned that a prism can disperse light into a spectrum. The spectra from various glowing objects differ from one another. By studying the spectra of various substances with a spectroscope (Fig. 11–24), it is possible to identify the substances. Recall that, by comparing the spectrum of light coming from a star with the spectra of the elements present on earth, scientists have succeeded in learning which elements are present in various stars.

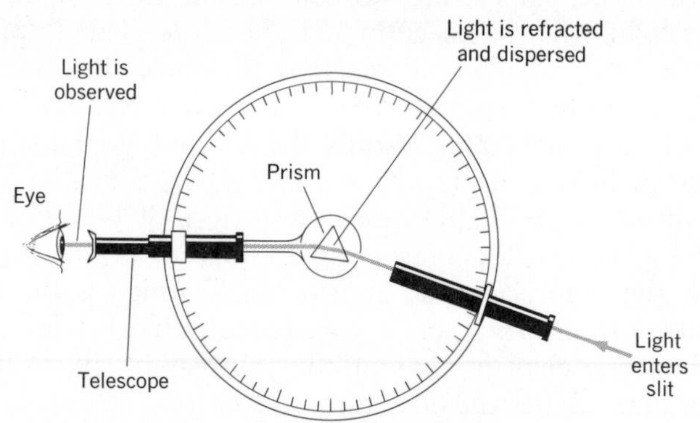

Fig. 11–24. A spectroscope.

TYPES OF SPECTRA

There are three important types of spectra: the *continuous spectrum*, the *bright-line spectrum*, and the *absorption spectrum*. Continuous and bright-line (discontinuous) spectra were observed in the laboratory experience in Chapter 7 (see pages 122–124).

Continuous Spectrum

The continuous spectrum is the type of spectrum you observe when you view white light through a glass prism or in a rainbow. In this spectrum, the colors blend into each other without separations. Gases under high pressure that are made to glow, as well as glowing solids and liquids, produce continuous spectra.

Bright-Line Spectrum

A bright-line spectrum is composed of several brightly colored narrow lines separated by large dark spaces. This type of spectrum is formed when a gas under low pressure is subjected to heat or electrical energy and is then observed through the spectroscope. Each element, when converted to a gas and made to glow, produces its own characteristic bright-line spectrum. This type of spectrum is thought to originate from the motions of electrons in the atoms of elements. It is possible to identify an unknown element by matching its spectral lines with the spectral lines of known elements.

Absorption Spectrum

It has been found that an element which emits specific wavelengths (colors) can also absorb these wavelengths *and no other*. For example, the bright-line spectrum of sodium vapor shows two bright yellow lines. Suppose a beam of white light, which contains all the colors of the spectrum, is passed through sodium vapor (Fig. 11–25). When the resulting light is observed in a spectroscope, we see a continuous spectrum, except for black lines in the exact position where the yellow sodium lines would normally appear. The sodium atoms apparently absorb the yellow wavelengths from the continuous spectrum. This type of spectrum, which has dark areas in it, is called an absorption spectrum.

Since the dark lines (absorbed wavelengths) are characteristic for each element, they can also be used to identify unknown elements. The dark lines we observe in the absorption spectrum of the sun were first noted by the German physicist *Joseph von Fraunhofer*, in 1817, and are called *Fraunhofer lines*.

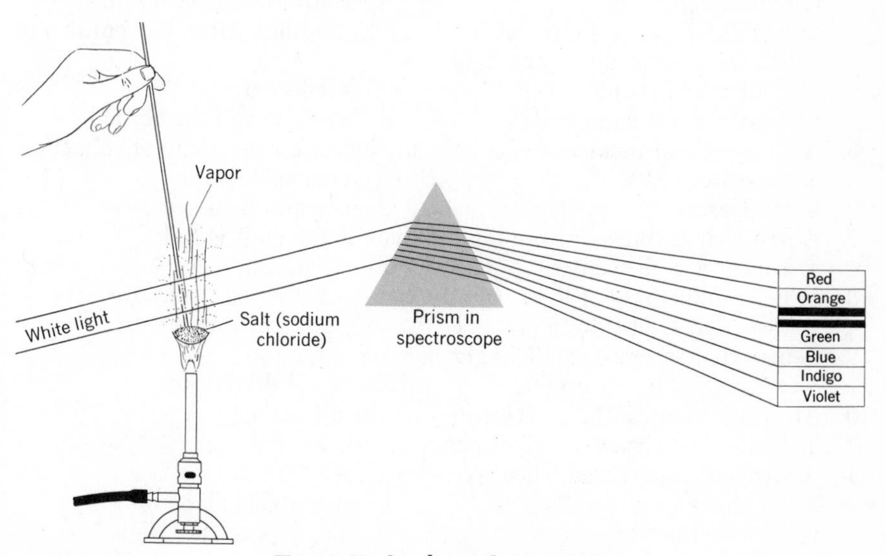

Fig. 11–25. An absorption spectrum.

Looking Back

In Chapter 10, we learned how light energy is useful in devices such as mirrors and polarizers. In this chapter, we learned how the refraction of light is useful in vision and in devices employing lenses and prisms.

Looking Ahead

Like light energy, sound energy is important to us in adjusting to our environment. We will study sound energy in Chapters 12 and 13.

Multiple-Choice Questions

1. The bending of light is known as
   a. reflection b. refraction c. diffraction d. dispersion
2. When a ruler is placed in water at an oblique angle, besides appearing bent, the ruler appears to be
   a. curved b. smaller c. magnified d. unaffected
3. When light enters a medium such as water or glass from the air, its speed
   a. decreases c. remains the same
   b. increases d. increases then decreases
4. When light passes at an oblique angle from a medium that is less dense to a medium that is more dense it
   a. continues in a straight line c. bends away from the normal
   b. is reflected d. bends toward the normal
5. When light passes from one medium to another, after the entire ray enters the new medium, the light
   a. continues to bend c. is reflected
   b. travels in a straight line d. bends toward the normal
6. As the angle of incidence of a light ray increases, the angle of refraction
   a. increases c. remains the same
   b. decreases d. increases then decreases
7. A lens that is thicker in the middle than at the ends is called
   a. concave b. convex c. diverging d. chromatic
8. When parallel rays of light pass through a convex lens, they are
   a. dispersed b. diverged c. converged d. diffracted
9. Lenses that separate parallel light rays are called
   a. convex b. converging c. prismatic d. concave
10. An image that can be projected on a screen is called
    a. real b. virtual c. dispersed d. natural
11. A virtual image is seen when we use a
    a. spotlight c. magnifying glass
    b. movie projector d. copying camera

12. In order to produce an image that is real, inverted, and smaller than the object, the object is placed
    a. at *F*
    b. beyond 2*F*
    c. between *F* and the lens
    d. between *F* and 2*F*
13. When the object on the principal axis is exactly on 2*F*, the image is formed on a screen at a point that is
    a. at 2*F*
    b. at *F*
    c. between *F* and 2*F*
    d. between the lens and *F*
14. When an object is placed at the principal focus of a convex lens, the rays emerging from the opposite side of the lens
    a. converge b. diverge c. are reflected d. are parallel
15. Compared to the object, images produced by concave lenses are
    a. virtual, upright, and smaller
    b. real, upright, and larger
    c. real, inverted, and smaller
    d. virtual, inverted, and larger
16. Eyeglasses used by nearsighted people consist of lenses that are
    a. convex b. converging c. concave d. chromatic
17. A reflecting telescope consists of a convex lens, a plane mirror, and a
    a. convex mirror
    b. concave lens
    c. magnifying glass
    d. concave mirror
18. Of the colors of light, the color that is refracted most when passing through a prism is
    a. green b. violet c. red d. yellow
19. The band of colors of light, ranging from red to violet, is called a
    a. mirage b. spectrum c. diffraction grating d. prism
20. A transparent object is the color of the light that the object
    a. transmits b. reflects c. absorbs d. refracts
21. When a beam of red light shines on a piece of blue glass, the glass appears to be
    a. red b. blue c. black d. white
22. When an object reflects all light, it appears to be
    a. black b. red c. green d. white

Modified True-False Questions

1. A spectrum composed of brightly colored narrow lines separated by large dark spaces is called *a continuous spectrum.*
2. A series of narrow dark lines that separate parts of a continuous spectrum is *an absorption spectrum.*
3. A convex lens converges light rays at a point called the *principal axis.*
4. The distance from the center of the lens to the principal focus is called the *focal length.*
5. An image that seems to be formed but cannot be projected is *a real image.*
6. A magnifying glass consists of *a concave lens.*
7. The scientist who determined that white light is composed of colored rays was *Isaac Newton.*

8. The separation of white light into its component colors is called *refraction.*
9. A red glass transmits *white light.*
10. When blue cloth is viewed in red light, the cloth appears *black.*
11. The color of an opaque object is the color that it *transmits.*

Thought Questions

1. Explain what happens to a ray of light in each of the following situations:
   a. Light passes from air to glass at an oblique angle.
   b. Light passes from water to air at an oblique angle.
   c. Light passes through a convex lens at the normal.
2. Complete the following table for convex lenses:

Object Distance	*Image Distance*	*Image Size*	*Type of Image*	*Erect or Inverted*
At infinity				
Greater than 2*F*				
At 2*F*				
Between *F* and 2*F*				
At *F*				
Between lens and *F*				

3. Describe how concave lenses can be used to help nearsighted people.
4. Explain the dispersion of light as it passes through a prism.
5. Explain the color observed for each of the following when struck with white light:
   a. a red transparent object
   b. a blue opaque object

CHAPTER 12
WHAT IS THE NATURE OF THE SOUND ENERGY IN OUR ENVIRONMENT?

When you have completed this chapter, you should be able to:

1. *Explain* how sound is produced and transmitted.
2. *Describe* the characteristics of sound waves.
3. *Find* the distance of an object from some point by means of sound.
4. *Discuss* how we hear.
5. *Relate* breaking the sound barrier to sound pollution.

In the laboratory experience that follows you will investigate how sound is produced and transmitted.

Laboratory Experience

HOW DOES SOUND TRAVEL?

A. Pour 2 centimeters of water into a pan and allow the water to stand until it is absolutely still. With one hand, hold an inverted tuning fork by the stem. With the other hand, strike a prong of the tuning fork with a rubber mallet.
   1. What happens to the prongs when the tuning fork is struck?
   2. What do you hear when the fork is struck?

B. Strike the tuning fork again and quickly immerse the tips of the prongs just below the surface of the water in the pan.
   3. Describe what happens to the water. Explain.

C. Hold one end of a clean rubber band tightly with your teeth and stretch the rubber band with one hand until the rubber band is about 15 centimeters long. With the other hand, pluck the rubber band.
   4. Describe your observations.

D. This part will be demonstrated by your teacher, who will set up the apparatus shown in Fig. 12–1.

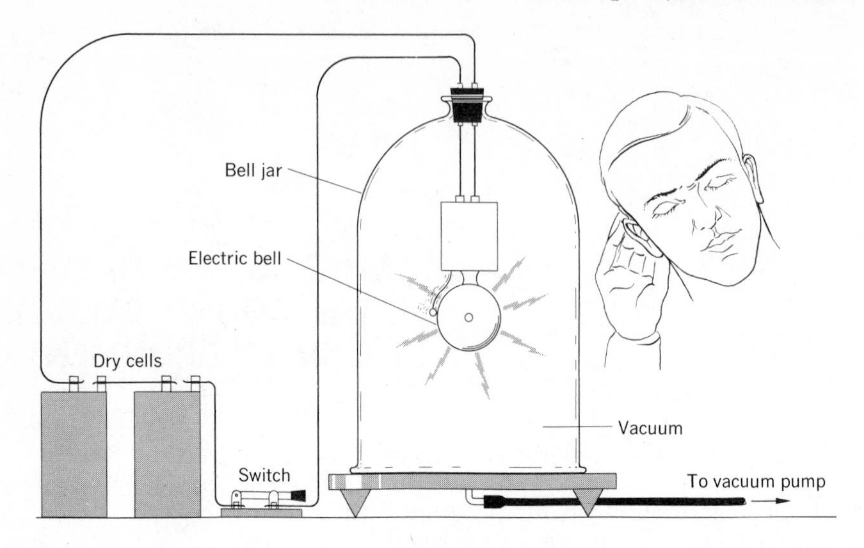

Fig. 12–1.

5. What do you observe when the switch is closed?
6. What do you observe when the switch is closed and the vacuum pump is started?
7. What happens a few minutes later?
8. What happens when the pump stops and air is allowed to enter the bell jar? Explain.
9. Explain how sound is produced and how it reaches your ears.

Introduction

Sounds plays a very important role in the lives of humans and many other organisms. Humans, as well as other animals, such as elephants, whales, porpoises, wolves, and robins, use sound as a means of communication.

We communicate with each other by making sounds with our vocal cords and shaping the sounds into words using the tongue and lips; that is, we talk. Our talking is often transmitted over great distances by devices such as the telephone, which changes sound to electrical impulses and then back to sound. We are all familiar with the sounds of music, of police sirens, or of traffic noise.

Although we depend on sound to improve our lives, we can be harmed by it at the same time. Sounds that are excessively loud for long periods of time can injure the nervous system and cause deafness. Unnecessarily loud sounds can be considered *sound pollution.* Understanding the nature and characteristics of sound can help us prevent and overcome sound pollution.

HOW SOUND IS PRODUCED

Sound is produced when matter vibrates—that is, moves back and forth rapidly. The human ear can generally hear vibrations between 20 and 20,000 per second.

You saw the relationship between sound and vibrating matter in your laboratory experience when you struck the tuning fork and plucked the rubber band. Similarly, when we disturb a string of a guitar or banjo, we hear a sound as we see the strings vibrate. When not disturbed, these objects are silent.

When you struck the tuning fork, you could hear a sound and see the fork vibrate at the same time. Sometimes the vibrations are so rapid that we cannot see them. You see the evidence for such vibrations by striking the fork and quickly placing the tips of its prongs just at the surface of a dish of water. The water splashes out of the container, and small waves can be seen on the surface of the water coming from the prongs of the tuning fork (Fig. 12–2). Since sound is produced when matter moves (vibrates), sound is really a form of mechanical energy.

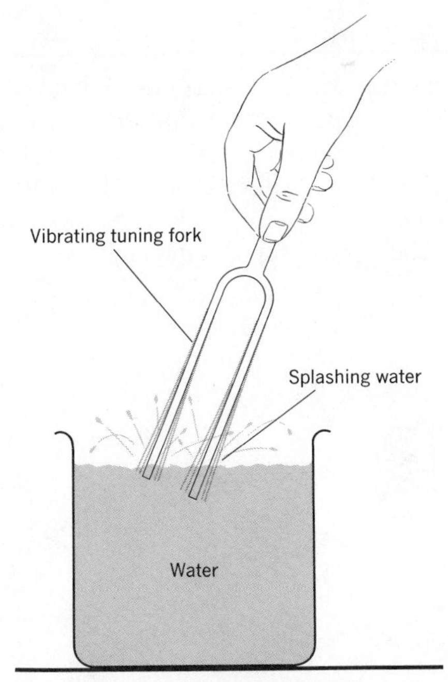

Fig. 12–2. A struck tuning fork vibrates.

HOW SOUND IS TRANSMITTED

You will recall that light can be transmitted through a vacuum. Sound results from the vibrations of matter and cannot be transmitted through a vacuum. In other words, sound can be heard only when vibrations from some source are transmitted or passed to our ears through a *carrying medium*.

In the laboratory, you discovered that when the switch is closed, the electric bell in the bell jar begins to ring and can be heard in all parts of the room. As the vacuum pump withdraws air from the inside of the bell jar, the sound of the bell becomes fainter and fainter until it almost disappears. When the pump is stopped and air is readmitted into the bell jar, the sound of the bell is again heard normally. This shows that sound cannot be transmitted in the absence of a carrying medium, in this case, air.

The carrying, or transmission, medium of a sound may be matter in any state—solid, liquid, or gas. Matter that transmits sound possesses the property of elasticity—that is, when its molecules are moved apart by a force, the molecules return to their original position after the force is removed. A coiled spring is a common example of a solid that possesses elasticity. A force may stretch the spring a little; when the force is removed, the spring returns to its original shape.

Sound Transmission by Solids

We can easily demonstrate that sound travels through a solid, as shown in Fig. 12–3. A student taps one end of a window pole while another student has an ear near the other end of the pole. The sound is clearly heard at the other end of the pole. Or, by placing an ear on a railroad track, it is possible to hear the sound of an approaching train even before the train comes into sight.

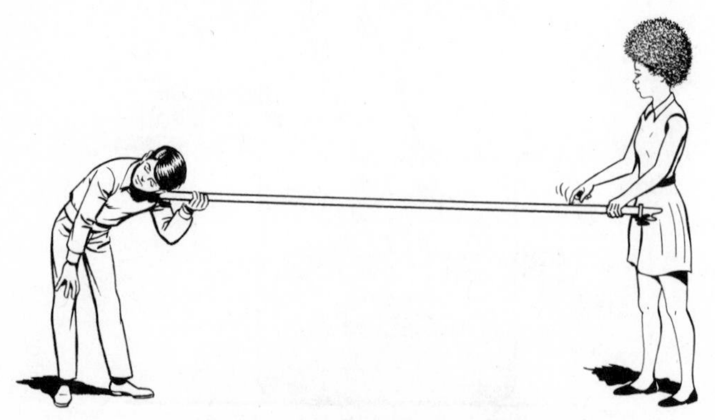

Fig. 12–3. Solids transmit sound.

Sound Transmission by Liquids

You may have had the opportunity to hear sounds while swimming underwater. You can verify that liquids transmit sound by placing your ear in the water of your bathtub as you gently scratch the side of the tub with your fingernail. The sounds you hear are the vibrations of the tub transmitted to your ear by the water.

Ships use a device called *sonar* to detect underwater objects. The word sonar is derived from *SO*und *NA*vigation *R*anging. The operation of this device depends on the time it takes a sound signal to reach an object and to be reflected back to the ship.

Sound Transmission by Gases

Since we constantly hear sounds traveling through the air, which is a gas, we know that gases transmit sound. Sound is transmitted more rapidly through less dense gases, such as hydrogen, than through denser gases, such as carbon dioxide (assuming the gases are at the same pressure). Apparently, the very small mass of the hydrogen molecules permits these molecules to vibrate more readily than the more massive carbon dioxide molecules.

In general, solids transmit sound faster than do either liquids or gases because solids are more elastic. Similarly, since liquids are more elastic than gases, they transmit sounds more rapidly than do gases.

Insulation Against Sound

To deaden sound, or to *insulate* against sound, we employ sound-resistant materials such as cork or fiber board. These materials are generally porous and inelastic. Thus, they absorb sounds but cannot transmit them effectively.

THE NATURE OF SOUND WAVES

Let us analyze the motion of a vibrating tuning fork and the air molecules around it (Fig. 12–4, page 226). Recall that air is elastic. As each prong of the vibrating fork moves in one direction, the air molecules surrounding a prong are pressed together, or crowded, by the prong. As a prong moves back in the other direction, the crowded air molecules bounce apart and separate. Thus, the movements of the prongs alternately crowd air molecules and then relieve the crowding. In other words, the molecules are first compressed into a smaller space and then are allowed to separate.

The region where the molecules of an elastic medium are crowded

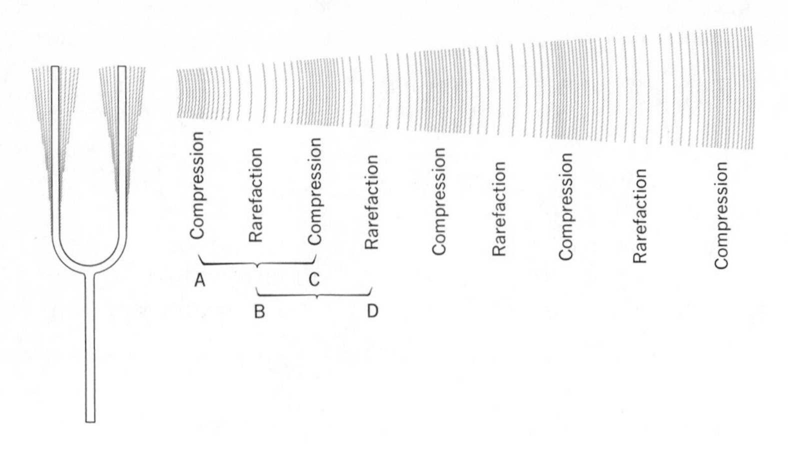

Fig. 12–4. The motion of the prongs of a struck tuning fork.

together is called a *compression.* The region where the molecules are farther apart is called a *rarefaction.* Successive compression and rarefaction regions make up sound waves, which travel outward in all directions.

In a sound wave, the vibrating particles move back and forth in the same direction as the wave. This type of wave, you will recall, is called a longitudinal wave. Recall that a light wave and a water wave are transverse waves, in which the vibrating particles move up and down at right angles to the direction of the wave (see Fig. 10–13, page 192). Longitudinal sound waves and transverse light waves, although different, have several characteristics in common. Both types of waves have speed, wavelength, and frequency.

SPEED OF SOUND

During a thunderstorm, you have probably noticed an interval of time between seeing a flash of lightning and hearing the sound of thunder. The lightning and the thunder occur simultaneously, but light, which travels at a speed of 300,000 kilometers per second, reaches us almost instantaneously. Sound, on the other hand, travels at a much slower rate. Depending on how far away the thunder occurred, the sound may take several seconds to reach us.

Finding the Speed of Sound

The speed of sound was first determined by firing a cannon on one hill while a person on another hill measured the interval of time between seeing the flash of the cannon and hearing the sound. By dividing the difference in time into the distance between the two hills, the speed of sound in air was determined.

It was also discovered that temperature affects the speed of sound. This is because temperature changes the density of the air without necessarily changing its pressure. Recall that gases with lower densities (hydrogen) transmit sound more rapidly than do gases with higher densities (carbon dioxide).

The speed of sound at 0°C is 327 meters per second. Scientists have found that for every Celsius degree increase in air temperature, the speed of sound increases by 0.6 meter per second. Thus, when the temperature is 5°C, the increase in the speed of sound is 5°C × 0.6 meter per second = 3 meters per second. Adding 3 meters per second to the speed of sound at 0°C, we obtain 3 meters per second + 327 meters per second = 330 meters per second, the speed of sound in air at 5°C.

At a temperature of 20°C, the increase in the speed of sound is 20°C × 0.6 meter per second = 12 meters per second. Adding 12 meters per second to the speed of sound at 0°C, we find that the speed of sound in air at 20°C is 12 meters per second + 327 meters per second = 339 meters per second.

The relationship of temperature to the speed of sound and our knowledge of the speed of light can help us determine how far away a bolt of lightning is. Suppose that the temperature of the air is 25°C and that the thunder is heard 3.4 seconds after the lightning is seen. Since light travels at 300,000 kilometers per second, we can assume that the light rays reach us instantaneously. To find out how far away the lightning is, we must first determine the speed of sound at 25°C. At 0°C, the speed of sound is 327 meters per second. Since the speed increases by 0.6 meter per second for each Celsius degree increase in temperature, the speed of sound at 25°C is 15 meters per second faster than at 0°C. Thus, the speed of sound is 15 meters per second + 327 meters per second = 342 meters per second at 25°C. Since it takes the sound of thunder 3.4 seconds to reach us, the distance traveled by the sound is 342 meters per second multiplied by 3.4 seconds:

$$342 \frac{\text{meters}}{\cancel{\text{seconds}}} \times 3.4\,\cancel{\text{seconds}} = 1163 \text{ meters}$$

Speed of Sound in Different Mediums

Careful experiments have shown that sound travels about 4½ times faster in water than in air. Therefore, the speed of sound in water is approximately 1470 meters per second at 0°C. In a solid, such as steel, sound travels about 14 times faster than in air, a speed of approximately 4600 meters per second at 0°C.

Differences in the speed of sound can be related to differences in elasticity and density of different mediums. The speed of sound in solids and liquids, unlike the speed of sound in gases, varies only slightly with changes in temperature. This is probably because the densities of solids and liquids are less affected by temperature changes than are the densities of gases.

WAVELENGTH OF SOUND

The compressions and rarefactions of sound waves are often represented as in Fig. 12–5. Wavelength is the distance between two successive compressions; this is the same as the distance between two successive rarefactions. For example, in Fig. 12–4 the wavelength was shown as either the distance between points A and C (compressions) or between points B and D (rarefactions). These distances are equal. Fig. 12–5 shows the same relationships in another way.

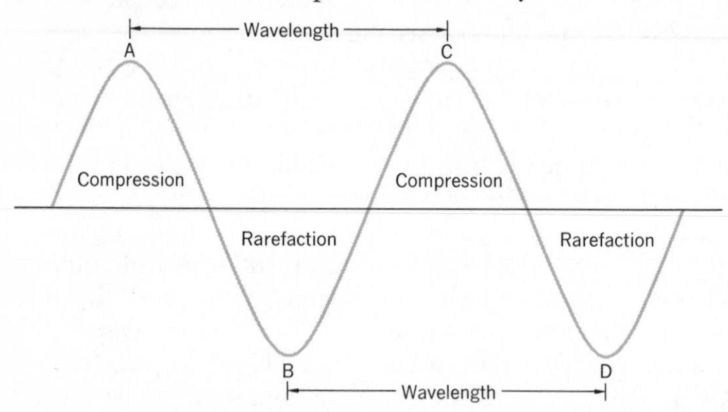

Fig. 12–5. Characteristics of a sound wave.

FREQUENCY OF SOUND WAVES

We have already defined frequency as the number of complete vibrations, or cycles, that pass a point in one second. Each vibration consists of a compression and a rarefaction. Fig. 12–5 shows a sound wave with a frequency of two cycles, or two vibrations, per second. Thus, the frequency of a sound wave is really the same as the number of vibrations per second made by the vibrating object.

The relationship between wavelength and frequency for sound waves is the same as it is for electromagnetic waves. That is, wavelength $(l) \times$ frequency $(f) =$ velocity (v).

CHANGING THE DIRECTION OF SOUND WAVES

When a sound wave strikes a smooth, hard surface such as a wall, floor, or mountain wall, it may be reflected back toward the source, much like a handball bouncing back from a wall. When such a sound reflection is heard, it is called an *echo*.

Distant echoes can only be heard when the reflecting surface is more than 16.5 meters away because the ear cannot detect different sounds that are less than $\frac{1}{10}$ second apart. This means that the sound must travel at least 16.5 meters to the reflecting surface and 16.5 meters back to the source, a total of 33 meters. Since sound travels about 33 meters in $\frac{1}{10}$ second, the reflecting surface must be further away than 16.5 meters so that the return of the sound occurs after one-tenth of a second.

To avoid echoes in large rooms or auditoriums, soft materials such as drapes, rugs, and special ceiling materials are used as insulators to absorb the sound waves. As we have indicated, sounds are absorbed by porous, inelastic materials.

Echoes are used in the operation of the sonar device mentioned earlier in this chapter. In using sonar, a vibrating signal of *ultrasonic* (very high) frequency is sent out. When this signal strikes an object, the signal bounces back and is picked up by a receiver. Knowing the speed of sound in the medium through which it is traveling, and knowing the time is takes for the sound to return, the distance of the reflecting object can be determined. For example, if a signal is sent out from a submarine and the echo is received 10 seconds later, we can determine the distance of the submarine from the object as follows:

1. Divide the time in half, since it will take half the time to reach the object and the other half to return to the sonar device. Thus, the time it will take for the sound to reach the object is 5 seconds.

2. In water, sound travels at a speed of about 1470 meters per second.

3. Multiply the speed of sound (1470 meters per second) by the time (5 seconds), or 1470 meters per second $\times$ 5 seconds $=$ 7350 meters. The distance from the submarine to the object is therefore 7350 meters.

SOUND WAVES AND HEARING

How does the human ear hear sounds? The human ear (Fig. 12–6) consists of three main parts: the *outer ear*, the *middle ear*, and the *inner ear*. The shape of the outer ear is fitted to collect sound waves and direct them into the *ear canal.* The ear canal leads the waves to the *eardrum,* which then begins to vibrate at the same rate as the sound waves. The vibrations of the eardrum cause three small bones in the middle ear to vibrate. The last bone transfers the vibrations to a membrane in the inner ear. The vibrations of this membrane, in turn, cause the fluid inside the inner ear to vibrate. Finally, the vibrations of the fluid cause nerve signals to start in the *auditory nerve.* When the signals reach the brain, the brain interprets them as sound.

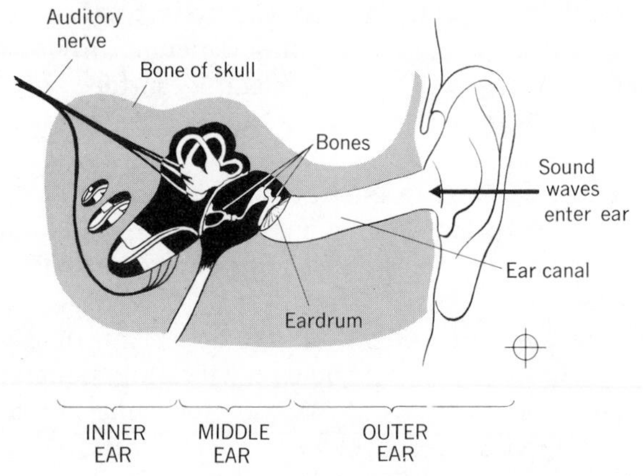

Fig. 12–6. The human ear.

The human ear is sensitive only to a certain range of vibrations. Thus, we can hear sounds between 20 and 20,000 vibrations per second. Longitudinal vibrations above 20,000 per second, which we cannot hear, are in the ultrasonic range. Ultrasonic vibrations, used in sonar devices, can be heard by dogs and other animals.

THE SOUND BARRIER

The speed of sound in air, 327 meters per second, is about 1200 kilometers per hour, and is referred to as a speed of *Mach 1.* The Mach number (named for the German physicist *Ernst Mach*) describes how fast a body is moving, compared to the speed of sound. An airplane moving at slower speeds sets up sound waves, which move in front of it at the speed of sound. These sound waves continue to pile up and reinforce one another. When the airplane reaches a speed of Mach 1, it has caught up with its own sounds which, by this time, have taken the form of a giant compression (longitudinal) wave. This wave, called the *sound barrier,* subjects the plane to tremendous stress. To continue in motion, the airplane must penetrate the compression wave in front of it; it must break the sound barrier.

High-speed jet planes are designed with sharpened noses and swept-back wings so as to reduce air friction which, in turn, permits them to break the sound barrier safely. The breaking of the sound barrier is also a problem faced by rocket ships, which must attain tremendous speeds to reach the velocity necessary to escape the force of gravity of the earth. This speed is about 40,000 kilometers per hour.

When a plane breaks through the sound barrier, an explosive sound, or *sonic boom*, is produced. The boom, often heard at ground level, can produce vibrations that are strong enough to damage buildings. Sonic booms caused by high-speed jet aircraft are an important source of sound pollution. This is one reason why the supersonic transport (SST), a huge plane that carries passengers faster than the speed of sound, is opposed by many people.

Looking Back

Sound is produced when matter vibrates and emits sound waves. Sound waves are longitudinal waves that travel in all directions away from the source of vibration if a carrying medium is present. The speed of sound varies with temperature and with the type of carrying medium. Sound pollution consists of sounds that are either excessively loud or unpleasant.

Looking Ahead

Sound, in the form of music, is a means of improving our environment. Musical sounds are the subject of the next chapter.

Multiple-Choice Questions

1. Of the following, the device used to detect underwater objects by means of sounds is
   a. laser b. radar c. maser d. sonar
2. Of the following, sound is most closely associated with
   a. mechanical energy c. heat energy
   b. chemical energy d. potential energy
3. Matter that transmits sound possesses the property of
   a. flexibility b. elasticity c. permeability d. ductility
4. Sound is transmitted best through
   a. liquids b. gases c. a vacuum d. solids
5. Of the following gases, sound is transmitted best by
   a. nitrogen b. oxygen c. hydrogen d. carbon dioxide

6. When the air in a bell jar containing a ringing bell is removed, the sound decreases because
   a. the removal of the air prevents an electric current from flowing
   b. sound cannot travel in a vacuum
   c. sound cannot travel through the glass
   d. sound cannot travel through air
7. In a sound wave, the portion of the elastic medium in which the molecules are crowded together is the
   a. compression b. rarefaction c. trough d. crest
8. In a sound wave, the molecules
   a. move up and down
   b. do not move
   c. move in all directions
   d. move in the same path as the wave
9. Sound is transmitted to the brain by the
   a. sensory nerve c. auditory nerve
   b. olfactory nerve d. vagus nerve
10. Humans can hear sounds whose highest frequency is
    a. 20 vps b. 100 vps c. 2000 vps d. 20,000 vps
11. In a sound wave, the distance between two successive compressions is called the
    a. wavelength b. frequency c. wave height d. amplitude
12. At 4°C the speed of sound in air is approximately
    a. 330 meters per hour c. 330 kilometers per hour
    b. 330 meters per second d. 330 kilometers per second
13. In steel, the speed of sound is approximately
    a. 327 meters per second c. 4600 kilometers per hour
    b. 4600 meters per second d. 4600 kilometers per second
14. When the temperature of a solid is increased, the speed of sound traveling in that solid
    a. increases greatly c. increases then decreases
    b. decreases greatly d. is not greatly affected
15. When a sound wave strikes a smooth hard surface, it is
    a. reflected b. absorbed c. transmitted d. refracted
16. Echoes can be heard only when the reflecting surface
    a. is soft c. is less than 16.5 meters away
    b. is more than 16.5 meters away d. absorbs sound

Modified True-False Questions

1. The rapid back-and-forth movement of matter that produces sound is known as *vibration*.
2. Sound-resistant materials are generally porous and *elastic*.
3. In a sound wave, the area of separation of molecules is called *compression*.
4. A sound wave is *a transverse* wave.

5. Sounds whose frequency is above 20,000 vibrations per second are called *ultrasonic.*
6. One compression and rarefraction in a sound wave is called *a cycle.*
7. Sound travels at a speed of 1470 meters per second in *water.*
8. A speed of 1200 kilometers per hour is referred to as *Mach 1.*
9. *An echo* is produced when an airplane breaks the sound barrier.
10. A sound reflection is known as *a noise.*

Thought Questions

1. A thunder clap is heard 5 seconds after a bolt of lightning is seen. Find how far away the lightning bolt struck if the air temperature is 10°C.
2. Explain how the sound barrier is formed.
3. a. A destroyer discovers a submarine by receiving a transmitted sonar signal 10 seconds after it was sent. How far away is the submarine?
   b. How deep is the ocean bottom if the echo of a transmitted sonar signal is received 20 seconds after it was sent?
4. List and discuss three characteristics of sound waves.

CHAPTER 13
HOW ARE MUSICAL SOUNDS PRODUCED IN OUR ENVIRONMENT?

When you have completed this chapter, you should be able to:

1. *Contrast* musical sounds and noise, including the production and characteristics of each.
2. *Explain*, with examples, how the pitch of sounds is changed in different musical instruments.
3. *Distinguish* between (*a*) pitch, amplitude, and quality of a musical tone (*b*) fundamental tone and overtone.
4. *Define* resonance, forced and sympathetic vibrations, interference of sound, and beats.
5. *Account* for the ability of the human body to produce sounds.

In the laboratory experience that follows, you will study how the pitch of certain vibrating bodies can be changed.

Laboratory Experience

HOW IS THE PITCH OF A SOUND RELATED TO ITS FREQUENCY?

A. Clamp a hacksaw blade to the edge of your desk so that the blade extends about 20 centimeters beyond the desk (Fig. 13–1). Force the overhanging end of the blade down about 15 centimeters and then release the blade suddenly.
   Observe the rate at which the blade vibrates and listen to the sound produced by the vibrating blade. The rate at which the blade vibrates is its *frequency*. The sound produced by the vibration is called its *pitch*.
B. Shorten the amount that the blade extends from the desk to 15 centimeters. Again, force the overhanging end of the blade down and then release the blade suddenly.
   1. How does the rate of vibration compare with the rate of vibration in part A?
   2. How does the pitch of the vibrating blade compare with the pitch produced in part A?

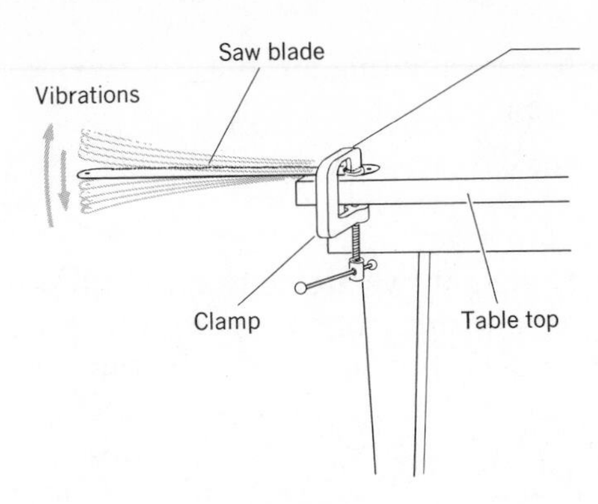

Fig. 13–1.

C. Shorten the amount that the blade extends from the desk to 10 centimeters. Again, force the overhanging end of the blade down and then release the blade suddenly.

3. How does the rate of vibration compare with the rates of vibration in parts A and B?
4. How does the pitch of the vibrating blade compare with the pitch produced in parts A and B?
5. What is the relation between the frequency at which the blade vibrates and the pitch produced by the blade?

D. Pour water into the five 15-centimeter test tubes as shown in Fig. 13–2. Place them in a rack.

E. Pick up the first test tube and blow gently across the opening. You will produce a sound having a certain pitch. Do the same with the other test tubes in turn.

6. What is the relation between the amount of water in each test tube and the pitch of the sound produced?
7. What similarity exists between the sounds produced by a vibrating hacksaw blade as you change its length and the sounds

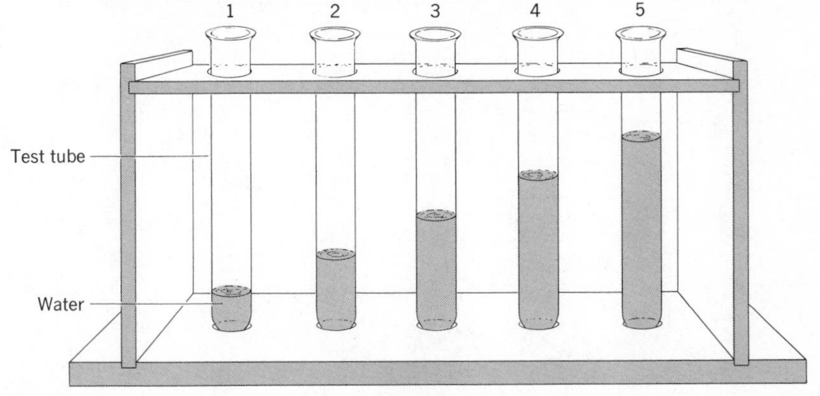

Fig. 13–2.

produced by the vibrating air in a test tube as the height of the water changes?

Introduction

In our daily environment, we are constantly exposed to many sounds —automobile horns, airplane engines, speech, music, explosions, hammering, and many others. In general, sounds can be classified as either *musical tones* or *noises* or combinations of both. Unnecessary noises and excessively loud music are often considered forms of sound pollution.

Musical tones are produced by the *regular vibrations* of an object— that is, vibrations that have a uniform number of compressions and rarefactions per second. Noises are produced by *irregular vibrations*. Sounds such as the roar of a train, an explosion, or the striking of a hammer are noises because the vibrations of the objects producing them are irregular.

REGULAR AND IRREGULAR VIBRATIONS

We can show the difference between regular and irregular vibrations by a simple device. Fig. 13–3*a* shows a disk that has one series of

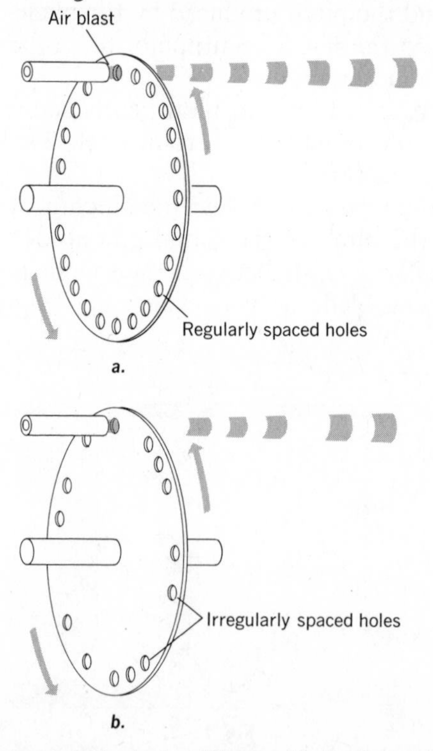

Fig. 13–3. Producing different kinds of sound.

evenly or regularly spaced holes, and Fig. 13-3*b* shows another disk with a series of irregularly spaced holes. When we rotate the disks, air blown through the evenly spaced holes produces regular vibrations. The sound we hear is a musical note—that is, a sound produced by a regular number of vibrations per second. Air blown through the irregularly spaced holes, however, produces an unpleasant noise. Patterns of these sounds are shown in Fig. 13–4. The smooth curve (regular vibrations) represents a pleasant sound, or musical note. The jagged curve (irregular vibrations) represents an unpleasant sound, or noise.

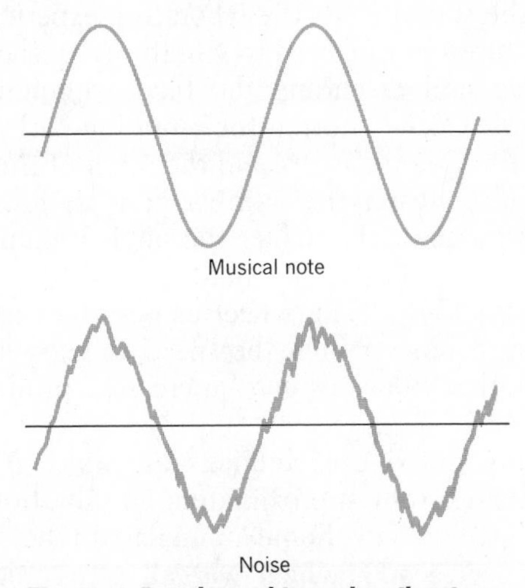

Fig. 13–4. Regular and irregular vibrations.

Fig. 13–5 shows a disk with several series of evenly spaced holes, each series a different distance from the center of the disk. When this disk is rotated, a blast of air directed through the holes produces notes of different numbers of vibrations per second. Why? This device can be used as a siren.

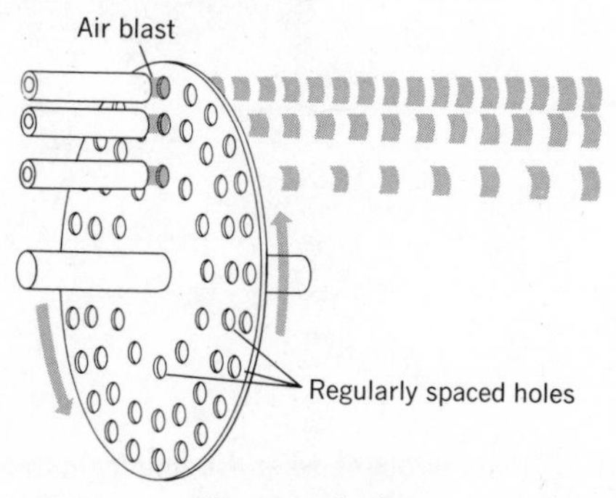

Fig. 13–5. A siren.

All musical tones, including sounds produced by the human voice or by any musical instrument, have three fundamental characteristics by which they can be identified. These characteristics are *pitch, amplitude,* and *quality*.

PITCH

When a musical note is played, pitch refers to the tone, or how high or how low the sound is. In the laboratory experience, we observed how the variation of pitch is related to vibrations by clamping a hacksaw blade onto a table and extending the blade different distances over the edge of the table. As we shorten the vibrating part of the saw blade, the frequency of vibration increases, and the pitch of the sound produced becomes higher. The greater the number of vibrations per second (or the greater the frequency), the higher the pitch becomes. This observation can also be demonstrated by holding a card against a rotating toothed wheel (Fig. 13–6). The wheel causes the card to vibrate and to produce a musical note. When the speed of the wheel is increased, the frequency of the vibrating card increases, producing a note of higher pitch.

We have already noted that humans are able to hear sounds of different pitch ranging from approximately 20 vibrations per second to 20,000 vibrations per second. Some animals can hear sounds beyond 20,000 vibrations per second, which we call ultrasonic sounds. A dog whistle, which dogs can hear but humans cannot hear, produces such ultrasonic sounds.

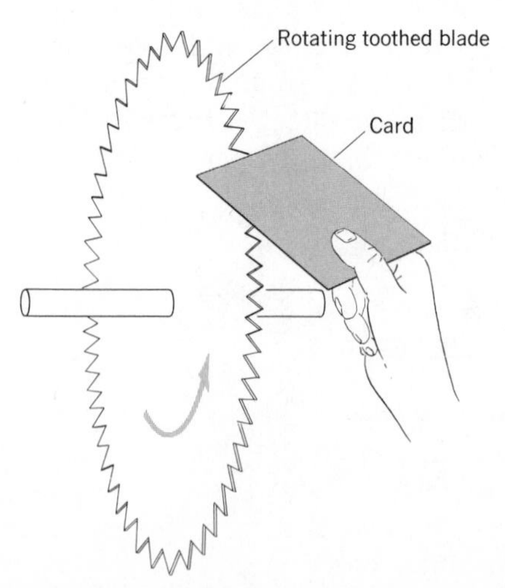

Fig. 13–6. Pitch increases when frequency increases.

Changing the Pitch of a Vibrating String

Stringed instruments such as the violin, banjo, and guitar produce a range of sounds, which results from varying the frequency of the vibrating strings. The frequency of a vibrating string can be varied in several ways:

1. *Varying the length of the string.* As a string is lengthened, its vibration frequency decreases. This means that a long string vibrates less rapidly than a shorter string. Since pitch depends upon the number of vibrations, a long vibrating string produces a low pitch. If the string is cut in half, each of the smaller strings when vibrating produces a higher pitch. When a violinist or guitarist wishes to increase the pitch of a string, he slides his finger "up the neck"; that is, he moves his finger along the string so as to shorten the length of the vibrating string. To produce a lower pitch from a string, the musician moves his finger the other way, thereby allowing more of the string to vibrate (Fig. 13–7).

Fig. 13–7. The pitch of a vibrating string depends on its length.

2. *Varying the thickness of the string.* In general, thick or heavy strings vibrate more slowly than do thin strings, and therefore thick strings produce musical notes of lower pitch. The strings of a violin vary in thickness. The thinnest of the four strings, the E string, produces a higher pitch than the thickest, the G string.

3. *Varying the tension, or tightness, of the string.* In the case of two strings of equal length and equal thickness, the tighter string produces a note of higher pitch than the looser string. We can hear the change of pitch with tension when a guitar or violin is tuned. As the tuning key is turned to loosen or tighten the vibrating string, we hear the changes in pitch, until the desired tension and pitch are reached.

Changing the Pitch of Pipes

A cylinder open at both ends is called an *open pipe*. A cylinder open at only one end is called a *closed pipe*. As with the length of a vibrating string, the length of the column of air in a pipe determines its pitch. Our experiment with the test tubes filled to various levels with water (Fig. 13–2, page 235) demonstrated that the shorter the pipe (that is, the shorter the air column in the test tube), the higher is the pitch.

The relation of pipe length to pitch can also be shown by trimming and tapering one end of a drinking straw. Place the tapered end of the straw into the mouth, and blow through it to produce a sound (you have made a crude oboe). Cut off a piece of the straw, and blow through it again. You will note that as the straw (pipe) becomes shorter, the pitch of the note produced becomes higher.

Musical instruments such as the flute, clarinet, and oboe are based on the principle that the pitch of a pipe can be increased by shortening the length of the air column in the pipe, and can be decreased by lengthening the air column in the pipe. By opening and closing the keys of a wind instrument, a musician in effect lengthens or shortens the vibrating air column, thereby varying the pitch.

AMPLITUDE

Amplitude of a sound wave generally corresponds to the loudness of the sound and depends on the force used in producing the sound. When a string is plucked gently, a soft note is produced. However, when the string is plucked violently, a much louder note is produced. Although the pitch of the two notes is the same, their loudness, or intensity, is different. The louder sound is produced because greater energy was applied to the string. This increase in energy causes the string to vibrate through a larger distance than before.

An increase in amplitude affects the compressions and rarefactions of the sound wave in opposite ways. During compression, the air molecules are crowded together even more. During rarefaction, the air molecules are spread apart even further. Thus, the loudness of a note depends upon the amount of energy given to a vibrating body —that is, the greater the energy given, the louder the sound that is produced.

QUALITY

When a trumpet and a violin sound the same note, we can easily distinguish between the two sounds. The difference in the sounds is called quality.

Investigation has shown that the difference in quality among musical instruments is based upon differences in the complexity of the vibrations of the instruments. All of the instruments playing the same musical note produce the same main tone called the *fundamental tone.* In a stringed instrument, the fundamental tone is produced when the string vibrates as a whole.

However, because of the materials of which different instruments are constructed, musical instruments vibrate in many complex ways. These complex vibrations produce additional tones called *overtones* (Fig. 13–8). In a stringed instrument, the first overtone is produced when the string vibrates in two parts; the second overtone is produced when the string vibrates in three parts; and so on. The sounds of the overtones differ in frequency, as shown in Fig. 13–8.

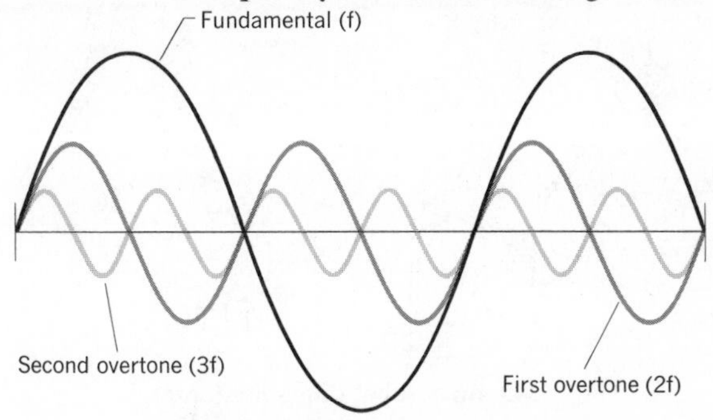

Fig. 13–8. Fundamentals and overtones.

When we listen to a musical instrument, what we actually hear is a combination of the fundamental tone plus the overtones. Since the fundamental tones of all instruments producing the same note are the same, the differences in the quality of the sounds they produce are caused by the differences in their overtones.

The human voice is produced by vibrating membranes, which are stretched across the *larynx,* or Adam's apple. These membranes are called the *vocal cords.* Muscles can change the tension on these cords, thus changing the pitch of the sounds. Correct usage of the palate, tongue, lips, and teeth provides for modulation, or regulation, of the voice. As with musical instruments, voice quality depends upon the proper blending of the overtones.

REINFORCEMENT OF SOUND

Have you ever watched an acrobat jumping on a trampoline (a stretched, flexible piece of canvas securely mounted on vertical supports)? To get the maximum bounce from each vibration of the canvas, acrobats must time their jumps properly. As shown in Fig. 13–9, the acrobat comes down when the canvas drops and jumps up when the canvas comes up. In this manner, the acrobat can increase the height of the jump greatly.

A sounding object—a vibrating body—is very much like the vibrating canvas of a trampoline. An elastic body in contact with or near the sounding body can be made to vibrate. If the frequencies of the two bodies match properly, the intensity of the sound that is produced increases. We call this matching of frequencies *resonance*.

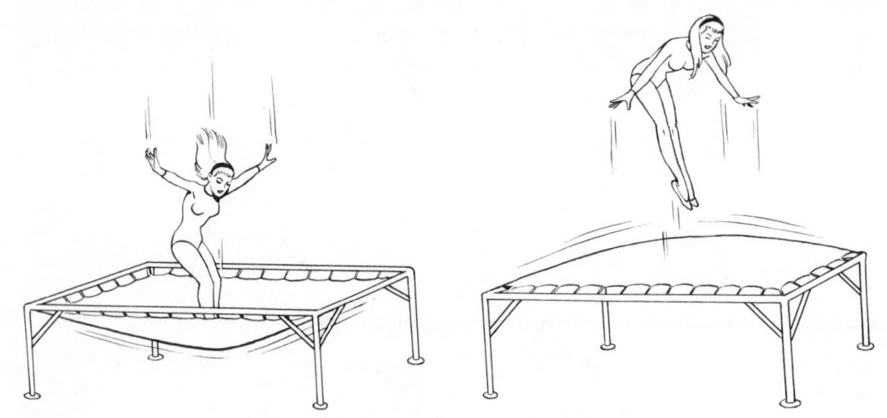

Fig. 13–9. An acrobat times her jumps.

Resonance

We have already described an open tube, or pipe, as a tube that is open at both ends. Stand an open tube in a cylinder of water, as shown in Fig. 13–10. Since one end of the tube is closed by the water, the tube is now a closed tube. Raising the tube in the water, without removing it completely, provides an air column of variable length. Now place a vibrating tuning fork over the open end of the tube, and slowly raise the tube. At some height of the air column, the intensity of the sound reaches a maximum—the sound becomes loudest. The air column is said to be *resonating*. At this point, the compressions and rarefactions of the vibrating tuning fork match the compressions and rarefactions of the sound wave that is reflected from the surface of the water in the tube. This increases the amplitude of the wave, and the intensity of the sound increases.

The reinforcement of sound by resonance is used in wind instruments such as a saxophone or harmonica. In these instruments, a vibrating air column resonates and reinforces the air jet produced by a vibrating reed.

Voice resonance is produced by the vibrations of the vocal cords

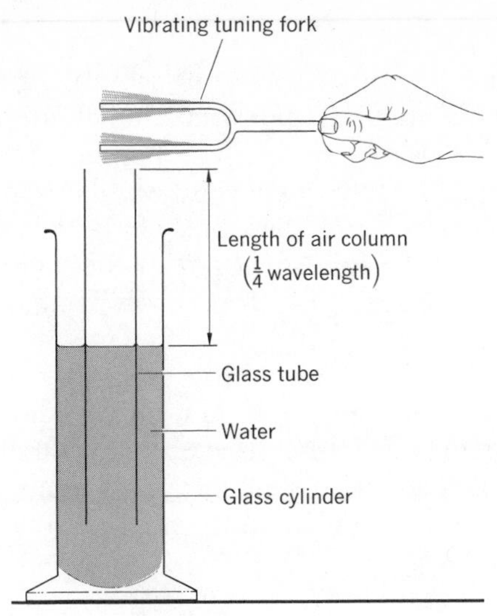

Fig. 13–10. Resonance.

reinforced by air in the *resonant cavities* formed by the base and roof of the mouth, or by the larynx, or by the nose. This is why a cold or a stuffed nose affects the resonance of the voice.

Forced Vibration

An elastic body has its own natural frequency of vibration. However, it may be forced to vibrate at another frequency by touching it with a vibrating body that has a different natural frequency of vibration. For example, suppose a tuning fork is struck and its stem is placed on a sound box (Fig. 13–11). The sound box is forced to vibrate at the same frequency as the tuning fork. The vibration of the sound box is called *forced vibration*.

The sound coming from the box has greater intensity than the sound of the tuning fork because the larger amount of air around the box has been made to vibrate. This is the same as saying that the amplitude of the sound wave has been increased. Forced vibrations are used to reinforce the sounds produced in a violin. The wood of the violin acts as a sound box, and the forced vibrations increase the intensity of the sound.

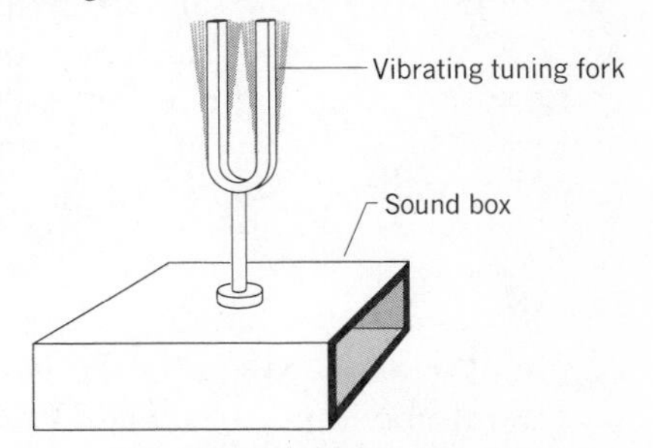

Fig. 13–11. Forced vibration.

Sympathetic Vibration

Sympathetic vibration occurs when one vibrating body causes another body, with the same natural frequency, to vibrate without being in contact with it. To demonstrate sympathetic vibration, set up two tuning forks of the same frequency on similar sound boxes a short distance apart (Fig. 13–12). When one of the tuning forks is struck, it causes the second tuning fork to vibrate at the same frequency. When the vibration of the first tuning fork is stopped, the second tuning fork continues to vibrate.

Some opera singers can cause a thin glass to shatter as they stand away from the glass and sing a certain note. This occurs when the singer reaches a note that causes the glass to vibrate sympathetically at the same frequency as the note. Since glass is not sufficiently elastic to bend rapidly as it vibrates, it shatters.

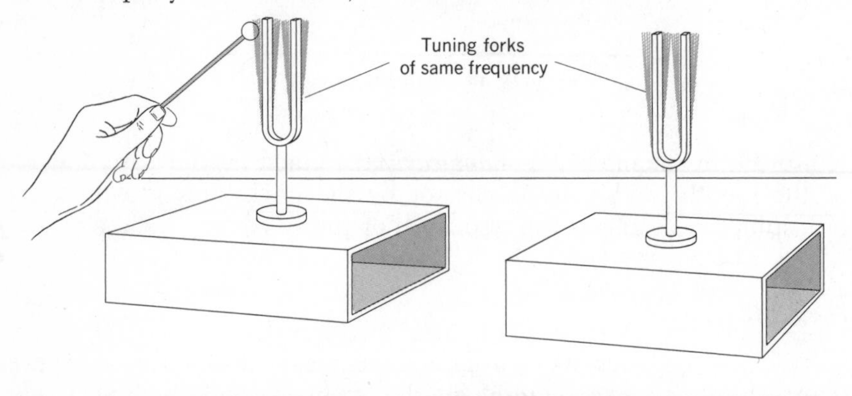

Fig. 13–12. Sympathetic vibration.

INTERFERENCE OF SOUND

We learned that when the frequencies of two vibrating bodies match—that is, when the compressions and rarefactions occur at the same time—reinforcement of the sound occurs. When this happens, the sound waves are said to be in step. In contrast, when the waves are out of step—that is, when one vibrating tuning fork produces a compression while the other vibrating tuning fork produces a rarefaction—the intensity of the sound can lessen to a point approaching complete silence. This effect is called *interference.*

BEATS

Sound waves of slightly differing frequencies may alternately interfere and reinforce one another. When this happens, a throbbing effect called *beats* is produced.

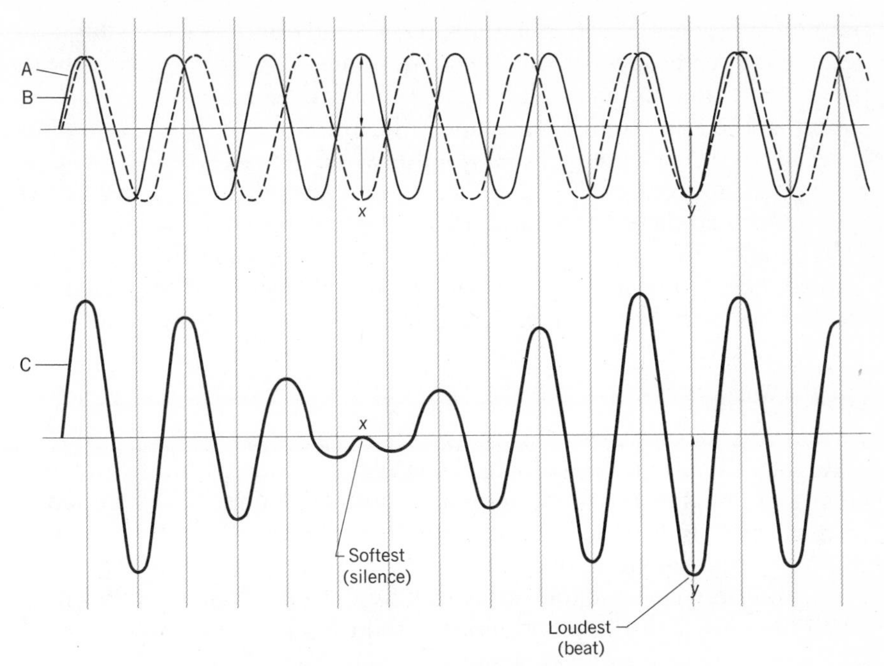

Fig. 13–13. Wave diagrams showing formation of beats.

Figure 13–13 shows how beats may be formed when two notes of slightly different frequencies are sounded at the same time. *A* and *B* represent the wave forms of the two notes. At point *x*, the two waves are out of step. The combined amplitude of waves *A* and *B*, shown in wave *C*, is the *difference* between the two amplitudes. The sound decreases in intensity (is softest) because interference between the two waves occurs at this point. At point *y*, on the other hand, the two waves are in step. The combined amplitude, shown in wave *C*, is the *sum* of the two amplitudes. The sound increases in intensity (is loudest) because reinforcement of sound waves occurs at this point. If these wave diagrams were continued, similar reinforcements between waves *A* and *B* would appear regularly. What we hear as beats, then, are the variations in sound caused by alternate interference and reinforcement.

We can readily calculate the number of beats per second produced by two notes of different frequencies by finding the difference between the frequencies of the notes. Assume that one tuning fork vibrates at the rate of 256 vibrations per second and a second fork at the rate of 259 vibrations per second. The difference between the two frequencies is 3 vibrations per second. The number of beats that can be heard in this case is 3 beats per second.

The human ear can distinguish only a limited number of beats per second. Some beat rates are pleasant to the ear; others are not. If the notes middle C (256 vibrations per second) and G (384 vibrations per second) are sounded at the same time, 128 (384 − 256) beats per second are produced. The ear cannot detect beats that are so close together, and a pleasing sound is heard. However if C (256 vibrations per second) and D (288 vibrations per second) are sounded at the same time, 32 (288 − 256) beats per second are produced. The ear can detect these beats, and an unpleasant sound is heard.

When we listen to a musical selection, we constantly hear beats. The sounds of music, however, are usually pleasant because the beats are blended with notes other than those that produced the beats.

Looking Back

Regular vibrations, pleasant to the ear, are considered music; irregular vibrations, unpleasant to the ear, are considered noise. The properties of musical sounds are pitch, amplitude, and quality. These properties can be reinforced by resonance, and by forced and sympathetic vibrations. Interference of sound waves of different pitch causes beats which, when blended with the proper notes, produce a pleasant musical sound.

Looking Ahead

Heat, light, and sound are forms of energy that are naturally present in our environment. Humans have also learned to produce many of these forms of energy by transformations from magnetism and electricity. We will study magnetism and electricity in Chapters 14, 15, 16, and 17.

Multiple-Choice Questions

1. Musical tones are produced
   a. by irregular vibrations
   b. by regular vibrations
   c. whenever matter is not vibrating
   d. whenever matter is vibrating
2. Noises are produced
   a. by irregular vibrations
   b. by regular vibrations
   c. whenever matter is not vibrating
   d. whenever matter is vibrating
3. The pitch of a sound depends upon the
   a. frequency
   b. wavelength
   c. amount of energy used
   d. amplitude
4. The pitch of a bicycle siren can be raised by
   a. riding more slowly
   b. riding more rapidly
   c. pressing the siren shaft to the tire and riding rapidly
   d. using an amplifier

5. As the length of a vibrating string is increased, the pitch of the sound produced
   a. increases then decreases
   b. increases
   c. decreases
   d. remains the same
6. As we increase the tension on a vibrating string, the pitch of the sound produced by the string
   a. is increased
   b. is decreased
   c. remains the same
   d. increases then decreases
7. The amplitude of a sound is determined by the
   a. frequency
   b. amount of energy used
   c. wavelength
   d. pitch
8. When the condensations and rarefactions of an air column match those of a vibrating tuning fork, the sounds produced
   a. are different in pitch
   b. have different wavelengths
   c. have different frequencies
   d. are resonating
9. Two vibrating objects produce 6 beats per second. If one of the objects has a frequency of 480 vibrations per second, the frequency of the second object is closest to
   a. 240 vps b. 486 vps c. 500 vps d. 120 vps

Modified True-False Questions

1. Very loud rock music is an example of *sound pollution.*
2. Musical tones are produced by *regular* vibrations of matter.
3. The main tone produced by a musical instrument is called *an overtone.*
4. The human voice is produced by membranes called *vocal cords.*
5. A *forced vibration* occurs when a vibrating object causes another object to vibrate without touching it.
6. When a violin bow is pressed harder on a string as the bow is moved, the *pitch* of the sound increases.

Thought Questions

1. List and discuss three characteristics of musical sounds.
2. Describe three ways by which the pitch of a vibrating string may be increased.
3. Explain why a violin sounds different from a cello.
4. Give a scientific reason for each of the following:
   a. A vibrating object at one end of a room causes a glass to shatter at the other end of the room.
   b. When a vibrating tuning fork is touched to a sound box, the sound becomes louder.
   c. The sound of a vibrating tuning fork lessens when the tuning fork is placed over a column of air.
5. Give a possible explanation why men's voices are usually lower-pitched than women's voices.

CHAPTER 14
WHAT IS THE NATURE OF MAGNETISM IN OUR ENVIRONMENT?

When you have completed this chapter, you should be able to:

1. *Distinguish* magnetic substances from nonmagnetic substances.
2. *Discuss* the theory of magnetic domains.
3. *Describe,* with reasons, how magnets are made and destroyed.
4. *State* the law of magnetic poles.
5. *Demonstrate* the magnetic field around magnets.
6. *Detect* and *use* the magnetic field of the earth.

In the laboratory experience that follows, you will explore the region around certain magnets.

Laboratory Experience

WHAT IS IN THE SPACE SURROUNDING A MAGNET?

A. Lay a bar magnet on your desk. Cover the magnet with a sheet of clear, stiff plastic. Sprinkle iron filings onto the plastic. Gently tap the edge of the plastic with your finger. Note what happens to the positions of the iron filings.
 1. Draw the pattern formed by the iron filings.
 Remove the plastic from the magnet and shake the iron filings into the dish intended for this purpose.

B. Lay two bar magnets on your desk. The magnets should be in line with each other, about 2 centimeters apart, and with similar poles facing each other.

 Cover the magnets with the sheet of plastic. Gently sprinkle iron filings onto the plastic, especially over the space between the two magnets. Tap the edge of the plastic with your finger. Note what happens to the positions of the iron filings.
 2. Draw the pattern formed by the iron filings.

Remove the plastic from the magnets and return the iron filings to the dish.

C. Position the two bar magnets on your desk so that they are in line with each other, about 2 centimeters apart, and with the north pole of one magnet facing the south pole of the other magnet.

Cover the magnets with the sheet of plastic. Gently sprinkle iron filings onto the plastic, especially over the space between the two magnets. Tap the edge of the plastic with your finger. Note what happens to the positions of the iron filings.

3. Draw the pattern formed by the iron filings.

Remove the plastic from the magnets and return the iron filings to the dish.

D. Lay a horseshoe magnet on your desk. Cover the magnet with the sheet of plastic. Gently sprinkle iron filings between the poles of the magnet. Tap the edge of the plastic with your finger. Note what happens to the positions of the iron filings.

4. Draw the pattern formed by the iron filings.

Remove the plastic from the magnet and return the iron filings to the dish.

5. Based on your findings in parts B and C, how would you describe the force that exists between the poles of the horseshoe magnet?
6. Based on your findings in parts B and C, draw a diagram showing the positions of iron filings when two horseshoe magnets are lined up with opposite poles near each other.

Introduction

Magnetism, like that of an ordinary magnet, appears to be present all around the earth and other heavenly bodies. Although magnetism is part of our environment, so far as is known, magnetism has no direct effect on us or on any other living thing. However, many everyday devices we use operate only because of magnetism. Among these devices are radios, televisions, telephones, electric generators, and electric motors.

MAGNETISM AND MAGNETIC SUBSTANCES

Thousands of years ago it was found that if a piece of rock called *lodestone* were suspended from a cord, one end of the rock would always point toward the north. Using this crude device, the captain of an ancient sailing ship could keep his vessel on course, even when the sky was overcast and the stars were hidden. Today we know that lodestone points toward the north because this rock possesses the property of magnetism. This property enables a substance to attract certain materials such as iron.

All substances can be classified as either magnetic or nonmagnetic. A *magnetic* substance is one that is attracted to a magnet. Examples include iron, cobalt, nickel, and lodestone. A *nonmagnetic* substance is not attracted to a magnet; however, magnetism passes through such a substance. If we place an iron nail on a sheet of thin cardboard and hold a magnet under the cardboard, the nail will be attracted to the magnet. As we move the magnet about, the nail will "follow" it. It is apparent that the magnetism passes through the nonmagnetic cardboard. Other examples of nonmagnetic substances are plastics, wood, and certain metals such as copper and silver.

HOW DO WE EXPLAIN MAGNETISM?

Magnetism is thought to be a force that exists around a magnet. The region around a magnetic substance is said to be a *magnetic field*. When a magnetic substance enters a magnetic field at the proper distance from a magnet, the substance is attracted to the magnet. A magnetic field is not only present around a magnet, but it is also present around moving electric charges, or electric currents, as you will see later.

It is known that matter consists of atoms that, in turn, contain a positively charged nucleus and negatively charged electrons moving around the nucleus. Not only do electrons revolve around the nucleus, but each electron spins around on its own axis, just as the earth does. The spinning motions of the electrons are thought to produce oppositely charged *magnetic poles* (*north* and *south* magnetic poles).

In most elements, the spins of electrons oppose one another. That is, the motions are in opposite directions, and thus the magnetic forces cancel each other. There is no magnetic field around such elements. Most substances, therefore, do not display any magnetic properties.

We will be concerned in this chapter with the magnetism of iron and some of its related elements. In such magnetic elements, spinning motions of the electrons do not oppose one another; instead, they reinforce one another.

The atoms in a piece of iron can be thought of as groups of tiny magnets called *domains*. Ordinarily, these domains are not arranged in any particular pattern; that is, they are arranged in a random fashion (Fig. 14–1*a*). Such an arrangement tends to weaken or cancel any net magnetic effect. However, when the domains are lined up, with all north poles facing one end and all south poles facing the other end (Fig. 14–1*b*), there is a net magnetic effect. The object becomes a magnet with a magnetic field around it.

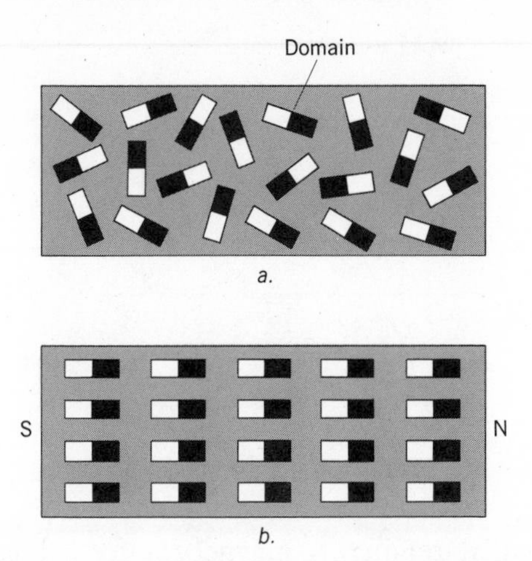

Fig. 14–1. Domains in an unmagnetized and a magnetized piece of iron.

Breaking or cutting a large magnet does not disturb the regular arrangement of magnetic domains. Thus, smaller pieces cut from a large magnet retain their magnetism.

NATURAL AND ARTIFICIAL MAGNETS

Lodestone is a *natural magnet.* It is a naturally occurring magnetic iron ore called *magnetite* (Fe_3O_4). Except for such iron ores, most magnets in use today are *artificial magnets.* Artificial magnets are usually made of iron alloys (combinations of iron and other metals). For example, a very powerful artificial magnet, called an *alnico magnet,* consists of aluminum, nickel, cobalt, and iron.

How Magnets Are Made

Magnets are made by several methods:

1. *By contact.* When a bar of a magnetic substance is stroked in *one direction* with a magnet, the bar becomes magnetized. It then possesses a magnetic field of its own. For example, when a bar of steel is stroked in one direction with a magnet, the steel itself becomes a magnet (Fig. 14–2). After being stroked with a magnet, the steel can attract several paper clips. This method is known as magnetizing by *contact.* According to the theory of magnetism, stroking a magnetic substance properly realigns the domains into a regular north-south arrangement.

It is interesting to note that when a bar of soft iron is magnetized, it does not remain a magnet for very long. It slowly loses its magnetism and is therefore called a *temporary magnet.* On the other hand, when

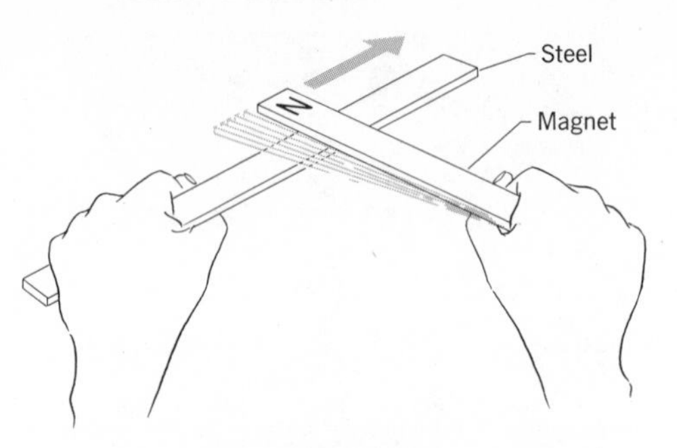

Fig. 14–2. Making a magnet by contact.

steel is magnetized, it retains its magnetism for a long period of time and is called a *permanent magnet.*

2. *By induction.* When a magnetic substance, such as a bar of soft iron, is brought close to a magnet—but does not touch the magnet—the soft iron itself becomes a magnet. As shown in Fig. 14–3, when an iron bar is held near (not touching) a magnet, the bar attracts paper clips. When the magnet is moved away, the paper clips fall from the iron bar. This method of making a magnet is known as *induction.* According to the theory of magnetism, the presence of a magnet near a magnetic object rearranges the domains in the magnetic object. Most of the north poles point in one direction, and most of the south poles point in the opposite direction. Apparently, the magnetic force, or

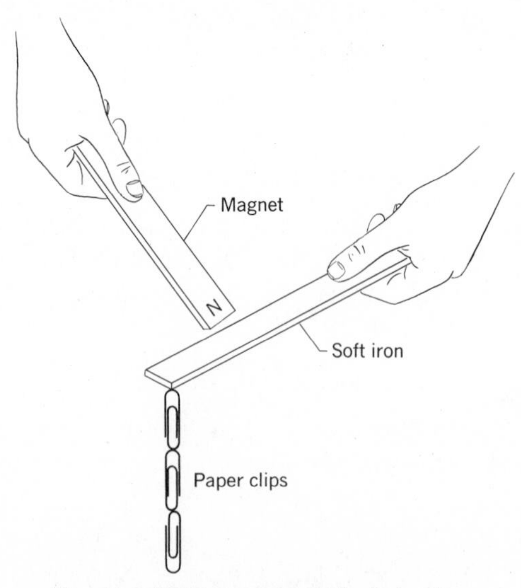

Fig. 14–3. Making a magnet by induction.

magnetic field, extends outward to some distance. Beyond this region, the magnetic field is too weak to affect magnetic substances.

3. *By electricity.* In 1819, the Danish scientist *Hans Christian Oersted* discovered that a wire carrying electricity possesses magnetic properties (Fig. 14–4). He found this to be so even though the wire is made of a nonmagnetic substance such as copper. In this case, note that the wire, which is a nonmagnetic substance, behaves like a magnet and attracts a magnetic substance.

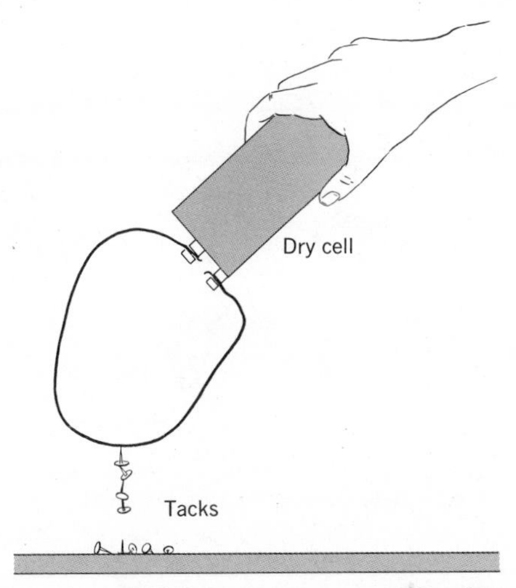

Fig. 14–4. Making a magnet using electricity.

In 1820, the French physicist *André Ampère* wound a long piece of nonmagnetic copper wire into a springlike coil. He then attached the ends of the coil to a source of electric current. He found that the coil attracted iron and acted like a bar magnet as long as electricity flowed in the wire. When the electricity stopped flowing, the coil lost its magnetism.

When a magnetic substance is inserted into a coil of wire and the wire is connected to the poles of a battery, the magnetic substance becomes a magnet. If this substance is soft iron, it becomes an *electromagnet* (a temporary magnet). If the substance is steel or some other hard iron alloy, it becomes a permanent magnet.

How Magnets Are Demagnetized

Magnets can be demagnetized by any method that disturbs the regular arrangement of magnetic domains (Fig. 14–5, page 254).

1. *By heat.* When a magnet is held in a flame and heated until it

is red hot, the excess energy absorbed by the magnet disarranges the domains of the magnet. As a result, the magnetic properties of the magnet disappear.

2. *By contact.* When one magnet is stroked by another magnet alternately in one direction and then the other, the domains of the stroked magnet become disarranged, and the stroked magnet becomes demagnetized. Note that this procedure is the opposite of the procedure used in making a magnet by stroking.

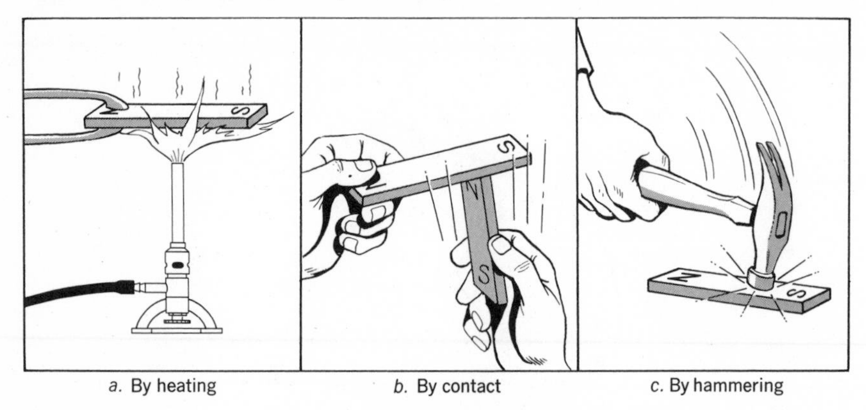

a. By heating *b.* By contact *c.* By hammering

Fig. 14–5. Demagnetizing magnets.

3. *By hammering or jarring.* When a magnet is repeatedly struck with a hammer, or when it is struck against a table top or some other hard object, the forceful vibrations of the magnet jar the domains out of their original alignment. Consequently, the magnet loses its magnetism. This can be shown as follows: First, pick up some paper clips with a magnet. Then remove the paper clips and strike the magnet solidly against a hard object four or five times. Now try to pick up the paper clips again. The clips are no longer attracted.

LAW OF MAGNETIC POLES

As you noticed in the laboratory experience, iron filings tend to concentrate at the ends of the magnet. It is at these ends, called *poles,* that the power of a magnet appears to be strongest (Fig. 14–6). When a bar magnet is suspended horizontally by a string from a ringstand, the magnet usually swings and then comes to rest in an approximate north-south position. The pole pointing toward the north is called the *north-seeking pole,* or N *pole,* of the magnet, while the pole pointing southward is called the *south-seeking pole,* or *S pole,* of the magnet.

When the north pole of a second magnet is brought close to the

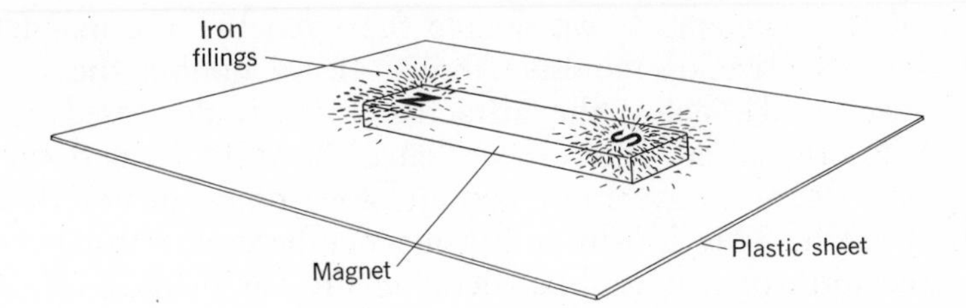

Fig. 14-6. The strength of a magnet is concentrated at its poles.

north pole of the suspended magnet, the two north poles repel each other. If the south pole of a magnet is brought close to the south pole of a suspended magnet, the two south poles also repel each other. On the other hand, when the south pole of a magnet is brought close to the north pole of the suspended magnet, the two poles attract each other (Fig. 14-7).

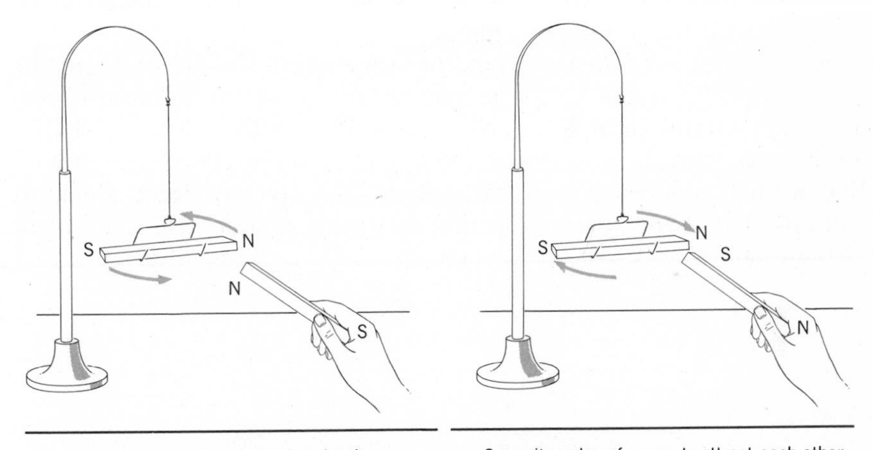

Fig. 14-7. The law of magnetic poles.

These observations are summarized in the *law of magnetic poles*. This law states that like poles of magnets repel each other, and unlike poles of magnets attract each other.

Experiments indicate that the force of attraction between two unlike poles, or the force of repulsion between two like poles, depends upon the strength of the magnets and the distance between the poles. At a given distance, stronger magnets produce stronger attractions or stronger repulsions. With magnets of the same strength, the attractions or repulsions increase as the distance between the poles becomes shorter.

In calculating the attractive or repulsive forces between two magnets, the distance between poles has a more pronounced effect than does the strength of the magnets. If we double the strength of a magnet, we double the attractive or repulsive forces. If we double the distance between two unlike poles, the attractive force is decreased to one-fourth of its original strength. If we halve the distance between two unlike poles, the attractive force becomes four times greater than the original strength. This is why a bar magnet becomes stronger when bent in the form of a horseshoe. Bending the bar magnet brings the poles closer together.

MAKING A MAGNETIC FIELD VISIBLE

We have seen that iron filings tend to cluster near the poles of a magnet. Magnetic effects can be observed not only at the poles of a magnet, but also for some distance away from the poles. The region around a magnet in which magnetic effects are observed we have already called the magnetic field. This field is invisible, but its effect can be observed with the aid of iron filings.

As you discovered in the laboratory experience, the field around the bar magnet is revealed by the pattern of lines made by the iron filings. The lines extend from the north pole to the south pole (Fig. 14–8). These lines, known as *magnetic lines of force*, form closed arcs around the magnet and never cross each other. The lines of force are most concentrated at the poles, indicating that the magnetic field is strongest at these points.

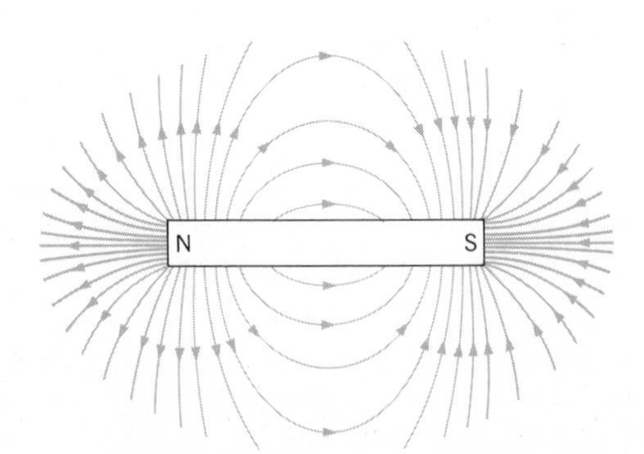

Fig. 14–8. Magnetic field around a bar magnet.

You have also observed the patterns showing the magnetic field between the poles of two magnets. Between two similar poles, the lines of force appear to repel one another (Fig. 14–9). When the north pole of one bar magnet is placed near the south pole of another magnet, the lines of force indicate the attraction between these poles (Fig. 14–10).

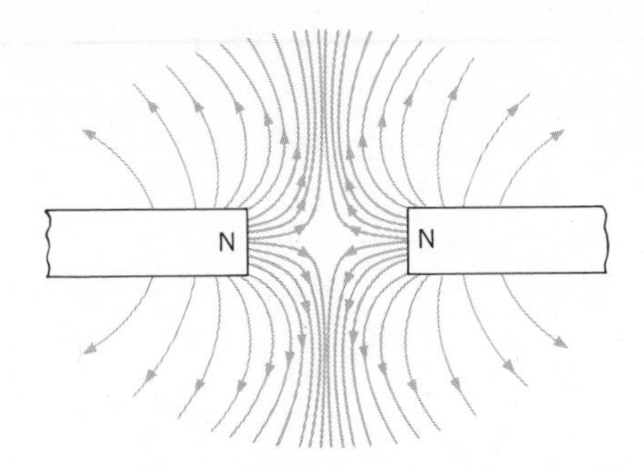

Fig. 14–9. Magnetic field between similar poles.

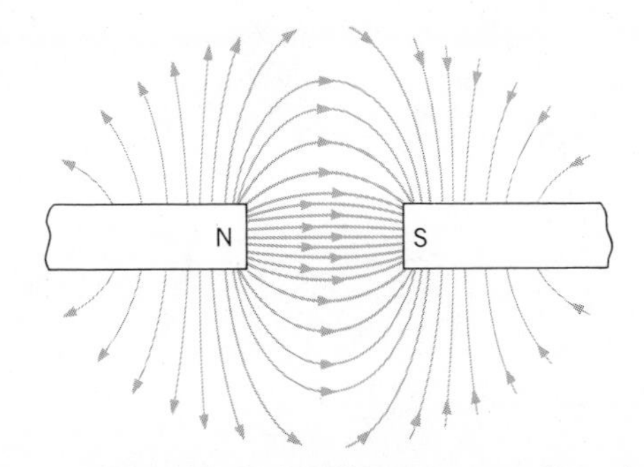

Fig. 14–10. Magnetic field between opposite poles.

THE MAGNETIC FIELD OF THE EARTH

In 1600, *William Gilbert*, an English scientist, published an essay in which he claimed that the earth behaved like a giant magnet. To support his view, he shaped a piece of lodestone into a sphere resembling the earth. He then demonstrated that a compass needle, placed anywhere on the sphere, took a north-south position. Recall that the same observation can be made when we suspend a bar magnet from a string. The freely suspended magnet also takes a north-south position.

If we represent the earth with a cardboard sphere or globe and place a bar magnet inside the sphere, as in Fig. 14–11, page 258, the lines of force around the bar magnet will correspond to the magnetic field of the earth.

We can demonstrate the magnetism of the earth itself in a simple way. Hold an iron rod in such a way that one end of the rod points north and the other end points south. In this position, the rod is aligned along the lines of force of the earth's magnetic field. Gently tap the south-pointing end of the rod with a hammer a few times.

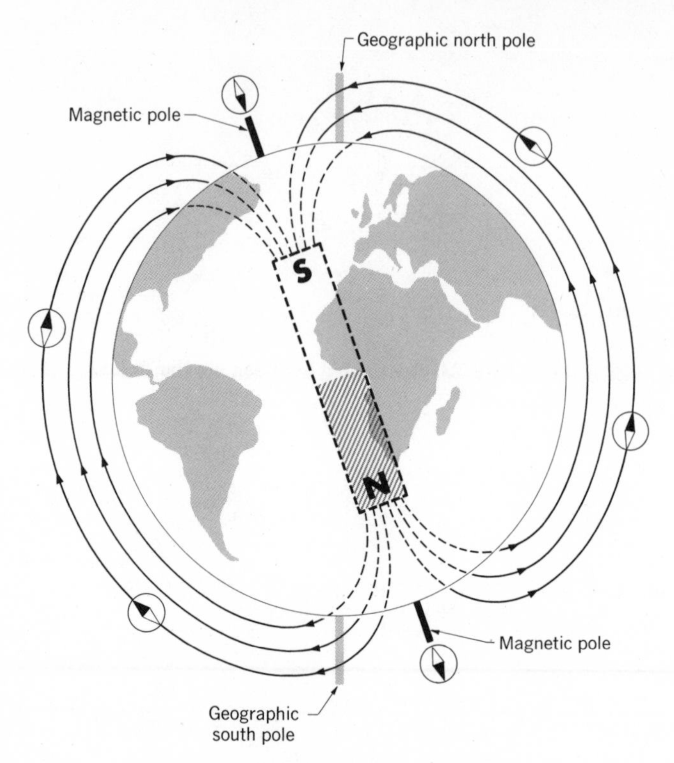

Fig. 14–11. The earth's magnetic field.

Tapping apparently shakes up the domains in the rod and enables the domains to rotate. Thus, as you tap the rod, the domains rotate within the rod and become aligned with the earth's magnetic field in a north-south direction. As a result, the rod becomes a magnet by the process of induction (see page 252).

MAGNETIC NEEDLES

Two devices used in navigation and in studies of the earth's magnetic field are the *compass* and the *dipping needle.*

The Compass

The compass is essentially a light iron needle mounted on a vertical pivot, so that it can swing freely in a horizontal plane. The needle responds to the earth's magnetism by aligning itself in a north-south direction.

The response of the compass to the earth's magnetism makes the compass useful as a navigational instrument. However, in most places on earth, the compass needle does not point to true north, by which we mean the geographic north pole. Instead, the compass needle points to the north magnetic pole, as shown in Fig. 14–11. The north magnetic pole of the earth is located in northern Canada, about 1900 kilometers south of the geographic north pole.

The angle formed by lines from an observer to the two different poles (magnetic and geographic) is called the *magnetic declination* of the particular location of the observer. In a few places on earth, the declination is 0°; that is, the geographic north pole, the magnetic north pole, and the observer are all aligned in a straight line. In these places only, the compass needle assumes a true north-south position. Navigators use special maps that show the declinations of different locations. By knowing the proper declination, and by using a compass, one can then determine the direction of true north—that is, the geographic north pole.

The Dipping Needle

The north and south magnetic poles of the earth can also be located by using a dipping needle (Fig. 14–12). This device is a compass needle suspended on a horizontal pivot, so that the needle turns in a vertical plane. A protractor that is part of the instrument permits us to measure the angle through which the needle moves. This angle, called the *angle of dip*, is the angle that the magnetic field of the earth makes with the horizontal at any specific location on the earth. At the equator, the angle of dip is 0°. As we move from the equator closer to the earth's north magnetic pole, the angle of dip increases

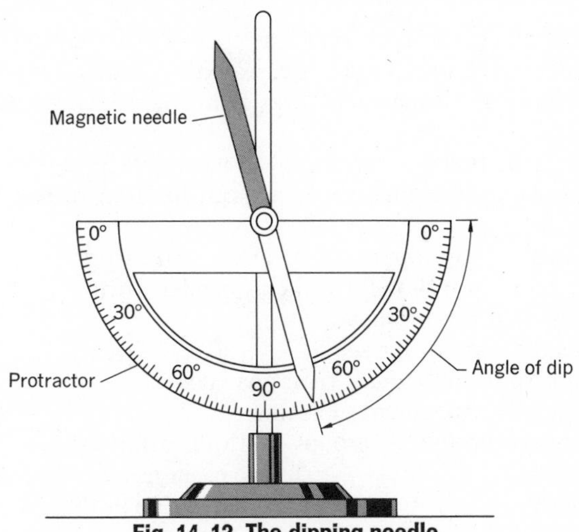

Fig. 14–12. The dipping needle.

until it reaches 90°—a vertical position—at the magnetic north pole. At the magnetic south pole, the dipping needle also indicates a 90° angle of dip.

From measurements of magnetic dip, it can be shown that the magnetic poles of the earth are continually shifting. Although these shifts are slight, they make it necessary for map makers to undertake regular magnetic surveys of the earth to keep their maps up to date.

Much remains to be learned about the reason that the earth behaves as a magnet.

Looking Back

Magnetism is an invisible force that exists around certain bodies in our environment. It is thought to be the result of the regular alignment of the atoms within those bodies. Magnetism can be detected around magnetic substances, around the earth and other heavenly bodies, and around wires carrying electricity. Magnets are made by contact, by induction, and by electricity flowing through coils of wire.

Looking Ahead

Magnetism is closely related to electrical energy. In the next chapter, we will discuss the nature of electrical energy.

Multiple-Choice Questions

1. Of the following, the rock that was used for navigational purposes was
   a. hematite b. lodestone c. bauxite d. calcite
2. Of the following, the element that is *not* considered to be a magnetic substance is
   a. cobalt b. nickel c. iron d. copper
3. Of the following, the substance that can be used to test for a magnetic substance is
   a. iron filings b. copper c. zinc d. sand
4. Magnetic effects are thought to be associated with
   a. electrons that do not move
   b. protons that do not move
   c. electrons spinning around their own axis
   d. an irregular arrangement of atoms
5. A magnet is composed of groups of atoms arranged
   a. in domains c. in random fashion
   b. irregularly d. none of these

6. Breaking a magnet in half results in
   a. the destruction of the magnet
   b. the formation of two half magnets
   c. the formation of two complete magnets
   d. disruption of the magnetic domains
7. Of the following, the element *not* present in the alloy used to make a powerful magnet is
   a. iron b. nickel c. cobalt d. copper
8. A magnet can be made by
   a. stroking a magnetic material in one direction with a magnet
   b. striking a magnetic material with a hammer
   c. heating a magnetic material
   d. stroking a magnetic material in both directions with a magnet
9. Placing a magnetic material near (but not touching) a magnet produces a magnet by
   a. contact b. induction c. conduction d. reaction
10. The discovery that a wire carrying an electric current has magnetic properties was first made by
    a. Volta b. Ampère c. Oersted d. Maxwell
11. Of the following, the procedure that does *not* destroy a magnet is
    a. hammering the magnet
    b. heating the magnet
    c. stroking the magnet in both directions with another magnet
    d. stroking the magnet in one direction with another magnet
12. The ends of a magnet are known as
    a. electrodes b. poles c. the field d. domains
13. When the S poles of two magnets are brought close together
    a. they attract each other
    b. they have no effect on each other
    c. they repel each other
    d. they first repel and then attract each other
14. The force of attraction between the poles of two magnets is most greatly affected by
    a. the distance between the poles
    b. the size of the magnets
    c. the strength of the magnets
    d. the composition of the magnets
15. When the distance between unlike poles of two magnets is increased, the force of attraction between these poles
    a. is decreased c. remains the same
    b. is increased d. cannot be predicted
16. Magnetic effects are observed in a region around a magnet called the
    a. magnetic domain c. magnetic pole
    b. magnetic field d. coil
17. A magnetic field is composed of
    a. domains b. iron filings c. charged atoms d. lines of force

18. An instrument currently used for navigation that operates on the principle of magnetism is a
    a. map b. lodestone c. compass d. magnetite
19. The theory that the earth is a giant magnet was proposed by
    a. Gilbert b. Maxwell c. Ampère d. Oersted
20. To locate the magnetic north pole of the earth, scientists use an instrument known as a
    a. domain b. dipping needle c. springlike coil d. sonar

Modified True-False Questions

1. A lodestone contains an ore of *copper*.
2. A substance that is not attracted to a magnet but allows magnetism to pass through it is said to be *artificial*.
3. A lodestone is an example of *a natural magnet*.
4. When steel is magnetized, it becomes *a temporary magnet*.
5. The observation that opposite magnetic poles attract each other is stated in the *law of domains*.
6. An invisible magnetic field can be detected by using *iron filings*.
7. The angle that the magnetic field of the earth makes with the horizontal as measured by a dipping needle is called the *angle of inclination*.
8. At the magnetic equator, the angle of dip is 90°.
9. The magnetic north pole is located in *northern Canada*.

Thought Questions

1. Define each of the following terms:
    a. magnetic substance
    b. natural magnet
    c. temporary magnet
    d. magnetic poles
    e. magnetic field
2. Explain the theory of magnetism. What evidence supports this theory?
3. Describe three methods for making a magnet.
4. Describe three methods for destroying a magnet.
5. Explain why a suspended magnet will line up in a north-south position when it comes to rest.
6. A magnet is freely suspended in air with its north and south markings covered. Explain how you could determine the north and south poles of the suspended magnet without touching it.
7. At your position, the angle of dip on a dipping needle measures 45°. What is your approximate geographic position with respect to the magnetic pole and the equator?

CHAPTER 15
WHAT IS THE NATURE OF THE ELECTRICAL ENERGY IN OUR ENVIRONMENT?

When you have completed this chapter, you should be able to:

1. *Distinguish* between (*a*) static electricity and current electricity (*b*) anode and cathode.
2. *State* the law of electrical attraction and repulsion.
3. *Describe* how static electricity is detected.
4. *Explain* the cause of lightning.
5. *Contrast* electrical conductors with electrical insulators.
6. *Trace* the flow of electrons in a closed circuit.
7. *Discuss* how electricity is produced in electrical cells and generators.

In the laboratory experience that follows, you will construct an electrical circuit and produce electricity to make the circuit operate.

Laboratory Experience

HOW CAN WE PRODUCE ELECTRICITY FROM CHEMICALS?

A. Connect a dry cell to an electric bell and switch, as shown in Fig. 15–1.
Close the switch.
1. What do you observe?

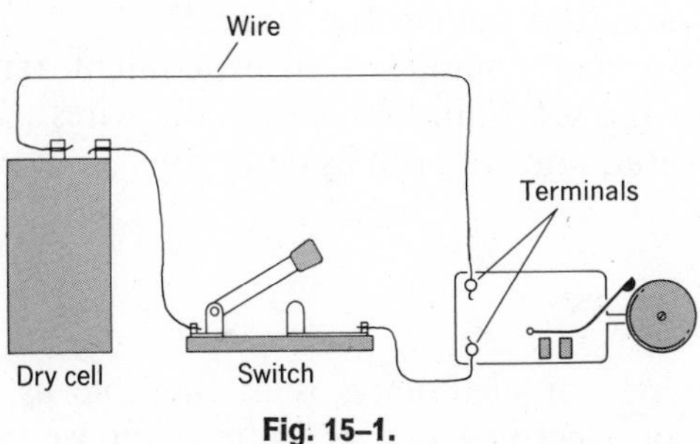

Fig. 15–1.

Open the switch to disconnect the apparatus.

2. Why doesn't the bell ring now?

B. With a piece of copper wire, tie a zinc bar to one terminal of the bell. Similarly, tie a carbon rod to the other terminal, as shown in Fig. 15–2*a*. (The carbon rod used here should be previously depolarized with nitric acid, as discussed on page 272.)

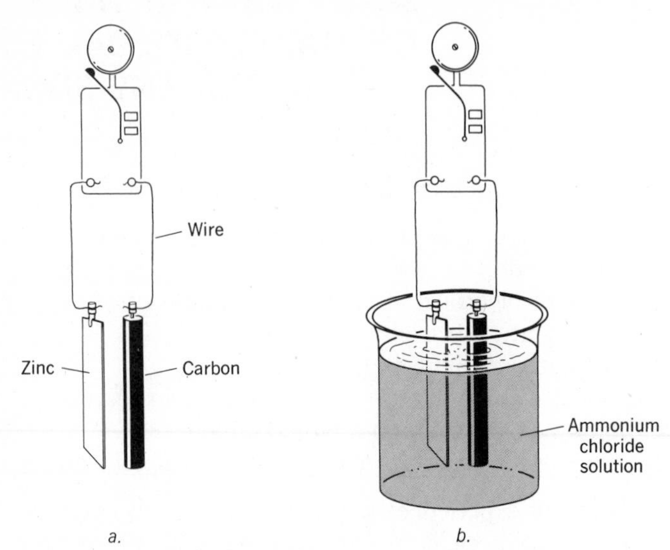

Fig. 15–2.

3. Does the bell ring? Explain.

Touch the zinc bar to the carbon rod.

4. What happens? Explain.

C. Fill a wide-mouth jar with a dilute solution of ammonium chloride to within 2 centimeters of the top of the jar. Hold the bell high so that the zinc bar and carbon rod hang straight down. Lower the bell slowly until the zinc and carbon rods are immersed in the ammonium chloride solution, without touching each other (Fig. 15–2*b*).

5. What happens? Explain.

6. What produced the electric current?

As soon as you have completed the experiment, remove the zinc and carbon from the solution. Disconnect the wires. Rinse the zinc and carbon in water, and set both aside to dry.

Introduction

Electrical energy, or electricity, is as invisible as heat energy. We become aware of electrical energy only when we receive an electric shock or when we observe what electrical energy does. Thus, when the electrical energy between clouds or between clouds and the earth is discharged, we see a flash of lightning. When we flick a switch, we observe the operation of many of our electrical appliances at home. Our present civilization is so dependent on electricity that new sources of this energy are constantly being sought.

ELECTRICAL ENERGY CAN ACCUMULATE ON OBJECTS

All matter is electrical in nature. This property of matter results from the presence of electrons and protons—charged particles—in atoms. When the numbers of electrons and protons in a sample of matter are equal, we say that such matter is electrically *neutral*; that is, the matter has no net electrical charge.

We can give an electric charge to certain materials by rubbing them. After rubbing, we find that these materials attract other materials. Thus, when we rub a glass rod with silk and a hard rubber rod with fur, the glass rod and the rubber rod attract each other. These rubbed objects also attract small pieces of paper or a fine stream of water (Fig. 15–3). In all of these cases, no attraction is observed until the articles are rubbed.

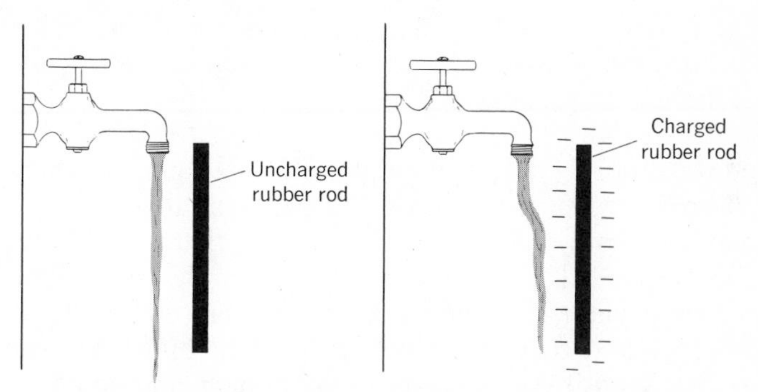

Fig. 15–3. The effect of static charges on a stream of water.

Rubbing apparently transfers electrons from one object to another, giving each of these objects an electric charge. A neutral object that gains electrons acquires a negative charge because it has more electrons (negative electrical particles) than it had before. For example, rubbing a rubber rod with fur transfers electrons from the fur to the rod. A neutral object that loses electrons has fewer electrons than it had before. Consequently, it now has more protons (positive electrical particles) than electrons and, therefore, has a positive charge. For example, rubbing a glass rod with silk transfers electrons from the rod to the silk.

Electric charges that accumulate on the surface of objects and remain

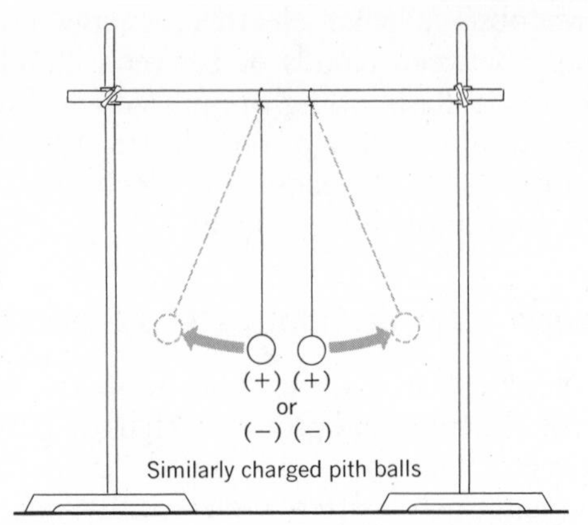

Fig. 15–4. Like electric charges repel each other.

there are referred to as static (nonmoving) electrical charges, or *static electricity*.

How Static Electricity Behaves

Pith, which is a very light material, is ordinarily electrically neutral because it has equal numbers of electrons and protons. When a small ball made of pith is touched with a positively charged glass rod, the pith ball also becomes positively charged.

Suspend two pith balls by threads, as in Fig. 15–4. Touch each with a charged glass rod, thereby giving each pith ball a positive charge. When we try to bring two such positively charged balls together, we find that they repel each other—that is, they move apart. Similarly, we can touch two suspended pith balls with a negatively charged rubber rod, thereby giving each a negative charge. When we try to bring two such balls together, they also repel each other. However, when a pith ball that has a positive charge is brought near another ball that has a negative charge, the two pith balls attract each other (Fig. 15–5).

Such observations led to the formulation of the *law of electrical attraction and repulsion*, which states that unlike electric charges attract each other, whereas like electric charges repel each other. Note the similarity between this law and the law of magnetic poles, studied in Chapter 14, pages 254–256.

How Static Electric Charges Are Detected

An *electroscope* is used to detect the presence of a static electric charge. This instrument (Fig. 15–6*a*) usually consists of an insulated metal rod with a metal knob on one end. Attached to the other end

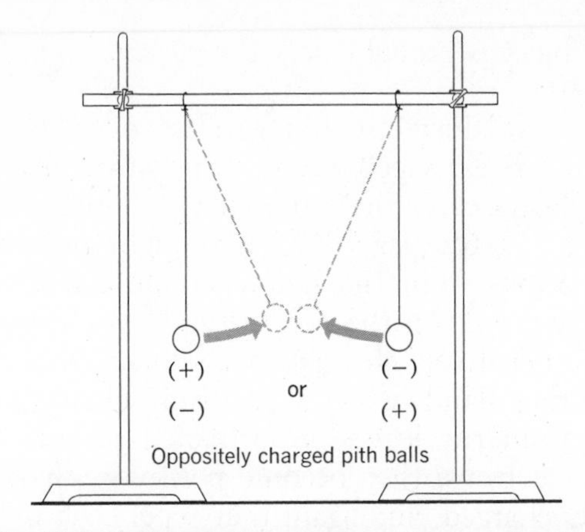

Fig. 15–5. Unlike electric charges attract each other.

of the rod are two thin pieces of metal foil, called *leaves*, which may be made of either aluminum or gold foil. The rod and leaves are enclosed in a container such as a flask. The container protects the delicate leaves. Only the knob projects from the flask.

When an electrically charged object is brought close to the metal knob of an electroscope, both leaves become similarly charged. Since the same charges repel each other, the leaves move apart. If a more

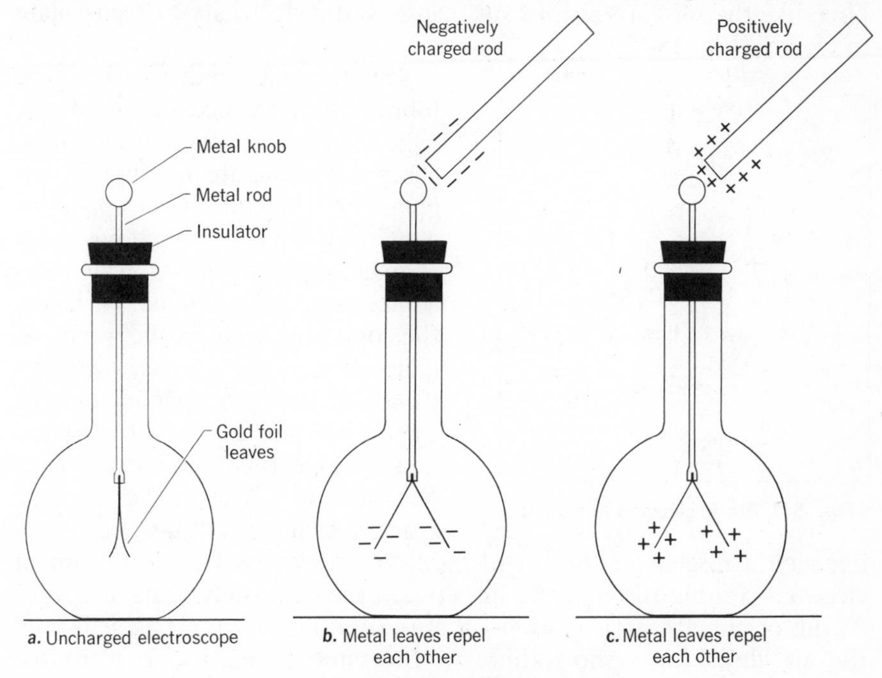

Fig. 15–6. Charging an electroscope.

highly charged object is brought near the electroscope, the leaves move even farther apart.

The leaves always draw apart, regardless of whether the charged object brought near the electroscope is negative or positive, because the two leaves always carry the same charge. Thus, when a negatively charged rod (Fig. 15–6*b*, page 267) is brought near the knob of an electroscope, electrons from the rod repel the electrons in the knob. These electrons move down the rod to the leaves, causing both of the leaves to become negatively charged. Accordingly, the leaves repel each other. On the other hand, when a positively charged rod is near the knob, electrons from the leaves are attracted to the knob. Since the leaves have lost electrons, they become positively charged. Both leaves are now similarly charged, and again they repel each other (Fig. 15–6*c*, page 267).

Static Electric Charges in the Atmosphere

Clouds are composed of water droplets so tiny that they are suspended in the air. Some of the droplets are larger than others, and this tends to make them move downward. Smaller droplets, on the other hand, tend to move upward with rising air currents. The water droplets rub against one another and against air molecules. This rubbing, like that of glass against silk, causes static electricity to accumulate in clouds (Fig. 15–7).

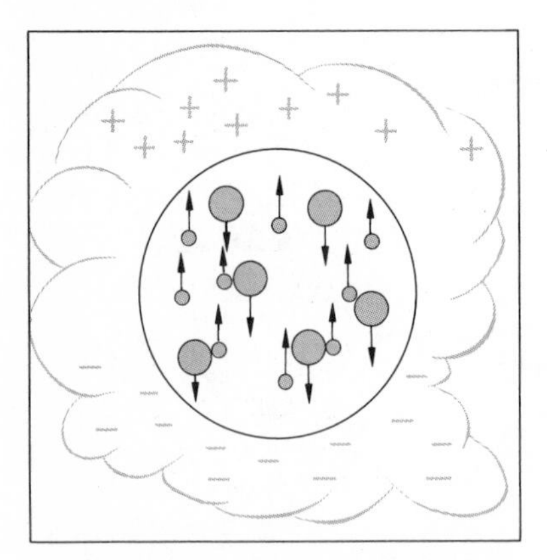

Fig. 15–7. Static charges in a cloud.

Scientists who study weather have found, as we learned in Chapter 6, page 110, that opposite electric charges accumulate in opposite regions of a cloud. The upper region of a cloud becomes positively charged, and the lower region becomes negatively charged. At times, the opposite charges between regions of a cloud (or between two clouds or between a cloud and the earth) become so great that a tremendous electrical discharge occurs. We see this discharge as a large spark, which we call lightning. During such a discharge, the bright light we see results from a stream of electrons rushing through the air between the oppositely charged points. As this occurs, the air is *ionized*—that is, its atoms become charged—and the air glows for a short time. At the same time, the air is heated to such a degree that it expands suddenly. Then, as cooler air rapidly moves into the space left by the sudden expansion of the heated air, a loud noise, which we call thunder, is produced.

ELECTRONS CAN FLOW

Electrons, moving steadily in a definite direction, constitute an electric current. This flow of electrons is also called *current electricity* to distinguish it from static electricity. In an electric current, electrons flow from a point where there is an excess of electrons to a point where there is a deficiency of electrons. In static electricity, there is an excess or a deficiency of electrons on the *surface* of a material; in current electricity, however, electrons flow continuously *through* a material.

Electrical Conductors

Materials through which electrons flow freely are known as *conductors*. Most metals are good conductors of electricity. Of all the metals, silver and copper are the best conductors. Copper is the more widely used conductor of electricity because it is cheaper than silver.

Electrical Insulators

Materials that greatly resist the passage of electrons through them are not good conductors of electricity. Such materials are known as *insulators*. Examples of insulators are rubber, glass, air, wool, and silk.

Although insulators do not conduct current electricity, they may store static electricity on their surfaces. Some insulators readily accept and hold electrons; other insulators readily give up electrons. As a result, some insulators can become negatively charged, and some insulators can become positively charged. These properties of insulators help us to understand why rubbing a rubber rod with fur charges the rod negatively and the fur positively. Similarly, rubbing a glass rod with silk charges the rod positively and the silk negatively. Although insulators do not conduct electrons well, insulators generally hold a charge of static electricity that has accumulated on them.

ELECTRONS FLOW IN CLOSED CIRCUITS

As we know, electrons flow from a point where they are in excess to a point where there is a deficiency of electrons. This condition, referred to as a *difference of potential*, produces a force called *electromotive force*. This force can push electrons through any conductor that provides a path for the electrons. Such a complete path is known as an *electrical circuit.*

A complete electrical circuit, shown in Fig. 15–8, consists of (1) a source of electrons (e^-), (2) a force that pushes the electrons through an appliance, or *load* (such as an electric light bulb), (3) a conducting path through which the electrons can flow to the appliance and then back to the source, and (4) a switch for closing or opening the circuit. How does this compare with the first part of your laboratory experience?

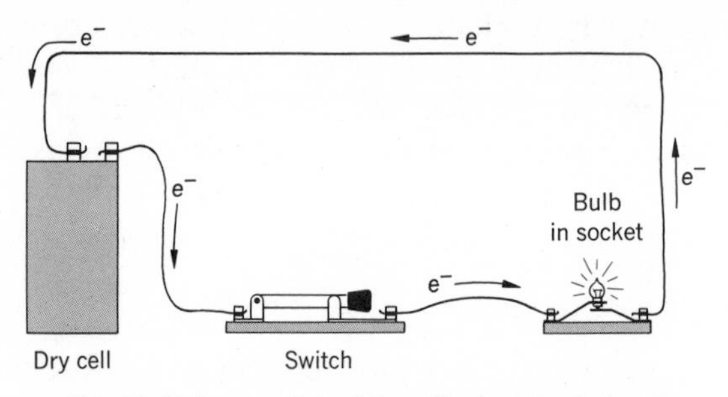

Fig. 15–8. A complete (closed) electrical circuit.

SOURCES OF ELECTRONS IN CIRCUITS

The most common sources of electrons are *electrochemical cells* (commonly called batteries) and electric *generators.* Electrochemical cells, such as dry cells, are generally placed near the appliance or machine requiring electrical energy. Generators, on the other hand, are much larger than cells and require extensive installations. Thus, they are usually set up some distance from homes, offices, or factories. Electric current supplied by generators reaches the appliance by means of connecting wires. Both electrochemical cells and generators require a conducting path to complete the electrical circuit.

Electrochemical Cells

Some chemical reactions release chemical energy stored within the substances that react. We already know that all forms of energy can be transformed to other forms. Early in the nineteenth century, *Alessandro Volta,* an Italian physicist, produced the first steady flow of electricity by chemical means. Volta transformed chemical energy into electrical energy in a device called an electrochemical cell. Today Volta's experiments can be repeated by using a device known as a *voltaic cell.* One type of voltaic cell is the *wet cell* with which you worked in your laboratory experience.

A wet voltaic cell is composed of strips of two different metals in an *electrolyte,* a liquid that conducts electricity. One such cell is shown in Fig. 15–9. In this cell, a strip of zinc and a strip of copper are placed in dilute sulfuric acid. As a result of the chemical reaction of the zinc with the acid, an excess of electrons accumulates on the zinc. This causes the strip of zinc to become negatively charged. The hydrogen atoms of the acid, on the other hand, are positively charged. These

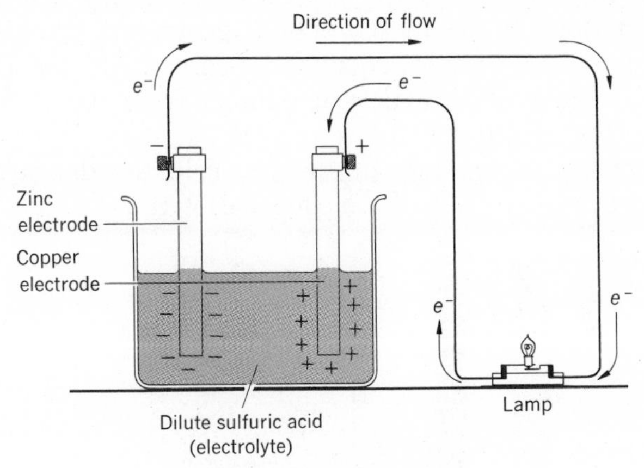

Fig. 15–9. A wet cell.

charged atoms, or *ions,* accept electrons from the copper strip. As a result, the charged hydrogen atoms become neutral, forming molecules of hydrogen gas, which escape from the solution in the form of bubbles. In giving away electrons to the hydrogen ions, the copper strip becomes positively charged.

The oppositely charged metals that are immersed in a conducting solution (such as zinc and copper in a voltaic cell) are called *electrodes.* The electrode that has an excess of electrons is the negative electrode, or *cathode.* The other electrode, which has a deficiency of electrons, is the positive electrode, or *anode.* When a conductor, such as copper wire, is connected to the electrodes of a voltaic cell, the excess electrons on the zinc electrode flow through the wire to the copper electrode, which has a deficiency of electrons. The flow of the electrons through the wire constitutes an electric current. In this type of cell, the accumulation of electrons usually continues until any one of the chemicals (acid, zinc, or copper) is used up.

Since a wet cell contains liquid, it is difficult to use a wet cell as a portable source of electric current. For example, consider the problem of using such a cell in a portable radio. A much more convenient type of electrochemical cell is known as a *dry cell.*

The dry cell is not really dry; it operates much like the wet cell you worked with in your laboratory experience. The inside of a dry cell is composed of a chemical paste made of manganese dioxide, water, and ammonium chloride (Fig. 15–10). The outer casing of the container is made of zinc, which serves as the negative electrode of the dry cell. The graphite (carbon) rod in the center of the dry cell serves as the positive electrode. The ammonium chloride paste serves as the electrolyte. The manganese dioxide acts as a depolarizer; that is, it aids in removing the hydrogen bubbles. These bubbles, if allowed to collect, would stop the chemical reactions generating the flow of electricity. (In your laboratory experience, the carbon rod was depolarized with nitric acid to remove hydrogen bubbles from the surface of the rod.) When the electrodes are connected, an electric current flows between them. As in the case of the wet cell, the dry cell produces electric current until any one of the chemicals within the cell is used up.

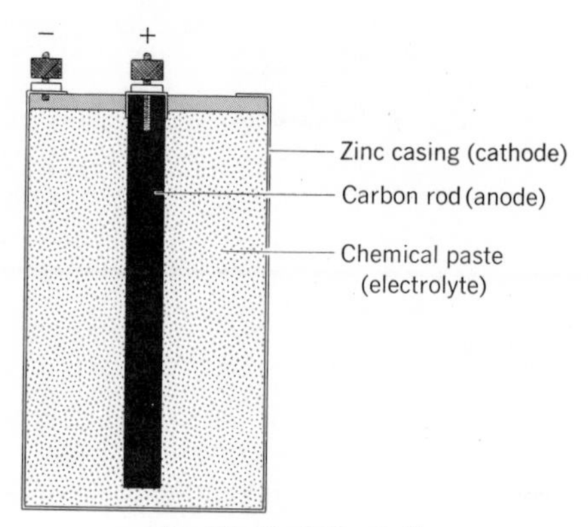

Fig. 15–10. A dry cell.

A more recent type of electrochemical cell is the *fuel cell.* One type of fuel cell, used in the Apollo space missions, has nickel and nickel oxide electrodes and a potassium hydroxide electrolyte. Such fuel cells may someday be used as energy sources in automobiles in place of gasoline. In this way, atmospheric pollution from gasoline engines may be reduced.

Generators

In the home, electrical appliances are usually plugged into a wall outlet. The plug then makes contact with wires connected to a generator. The generator may be many miles away from the outlet. Most generators of electricity are driven mechanically. They produce a continuous source of flowing electrons ready to operate an appliance as soon as a closed circuit is provided. (We will discuss how a generator supplies electrons in Chapter 17.)

COMPONENTS OF A CLOSED ELECTRICAL CIRCUIT

When a generator or electrochemical cell is used as a source of electrons, electricity will flow as soon as a complete circuit is available. When a switch in a circuit is in the "on" position, electricity flows as follows (Fig. 15–11): Electrons (e^-) from the negative electrode, or terminal of the *current source*, flow through one prong of the plug (1),

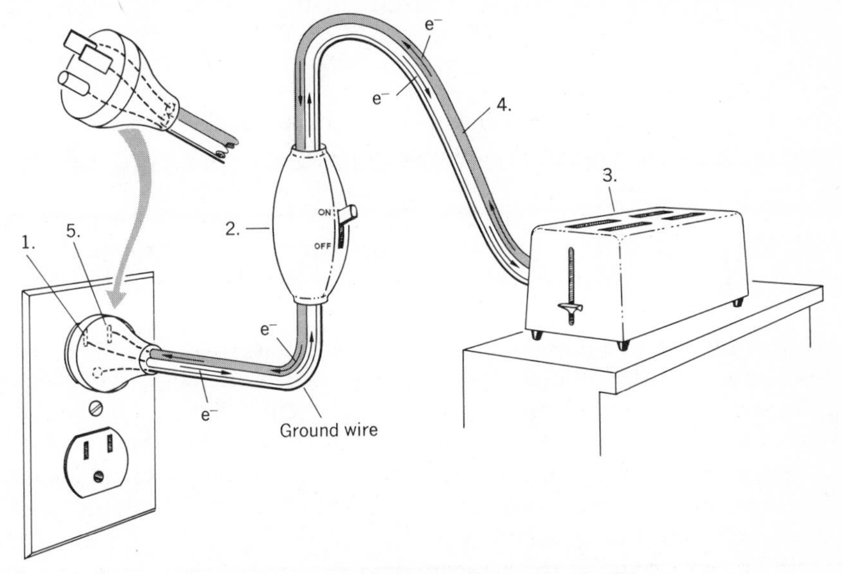

Fig. 15–11. A closed electrical circuit in the home.

along a wire through the switch (2), and into the load (3). Then, the electrons flow back from the load, through another wire (4), through the other prong of the plug (5), and back to the positive terminal of the current source.

Plugs

Many modern appliances have plugs with three prongs. Only two of these prongs are part of the circuit. The third prong is not. It is a safety device connected to the outer case of the appliance by means of a third wire. The third prong makes contact with a matching conductor that leads from the socket to the ground. Current that leaks from an appliance can give an electric shock to anyone who touches the appliance. Should current leak from the appliance, the leaking current is conducted into the ground where it can do no harm. Thus, the third wire is called a *ground wire.*

Loads

A load is the electrical appliance, properly connected in the circuit, that is powered by moving electrons (electrical energy). Since a load generally opposes the flow of electrons, a load is often referred to as a *resistance*. Examples of loads in a circuit include lamps, radios, buzzers, television sets, and motors. Electrons from the source must move through the load before they can return to the source.

Switches

In a complete circuit, electrons flow continuously. A switch is a convenient way of closing or opening the circuit. By closing a switch, we close, or complete, an electrical circuit and provide a complete path through which electrons flow. By opening a switch, we open, or break, the circuit, and the flow of electrons stops. The control of circuits by this means is often provided by a knife switch, a push button, a snap switch, a fuse, or a circuit breaker.

Fuses and circuit breakers are placed in the electrical circuits of our homes and in other places as automatic safety switches. Too many appliances used at one time may overload a circuit; that is, the excessive number of appliances may require too large a current to flow through the wires. When this happens, the wires may become hot and cause a fire. The fuse or circuit breaker is designed to break the circuit under these conditions and therefore stop the current. The use of fuses and circuit breakers reduces the danger of fire.

Looking Back

There are two kinds of electricity, or electrical energy: static electricity and current electricity. Static electricity is the result of an accumulation or a deficiency of electrons on the surface of an object. Such accumulations and deficiencies can result from rubbing together certain materials. Current electricity is the flow of electrons from a source that pushes them through a closed circuit. Such a circuit consists of a conducting path, an appliance, and another conducting path leading back to the source. Sources of electrons are wet cells, dry cells, and generators.

Looking Ahead

When electrical energy flows through an appliance, the electrical energy does work for us. The factors that affect the flow of electricity are explained in the next chapter.

Multiple-Choice Questions

1. When the numbers of electrons and protons in a sample of matter are equal, the matter is
   a. neutral
   b. positively charged
   c. negatively charged
   d. insulated
2. Rubbing one substance against another causes
   a. nothing to happen
   b. a loss of protons
   c. a transfer of electrons
   d. a gain of protons
3. Two positively charged pith balls, brought close together,
   a. have no effect on each other
   b. repel each other
   c. attract each other
   d. first repel and then attract each other
4. An electroscope contains two thin pieces of metal foil called
   a. sheets b. electrodes c. branches d. leaves
5. In a cloud, the rubbing of water droplets against air molecules produces
   a. current electricity
   b. magnetism
   c. static electricity
   d. thunder
6. A bolt of lightning is seen because
   a. the electrons ionize the air
   b. the air expands suddenly
   c. protons are released
   d. the heat produced ignites the air
7. In an electric current, electrons generally flow
   a. from a point of deficiency to a point of excess
   b. from a point of excess to a point of deficiency
   c. from the anode to the cathode
   d. from a large electrode to a small electrode
8. Of the following, an example of an insulator is
   a. copper b. iron c. silver d. rubber
9. Insulators
   a. conduct electrons
   b. cannot hold a static charge
   c. can hold a static charge
   d. conduct protons
10. The first steady flow of electric current by chemical means was produced by
    a. Volta b. Ohm c. Ampère d. Galvani
11. Two strips of different metals, placed in a liquid electrolyte, constitute a
    a. dry cell b. voltaic cell c. generator d. none of these
12. An electrode that has a deficiency of electrons is called the
    a. cathode b. electrolyte c. conductor d. anode
13. A convenient, portable source of electric current is a
    a. dry cell b. wet cell c. small generator d. charged rubber rod
14. The outer casing of a dry cell is generally made of
    a. lead b. carbon c. zinc d. manganese
15. A source of household electric current is a
    a. lamp b. motor c. transformer d. generator

16. Control of an electric circuit is provided by a
    a. load   b. switch   c. source   d. resistance
17. An example of a protective device used in an electric circuit is a
    a. fuse   b. resistance   c. load   d. switch
18. A recently devised electrochemical cell is a
    a. dry cell   b. fuel cell   c. wet cell   d. battery

Modified True-False Questions

1. When an object loses electrons, it takes on *a positive charge.*
2. Electric charges that accumulate on the surface of objects and remain there are called *current electricity.*
3. A device used to detect the presence of a static electric charge is *a dry cell.*
4. A large discharge of static electricity in the atmosphere is called *lightning.*
5. A flow of electrons in a definite direction is called an electric *charge.*
6. Materials through which electrons can flow freely are called *cathodes.*
7. A sudden expansion of heated air, followed by cooler air rushing in to take the place of this air produces a sound called *thunder.*
8. Materials that resist the passage of electrons are called *insulators.*
9. Volta transformed chemical energy to electrical energy in *a generator.*
10. Strips of metal placed into a wet cell are called *anodes.*
11. The electrolyte of a dry cell consists of a paste of *manganese dioxide.*
12. A complete path for electrons through a conductor is called *an electrical circuit.*
13. In an electric circuit, a load is sometimes referred to as *a source.*

Thought Questions

1. Explain the differences between each of the following pairs of terms:
    a. static and current electricity
    b. anode and cathode
    c. conductor and insulator
2. Explain the cause of a lightning discharge.
3. Explain how the use of fuel cells can eliminate an important source of atmospheric pollution.

CHAPTER 16
WHAT FACTORS AFFECT THE FLOW OF ELECTRICITY?

When you have completed this chapter, you should be able to:

1. *List* the factors and units used in measuring the flow of electricity.
2. *State* Ohm's law.
3. *Describe* the characteristics of series circuits and of parallel circuits.
4. *Distinguish* between an ammeter, a voltmeter, and an ohmmeter.

In the laboratory experience that follows, you will set up a series circuit and a parallel circuit. Then, you will study the characteristics of these circuits.

Laboratory Experience

HOW DOES A SERIES CIRCUIT DIFFER FROM A PARALLEL CIRCUIT?

A. Connect two dry cells, two lamp sockets, two lamps, and a knife switch, as shown in Fig. 16–1. In this type of electrical circuit, called a series circuit, electricity flows in a single path from the dry cells, through the switch when closed, through the lamps, and back to the dry cells again. The symbol e^- represents electrons, and the arrows indicate direction of flow.
Close the switch, and observe how brightly the lamps light. Open the switch again.

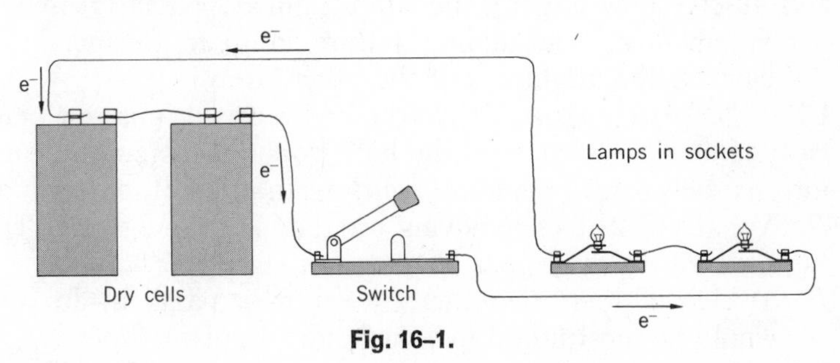

Fig. 16–1.

B. Disconnect the wire between the knife switch and the lamp socket. Add a third lamp in series to your circuit.

Close the switch again, and observe how brightly the three lamps light. Open the switch again to conserve the dry cells.

1. What effect does adding a third lamp have on the brightness of all three lamps?
2. How does the brightness of each lamp compare with that of the others?

C. Close the switch again. While the lamps are lit, unscrew one of the lamps from its socket until the light goes out. Screw the lamp back into its socket until the lamp lights again. Open the switch.

3. What effect does removing one lamp from the series circuit have on the brightness of the other lamps?

D. Disassemble the series circuit. Reassemble the parts as shown in Fig. 16–2. This type of electrical circuit is called a parallel circuit. In a parallel circuit, electricity flows through two or more paths at the same time. Electricity flows from the dry cells, through the closed switch, through each lamp separately, and back to the dry cells again.

Close the switch, and observe how brightly the lamps light. Open the switch again.

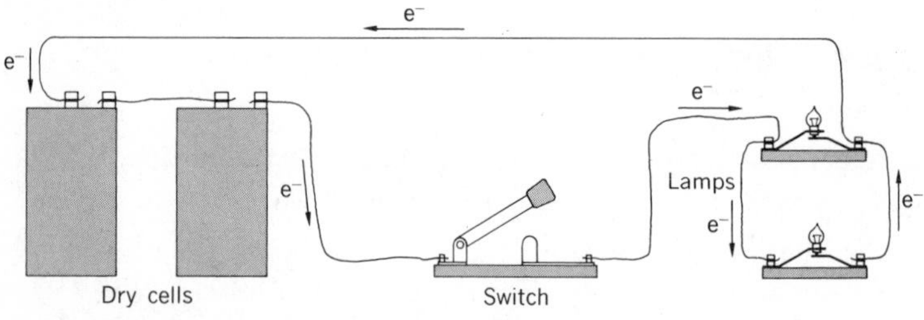

Fig. 16–2.

E. Add a third lamp in parallel to the circuit. Close the switch again, and observe how brightly the lamps light. Open the switch.

4. What effect does adding a third lamp to the parallel circuit have on the brightness of the other lamps?

F. Close the switch again. While the lamps are lit, unscrew one of the lamps from its socket until the light goes out. Screw the lamp back into its socket until the lamp lights again. Open the switch again.

5. What effect does removing one lamp from the parallel circuit have on the brightness of the other lamps?
6. Which of these two circuits—series or parallel—do you think would be most useful in your home? Explain.

Introduction

A flow of electrons exhibits many characteristics. When you understand these characteristics, you will be able to use electrical circuits safely and efficiently.

FACTORS AFFECTING THE FLOW OF ELECTRONS

We can understand the characteristics of a flow of electrons through the wires of an electrical circuit by using a model in which water flows through a hose. Like all models, the water model is limited in its application. However, a number of similar factors can be observed and measured in the flow of water and the flow of electrons.

Rate of Flow

When a hose is attached to a faucet and the valve is opened, water flows from the faucet and through the hose. By using a stopwatch and a container marked to measure liters, we can study the rate of flow of the water. We can observe the number of liters that leave the hose and enter the measuring container each second. The quantity of water flowing into the container in some unit of time is the rate of flow of the water. We can express the rate of flow of water as the number of liters of water per second.

Similarly, we can determine the rate of flow of electrons, or current, by measuring the number of electrons flowing past a given point in a unit of time. This flow is expressed in terms of a unit called a *coulomb*, which is equal to a flow of 6,300,000,000,000,000,000 electrons. A rate of flow of one coulomb per second is called an *ampere*, after the French physicist André Ampère. More generally, the rate of flow of electrons is known as *amperage*. The amperage of an electric current can be measured with an instrument called an *ammeter*.

Driving Force

Water flows through a hose because there is a driving force behind the water. We can increase the rate of flow of the water by increasing the driving force. To do this, we might add one or more water pumps to the line.

In an electrical circuit, the electromotive force (difference of potential) that causes electrons to move is produced in the source of the current. The electrochemical cell and the generator are common examples of sources of current. As the electromotive force is increased, the number of electrons flowing in the circuit increases. This electromotive force, abbreviated *emf*, is also known as *voltage*. It is measured in a unit called the *volt*, named after Volta, the Italian physicist. To measure voltage, an instrument known as a *voltmeter* is used.

Resistance to Flow

Water molecules, moving through a pipe, rub against the walls of the pipe and slow down. The walls of the pipe oppose or offer resistance to the flow of water. Longer and narrower pipes offer more resistance to the flow of water than do shorter and wider pipes.

In a somewhat similar fashion, electrons flowing through a wire encounter resistance to flow. Longer and thinner wires offer more resistance to electron flow than do shorter and thicker wires of the same material. In addition, the nature of the conducting material influences the flow of electrons. For example, nichrome wire offers greater resistance than the same length and thickness of copper wire. When the resistance of a material to the flow of electrons is great enough, electrons do not flow. Such a material makes a good insulator. Electrical resistance is measured in a unit called the *ohm*, after *Georg Ohm*, a German physicist. An instrument called an *ohmmeter* is used to measure resistance.

Table 16–1 summarizes the major factors that influence the flow of electrons in a circuit.

Table 16–1. Factors Affecting Electron Flow

Name	*Symbol*	*Meaning*	*Unit of Measurement*	*Measuring Instrument*
Current	*I*	Rate of flow of electrons	Ampere	Ammeter
Voltage	V	Driving or electromotive force behind electrons	Volt	Voltmeter
Resistance	*R*	Opposition to the flow of electrons	Ohm	Ohmmeter

OHM'S LAW

In 1827, Ohm studied the voltage, current, and resistance relationships in an electrical circuit. He summarized his findings in a statement known as *Ohm's law:* In a complete or closed electrical circuit, current and voltage are directly proportional, whereas current and resistance are inversely proportional. Thus, an increase in voltage causes an increase in current, and a decrease in voltage causes a decrease in current. However, an increase in resistance causes a decrease in current, and a decrease in resistance causes an increase in current. Mathematically, Ohm's law states:

$$\text{current} = \frac{\text{voltage}}{\text{resistance}} \tag{1}$$

Since current is measured in amperes, voltage is measured in volts, and resistance is measured in ohms,

$$\text{amperes} = \frac{\text{volts}}{\text{ohms}} \tag{2}$$

Using symbols (see Table 16–1), Ohm's law may be written as

$$I = \frac{V}{R} \tag{3A}$$

The formula for Ohm's law can also be expressed in equivalent ways:

$$\text{volts} = \text{amperes} \times \text{ohms} \quad \text{or} \quad V = IR \tag{3B}$$

$$\text{ohms} = \frac{\text{volts}}{\text{amperes}} \quad \text{or} \quad R = \frac{V}{I} \tag{3C}$$

You can use Ohm's law to calculate either amperage, or voltage, or resistance of a circuit providing that you know any two of these factors.

1. Find the amperage in a circuit that has a voltage of 120 volts and a resistance of 60 ohms.

Write Ohm's law: $I = \frac{V}{R}$

From the problem, $V = 120$ volts and $R = 60$ ohms.

Substitute: $I = \frac{120 \text{ volts}}{60 \text{ ohms}}$

Solve the equation: $I = 2 \frac{\text{volts}}{\text{ohms}}$

$I = 2$ amperes

Notice that each factor affecting electric current has a numerical value as well as a unit. We must always divide (or multiply) the units as well as the numbers. Thus, 120 divided by 60 is 2; similarly, volts divided by ohms is amperes (Equation 2). Be sure always to include units in the answer.

The units we obtain as part of our answer act as a check on our work. In the preceding problem, suppose we accidentally wrote Ohm's law as $I = \frac{R}{V}$. We would get a numerical value of $\frac{1}{2}$ by dividing 120 into 60. But when we tried to divide volts into ohms, we would realize that something was wrong. None of our equations for Ohm's law gives $\frac{\text{ohms}}{\text{volts}}$. Therefore, we would have to start over, and we would realize that our equation $I = \frac{R}{V}$ was incorrect.

2. Determine the voltage in a circuit that has a current of 3 amperes and a resistance of 20 ohms.

Write the formula for Ohm's law that has voltage (V) on the left:

$$V = I \times R$$

From the problem, $I = 3$ amperes and $R = 20$ ohms.

Substitute: $V = 3 \text{ amperes} \times 20 \text{ ohms}$

Solve the equation: $V = 60 \text{ (amperes} \times \text{ohms)}$

$$V = 60 \text{ volts}$$

3. Find the resistance of a circuit that has a voltage of 120 volts and a current of 4 amperes.

Write the formula for Ohm's law that has resistance (R) on the left:

$$R = \frac{V}{I}$$

From the problem, $V = 120$ volts and $I = 4$ amperes.

Substitute: $R = \frac{120 \text{ volts}}{4 \text{ amperes}}$

Solve the equation: $R = 30 \frac{\text{volts}}{\text{amperes}}$

$$R = 30 \text{ ohms}$$

HOW ELECTRICITY FLOWS IN A SERIES CIRCUIT

Fig. 16–1 (page 277) illustrates a circuit in which the electrons flow along a single path through two loads. This type of arrangement is known as a *series circuit.* The distinguishing feature of such a circuit is that the electrons flow along a *single path* only, and pass through two or more loads before returning to the source. Measurements and tests reveal that a series circuit has several important characteristics.

1. *Any break in a series circuit stops the entire electron flow.* In a series circuit, electrons must flow from the source through each load or section of the circuit and back to the source again. Any gap in this single pathway or line interrupts the flow of electrons. Thus, if one of the lamps in Fig. 16–1, page 277, is removed from the circuit, as you did in your laboratory experience, the circuit will be open, and the other lamp will go out. Similarly, a break in a wire or a loose connection can prevent the electrons from flowing.

This situation can be compared to the model of water flowing through a small hose to a point 20 meters from the faucet. Any break in the hose prevents the water from reaching its destination, since the single path that the water follows has been broken. (The water model does not quite fit the electrical situation. A break in a wire permits *no* flow of electrons, whereas water still flows from a break in a hose, although not to its destination.)

2. *When there are two or more loads in a series circuit, the voltage across each load is a fraction of the total voltage supplied by the source.* Every time an additional load is wired into a series circuit, the voltage across each load already in the circuit decreases. Fig. 16–3 shows a lamp with a resistance of 1 ohm connected to a 3-volt source. When a volt-

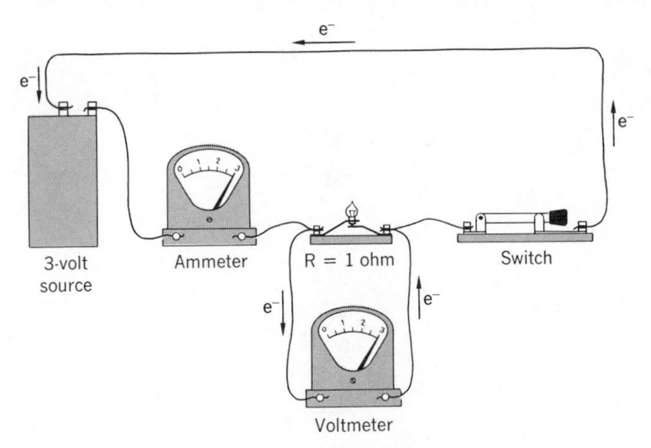

Fig. 16–3. Series circuit: single resistance.

meter is connected across the lamp, the voltage reading is 3 volts. An ammeter in the circuit reads 3 amperes.

Fig. 16–4 shows the same series circuit, but with a second lamp of 1-ohm resistance added. When a voltmeter is connected across each of the lamps, the voltage reading is 1.5 volts. Since the voltage source is still 3 volts, the voltage across each lamp has decreased. An ammeter in the circuit reads 1.5 amperes.

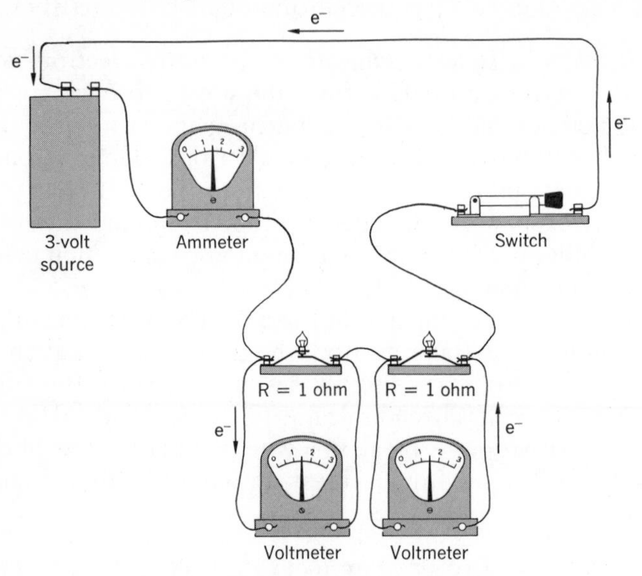

Fig. 16–4. Series circuit: two resistances.

Fig. 16–5 shows the same series circuit, but with a third lamp of 1-ohm resistance added. The voltage reading across each of the lamps is now 1 volt, a further decrease in voltage. An ammeter in the circuit reads 1 ampere.

Notice that, in each series circuit, the *sum* of the voltages across each lamp is equal to the voltage source. In Fig. 16–4, 1.5 volts + 1.5 volts = 3 volts; in Fig. 16–5, 1 volt + 1 volt + 1 volt = 3 volts.

Ohm's law applies to all parts of an electrical circuit as well as to the entire circuit. According to Ohm's law, the current in the circuit in Fig. 16–3, page 283, is 3 amperes:

$$I = \frac{V}{R}$$

$$I = \frac{3 \text{ volts}}{1 \text{ ohm}}$$

$$I = 3 \text{ amperes}$$

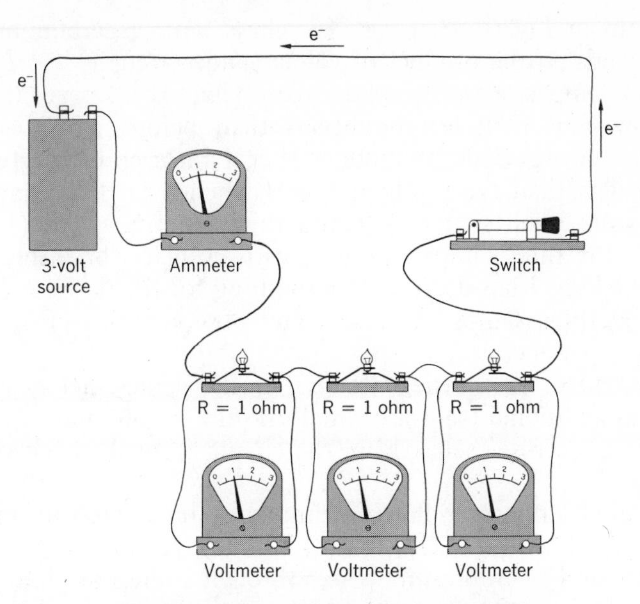

Fig. 16–5. Series circuit: three resistances.

This agrees with the ammeter reading. In Fig. 16–4, the current through either lamp is

$$I = \frac{V}{R}$$

$$I = \frac{1.5 \text{ volts}}{1 \text{ ohm}}$$

$$I = 1.5 \text{ amperes}$$

This also agrees with the ammeter reading. (Note that we use a voltage of 1.5 volts—the voltmeter reading—for this calculation since we are concerned with only *part* of the circuit.) In Fig. 16–5, the current through any of the lamps is

$$I = \frac{V}{R}$$

$$I = \frac{1 \text{ volt}}{1 \text{ ohm}}$$

$$I = 1 \text{ ampere}$$

Once again, Ohm's law and the ammeter reading are in agreement.

The lamp in Fig. 16–3, page 283, glows with a certain brightness, which depends on the product of voltage and current ($V \times I$). When the second lamp is added to the circuit (Fig. 16–4, page 284), both lamps glow—but with less brightness than before. This decrease in brightness indicates that the product $V \times I$ for each of the two lamps in series is less than the product $V \times I$ when a single lamp was used with the same 3-volt source. When a third lamp is added (Fig. 16–5, page 285), the three lamps will glow with even less brightness. Again, the product $V \times I$ has decreased, accounting for the decrease in brightness of the three lamps in series. You observed this effect in your laboratory experience.

To summarize: In a series circuit, (1) the voltage across each load decreases as additional loads are wired into the circuit, and (2) the sum of the voltages across each load in the circuit is equal to the voltage of the source.

In the model of water flowing through a hose, pressure or driving force is similar to voltage (electromotive force). Assume that water from some source at a given pressure passes through a series of pipes of different lengths and diameters and then returns to the source. If the driving force behind the water in each of the pipes is measured, we find that the sum of the driving forces in each of the pipes equals the driving force of the water at the source.

3. *The current is the same in all parts of a series circuit.* In the circuit shown in Fig. 16–3, page 283, for example, the ammeter will read 3 amperes when it is properly wired to *any point* in the series circuit. In any electrical circuit, all the electrons flowing from the source eventually return to the source. Since, in a series circuit, only one path is provided for the flow of electrons, all the electrons must pass through each of the loads in the circuit in order to reach the source again. This means that the current is the same in all parts of a series circuit.

4. *The resistance increases in a series circuit as the number of loads increases.* In a series circuit, where only one path is provided for the electrons, the wires and loads in the circuit offer resistance to the flow of electrons. Since the electrons travel along each wire and through each load in returning to the source, the total resistance of the circuit is equal to the sum of the resistances of each wire and load. In the series circuit shown in Fig. 16–4, page 284, for example, the total resistance offered by the two 1-ohm lamps is 2 ohms. Knowing the total resistance in the circuit, we may calculate the current by using Ohm's law:

$$I = \frac{V}{R}$$

$$I = \frac{3 \text{ volts}}{2 \text{ ohms}}$$

$$I = 1.5 \text{ amperes}$$

(Note that, since we use the total resistance, we must use the total voltage, that is, the voltage of the source.) With three 1-ohm lamps (Fig. 16–5), the total resistance is 3 ohms, and the current in this circuit is

$$I = \frac{V}{R} = \frac{3 \text{ volts}}{3 \text{ ohms}} = 1 \text{ ampere}$$

HOW ELECTRICITY FLOWS IN A PARALLEL CIRCUIT

Fig. 16–2, page 278, illustrates a circuit in which electrons flow through more than one path or branch. This type of arrangement is known as a *parallel circuit,* also called a *branching circuit.* The distinguishing feature of such a circuit is that the electrons can flow through *any one of the branches* of the circuit before returning to the source. Several important characteristics of parallel circuits follow:

1. *A break in one branch of a parallel circuit does not stop the flow of current in the other branches.* In Fig. 16–2, page 278, each of the lamps can be considered to be connected to the same source independently. The removal of one of the lamps from the circuit, as you did in the laboratory experience, eliminates only one branch of the circuit (Fig. 16–6). The electrons continue flowing in the other branch. This situation can be compared to the model of water flowing out of a can that has three spouts in its bottom, as shown in Fig. 16–7, page 288. When all three spouts are open, water flows from all three. When a cork is placed in one of the spouts, the water stops flowing from this spout, but it continues to flow from the other two.

2. *The total resistance in a parallel circuit decreases as the number of loads or individual resistances increases.* In a series circuit, all the

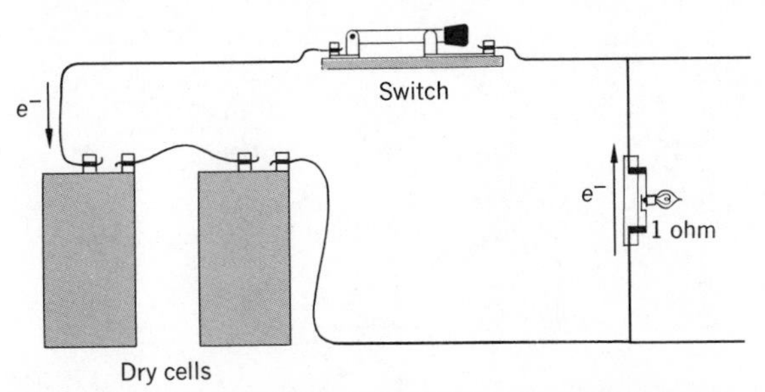

Fig. 16–6. Removing a resistance from a parallel circuit.

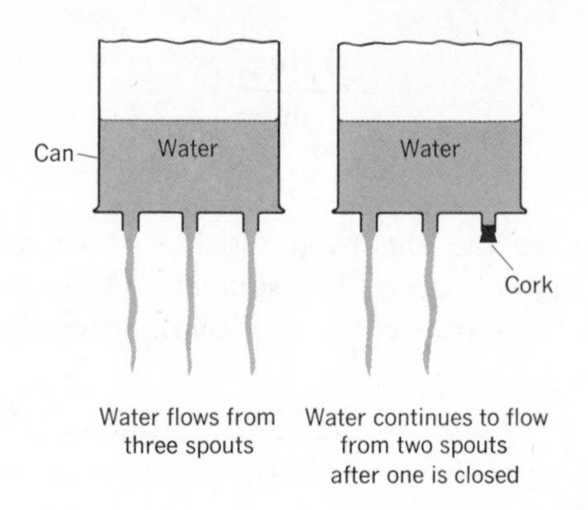

Fig. 16–7. Breaking a parallel circuit: water analogy.

electrons flow through each load by way of a single path and therefore meet more and more resistance along the way. On the other hand, in a parallel circuit, electrons flow into several branches containing loads or resistances. All the branches together act as one broad pathway which offers less resistance to the flow of electrons than does a narrow pathway. In fact, the total resistance in a parallel circuit is *less* than the smallest single resistance in the circuit.

If, for example, each lamp in Fig. 16–2, page 278, has a resistance of 1 ohm, the total resistance of the circuit is $\frac{1}{2}$ ohm. (In a series circuit, such as that shown in Fig. 16–4, page 284, two 1-ohm lamps would have a total resistance of 2 ohms.) When a third 1-ohm lamp is wired into a parallel circuit (Fig. 16–8), the total resistance of the three 1-ohm lamps is $\frac{1}{3}$ ohm. (In a series circuit, such as that shown in Fig. 16–5, three 1-ohm lamps would have a total resistance of 3 ohms.)

This situation can be compared to a pipe of given diameter that branches into three pipes of smaller diameter. The three pipes offer less resistance to the flow of water than does the single pipe.

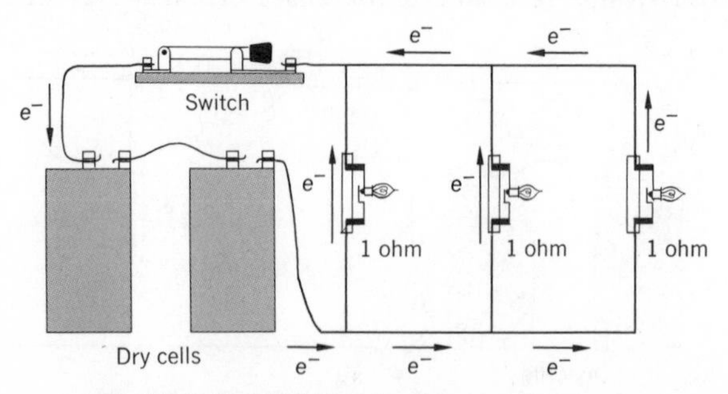

Fig. 16–8. Parallel circuit: three resistances.

3. *The voltage is the same in all branches of a parallel circuit.* Recall that Ohm's law applies to portions of an electrical circuit. Given a 3-volt source and a lamp with a resistance of 1 ohm, the current is 3 amperes. The lamp glows with a certain brightness, which depends on the product of voltage and current ($V \times I$). When two such lamps are connected in parallel to the same source, as in Fig. 16–2, the brightness of each lamp remains unchanged. This means that the product $V \times I$ through each lamp is also unchanged. Why?

We know that the total resistance of a parallel circuit is less than the smallest single resistance. In fact, two 1-ohm resistances connected in parallel have a total resistance of $\frac{1}{2}$ ohm. Substituting into Ohm's law:

$$I = \frac{V}{R}$$

$$I = \frac{3 \text{ volts}}{\frac{1}{2} \text{ ohm}} \quad [3 \div \frac{1}{2} = 3 \times 2 = 6]$$

$$I = 6 \text{ amperes}$$

Thus, 6 amperes flow through the entire circuit. However, the circuit has two branches of equal resistance, and each branch must carry half the current, or 3 amperes. This was the current in the 1-lamp circuit previously used. The voltage across each lamp equals $I \times R = 6$ amperes $\times \frac{1}{2}$ ohm $= 3$ volts, which is the same as the voltage of the source. Thus, the product $V \times I$ remains unchanged, as does the brightness of each lamp.

We can use the same reasoning to show that the addition of another lamp (or any number of lamps) does not diminish the brightness of each lamp in the parallel circuit. The current in each lamp must remain 3 amperes. The total resistance using three lamps in parallel is $\frac{1}{3}$ ohm (Fig. 16–8). The total current $I = \frac{V}{R} = \frac{3 \text{ volts}}{\frac{1}{3} \text{ ohm}} = 9$ amperes. The current divides into three branches, each carrying $\frac{1}{3}$ of the total, or 3 amperes. The voltage is still $I \times R = 9$ amperes $\times \frac{1}{3}$ ohm $= 3$ volts. Thus the product $V \times I$ remains unchanged.

4. *The amperage (current) is not necessarily the same in all branches of a parallel circuit.* In a parallel circuit, as in a series circuit, all the electrons flowing from the source eventually return to the same source. In a parallel circuit, however, electrons flow through separate branches of the circuit before reaching the source again. Since each branch may offer different resistance, the flow of electrons in one branch may differ from the flow in another. The sum of all the currents in the branches of the circuit must equal the total amount of electricity flowing in the circuit. We have illustrated this idea in the previous paragraph. The total current in the 2-lamp parallel circuit is 6 amperes, and the current in each lamp is 3 amperes.

Fig. 16–9. Current in a parallel circuit: water analogy.

This is similar to the situation shown in Fig. 16–9. If the can holds 3 liters of water, about 1 liter will flow from each large spout, and about $\frac{1}{2}$ liter will flow from each half-size spout. The two half-liters equal one single liter.

SYMBOLS USED TO REPRESENT PARTS OF A CIRCUIT

In chemistry, chemical symbols make it much easier to represent chemical elements and compounds. For example, H is the symbol for hydrogen; O, for oxygen; and H_2O represents water. Representing electrical circuits through actual drawings, as we have done, is time consuming and difficult. Fig. 16–10 uses common electrical symbols to illustrate a series circuit containing two dry cells, two lamps, an ammeter, and a single-pole switch. Fig. 16–11 shows the same items connected in a parallel circuit. See Fig. 16–12 for other common electrical symbols that are used to represent parts of electric circuits.

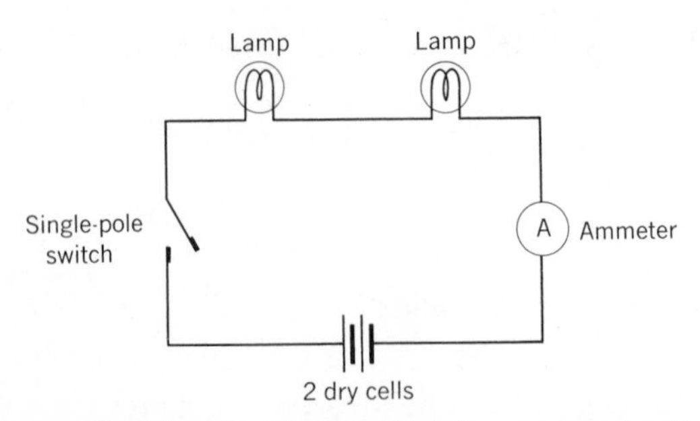

Fig. 16–10. Using electrical symbols in a series circuit.

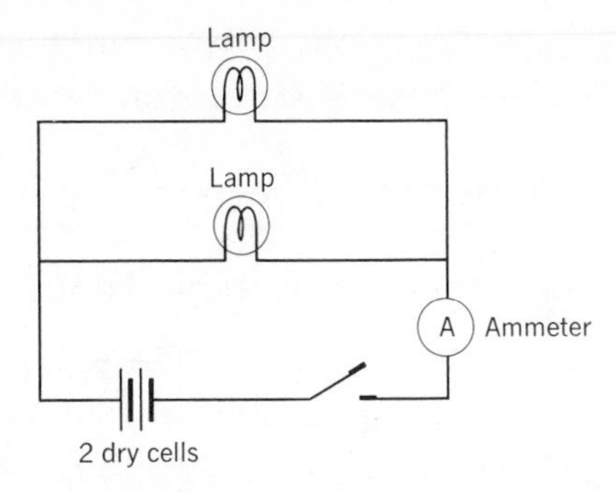

Fig. 16–11. Using electrical symbols in a parallel circuit.

Name	Electrical Symbol	Name	Electrical Symbol
Dry cell	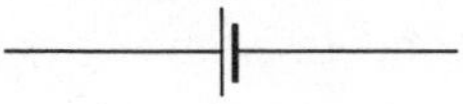	Knife switch (single pole)	
Dry cells in series	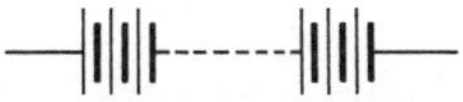	Fuse	
Lamp	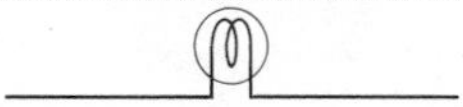	Resistance	
Ammeter	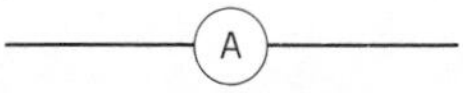 A	Resistances in series	
Voltmeter	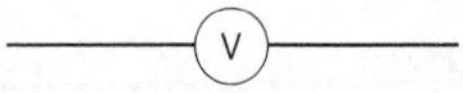 V	Resistances in parallel	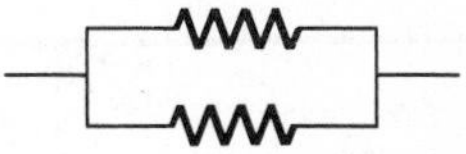
Galvanometer	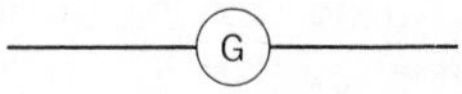 G		

Fig. 16–12. Common electrical symbols.

Looking Back

The factors that affect the flow of electricity are voltage and resistance, as stated in Ohm's law: current $= \frac{\text{voltage}}{\text{resistance}}$. Ohm's law applies to all parts of either a series or a parallel circuit.

The main features of a series circuit may be summarized as follows:

1. The current is the same in all parts of the circuit.

2. Each resistance gets only a fraction of the total voltage supplied by the source. The sum of all the fractional voltages equals the voltage of the source.

3. The total resistance equals the sum of the individual resistances. For n loads in a circuit, the total resistance may be calculated as follows:

$$R\,(\text{total}) = R_1 + R_2 + \ldots\ldots + R_n$$

The main features of a parallel circuit may be summarized as follows:

1. The current divides in each of the branches. The sum of the currents in all the resistances equals the total current flowing through the circuit.

2. The voltage across each resistance remains unchanged and equals the voltage at the source.

3. The total resistance in a circuit is less than the smallest single resistance. For n loads in a circuit, the total resistance may be calculated as follows:

$$\frac{1}{R\,(\text{total})} = \frac{1}{R_1} + \frac{1}{R_2} + \ldots + \frac{1}{R_n}$$

Looking Ahead

Now that you have some understanding of the flow of electricity, you will be better able to understand how various electrical devices operate. Several of these devices are discussed in Chapter 17.

Multiple-Choice Questions

1. In general, the greatest resistance is offered by
   a. short thick wires c. long thin wires
   b. long thick wires d. short thin wires
2. In a complete electric circuit, when the current increases, the voltage
   a. remains the same c. increases
   b. decreases d. decreases then increases
3. In a series circuit, electrons
   a. do not flow c. are produced
   b. flow along several paths d. flow along a single path
4. In a series circuit containing four lamps, when one lamp burns out,
   a. all four lamps go out
   b. the remaining three lamps remain lit
   c. one other lamp goes out
   d. the brightness of the lamps increases

5. In a series circuit, the sum of the voltages in each load
   a. is less than the voltage at the source
   b. is greater than the voltage at the source
   c. is equal to the voltage at the source
   d. equals the voltage across the smallest resistance
6. In a series circuit, as the number of loads increases
   a. the total amperage increases
   b. the total resistance increases
   c. the total voltage increases
   d. the total amperage decreases
7. In a parallel circuit, a break in one branch of the circuit
   a. stops the flow of electrons in all branches
   b. decreases the flow of electrons in other branches
   c. does not stop the flow of electrons in other branches
   d. produces a short circuit
8. In all branches of a parallel circuit,
   a. the voltage across each load is the same as the voltage of the source
   b. the voltage across each load varies
   c. the amperage is the same
   d. the resistance is the same
9. The rate of flow of electrons is known as
   a. voltage b. amperage c. resistance d. conductance
10. As the electromotive force in a circuit increases, the number of electrons flowing in the circuit
    a. increases
    b. decreases
    c. remains the same
    d. splits into two parts

Modified True-False Questions

1. Electrical resistance is measured in a unit called the *ohm.*
2. In a series circuit, the current in all parts of the circuit is *the same.*
3. A circuit which has more than one path open to the flow of electrons is called *a series circuit.*
4. The voltage is the same in all branches of *a parallel circuit.*
5. Electric circuits are easily represented by using *electrical symbols.*

Matching Questions

Column A	Column B
1. unit of electric pressure	a. ohm
2. device that measures current	b. ohmmeter
3. relates current, voltage and resistance	c. volt
4. unit of rate of electron flow	d. voltmeter
5. device that measures electric pressure	e. electric current
6. electrons in motion	f. ampere
7. unit of resistance	g. Ohm's law
8. device that measures resistance	h. ammeter

Thought Questions

1. Complete the table.

Name	*Meaning*	*Unit of Measurement*	*Measuring Device*
Current			
Voltage			
Resistance			

2. Explain the differences between the terms in each of the following pairs.
   a. series and parallel circuits
   b. amperage and voltage
3. Solve each of the following problems using Ohm's law.
   a. Find the amperage in an electric circuit when the voltage is 120 volts and the resistance is 40 ohms.
   b. Find the voltage in an electric circuit when the amperage is 5 amperes and the resistance is 25 ohms.
   c. Find the resistance of an electric circuit when the voltage is 220 volts and the amperage is 5 amperes.
4. A series circuit with a current of 2 amperes is connected to a 12-volt source containing three resistances. The first resistance equals 3 ohms; the second resistance is 2 ohms; the third resistance is 1 ohm.
   a. What is the total resistance in the circuit?
   b. What is the voltage across each resistance?
5. A parallel circuit with a total current of 3 amperes is connected to a source. The circuit contains two 1-ohm resistances.
   a. What is the total resistance in the circuit?
   b. What is the current in each resistance?

CHAPTER 17
WHAT ARE SOME USES OF ELECTRICITY AND MAGNETISM?

When you have completed this chapter, you should be able to:

1. *Explain* how to vary the strength of electromagnets.
2. *Trace* the flow of electrons in the circuits of an electric bell, a telegraph, and a telephone.
3. *Discuss* the operation of an electric motor, radio, and television.
4. *Distinguish* between a galvanometer, an ammeter, a voltmeter, and an ohmmeter, and explain how each is connected in a circuit.
5. *Contrast* alternating current and direct current.
6. *Appreciate* how electricity is produced by means of electromagnetic induction.
7. *Describe* the value of transformers and how to calculate the voltages they produce.

In the laboratory experience that follows, you will construct an electromagnet and study how to vary its strength.

Laboratory Experience

WHAT ARE THE PROPERTIES OF ELECTROMAGNETS?

Note: Be sure to use the same length of bell wire for all the experiments in this laboratory experience.

A. Using a 30-centimeter length of bell wire (insulated copper wire), wind 10 turns around an iron nail. Connect the bell wire, the dry cell, and the knife switch, as shown in Fig. 17–1, page 296. Leave the switch open.
   Place a few paper clips on your desk, and touch one end of the nail to them.
   1. Describe what happens.

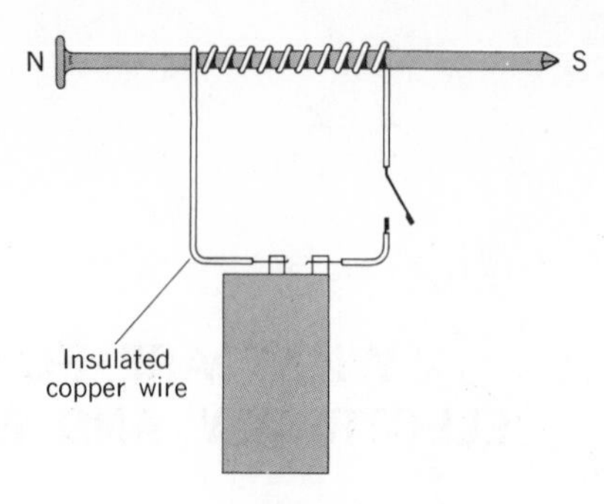

Fig. 17–1.

B. Close the switch in the circuit, and again touch the end of the nail to the paper clips. You have made an electromagnet. Open the switch again.

2. Describe what happens when the switch is closed.
3. How many paper clips can you pick up with your electromagnet?

C. Repeat part B. This time, however, wind 20 turns of bell wire around the nail before closing the switch. Open the switch.

4. How many paper clips can you pick up with the electromagnet now?
5. What happens to an electromagnet when you increase the number of turns around the nail?

D. Wind 20 turns of bell wire around *two* iron nails. Close the switch on the electromagnet, and touch the ends of the nails to the paper clips. Open the switch again.

6. How many paper clips can you pick up with the electromagnet now?
7. What happens to an electromagnet when you increase the thickness of the core, that is, increase the number of nails?

E. Connect a second dry cell into the circuit in series. There are still 20 turns of bell wire wrapped around two iron nails. Close the switch on the electromagnet.

8. How many paper clips can you pick up with the electromagnet now?
9. What happens to an electromagnet when you increase the current through the circuit?

F. Remove the second dry cell from the circuit. Place a magnetic compass near the nails, and close the switch on the electromagnet. Open the switch.

10. What effect does the electromagnet have on the compass needle? Explain.

G. Reverse the wires connected to the dry cell, and close the switch again. Observe the compass needle. Open the switch.
   11. What effect does reversing the wires have on the compass needle? Explain.

Introduction

If you take apart electrical appliances such as telephones, television receivers, or electric motors, you will find that magnets and electric wires are the heart of these devices. A magnetic substance, such as iron, can be made into a magnet with the aid of an electric current. It is also true that a magnet can be used to make, or generate, an electric current. Electricity and magnetism seem to be inseparable.

MAKING MAGNETS WITH ELECTRICITY

We have learned before that when an electric current passes through a straight or coiled wire, a magnetic field is produced in the space surrounding the wire. You can verify this statement by winding an insulated copper wire around a pencil to form a coil. Remove the pencil, and place a compass near one end of the coil. Observe that the coil has no effect upon the compass needle. Now connect the ends of the wire through a switch to a dry cell, and close the switch. Observe that one end of the coil attracts one pole of the compass needle and repels the other. When the compass is placed near the other end of the coil, the reverse happens (Ampère's experiment, Fig. 17–2).

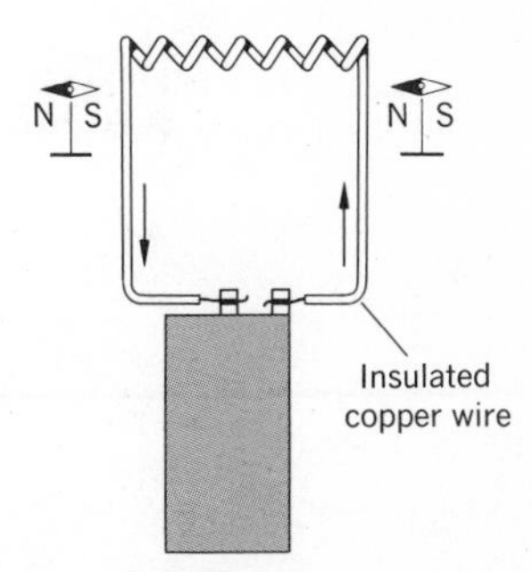

Fig. 17–2. Ampère's experiment.

The behavior of a compass needle near a coil of wire carrying electric current resembles its behavior near a bar magnet. Recall that attraction occurs when unlike poles are brought together and that repulsion occurs when like poles are brought together. Thus, the behavior of the compass needle near a coil carrying an electric current shows that the coil has magnetic properties very much like a bar magnet. The coil behaves in this fashion because each loop of wire acts as a separate small magnet, and all the loops aligned together act as one larger magnet.

As you observed in your laboratory experience, an iron nail placed in a coil of insulated copper wire connected to a switch and a dry cell (Fig. 17–1) becomes a magnet and attracts magnetic substances such as tacks or paper clips. Such a magnet, produced by electrons flowing through a coil of wire, is called an *electromagnet.* The nail is called the *core* of the electromagnet.

Recall what happened to your electromagnet when you reversed the wires connected to the dry cell. The polarity of the magnet was reversed. To determine which end of the core is the north pole, we use a procedure known as the *left-hand rule* (Fig. 17–3) as follows: Wrap the four fingers of your left hand around the coil so that the fingers point in the direction in which the electrons are flowing, that is, from the negative terminal of the dry cell to the positive terminal. When you extend your left thumb along the core, the thumb points to the north pole of the electromagnet. In Fig. 17–1, page 296, the north pole is at the head of the nail.

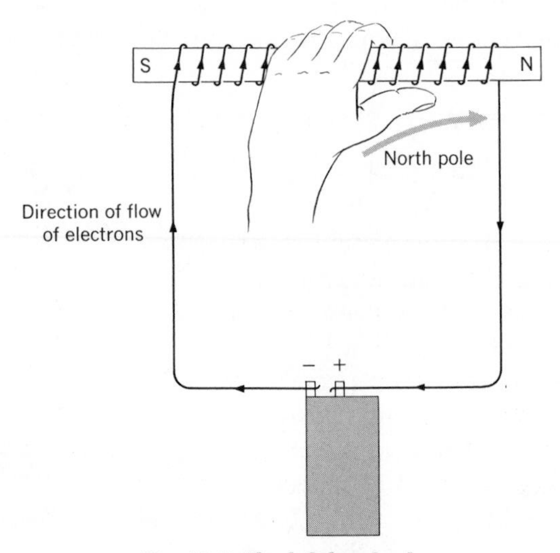

Fig. 17–3. The left-hand rule.

VARYING THE STRENGTH OF ELECTROMAGNETS

The strength of an electromagnet can be changed in several ways:

1. *Varying the number of turns of wire around the core.* When we increase the number of turns or loops of insulated wire around a core, the strength of the electromagnet increases. In the laboratory, when we increase the windings of the coil from 10 turns to 20, the core picks up many more clips than before.

2. *Varying the current.* When we increase the amount of the current through the coil of wire by increasing the voltage, more electrons pass through the wire in a given period of time. As a result, the magnetic field becomes stronger, and the strength of the electromagnet increases. For example, when we add, in series, a second dry

cell to the circuit containing a coil of 20 turns of wire, our electromagnet picks up still more clips.

3. *Changing the core.* As we learned earlier, when an empty coil of wire is connected to a source of voltage, a compass needle indicates the presence of a magnetic field at the ends of the coil. Some substances become magnetized by induction when they are in a magnetic field. These substances concentrate the lines of force of the field. This effect on the lines of force is called *magnetic permeability.* Iron and cobalt (both magnetic substances) possess magnetic permeability. If a wooden core is inserted in the coil, the strength of the electromagnet does not change because wood lacks magnetic permeability. When a magnetic substance such as iron is used as a core, the strength of the electromagnet may be increased as much as 1000 times. When a weaker magnetic substance, such as cobalt, is used as a core, the strength of the electromagnet is increased only about 170 times. Both iron and cobalt are used as cores to strengthen electromagnets.

4. *Varying the thickness of the core.* When the thickness of the core of an electromagnet is increased, the strength of the electromagnet is also increased because more magnetic domains are provided. Therefore, when we wind a coil of wire around two nails instead of only one, the electromagnet becomes stronger.

SOME USES OF ELECTROMAGNETS

Electromagnets of varying strength are used in many household and industrial devices. These devices include the electric bell, the telegraph, the telephone, radio, television, and the electric motor.

The Electric Bell

A common type of electric bell consists of a horseshoe electromagnet, a soft iron armature, a clapper or hammer, a contact screw, wires, a spring, and a gong (Fig. 17–4*a*, page 300). The bell is connected through a switch or push button to a source of voltage. As shown in Fig. 17–4*b*, page 300, when the button is pushed, the circuit is closed. Electrons flow through the coils of the electromagnet, causing the iron core to become magnetized. The poles of the electromagnet attract the armature and hammer, causing the hammer to strike the gong. However, as the armature and hammer move toward the gong, the armature also moves away from the contact screw. Thus, the circuit is broken at the contact point, and the flow of electrons stops. The iron core of the electromagnet loses its magnetism, and the hammer is pulled back to its original position by the spring. In this position, the hammer makes contact

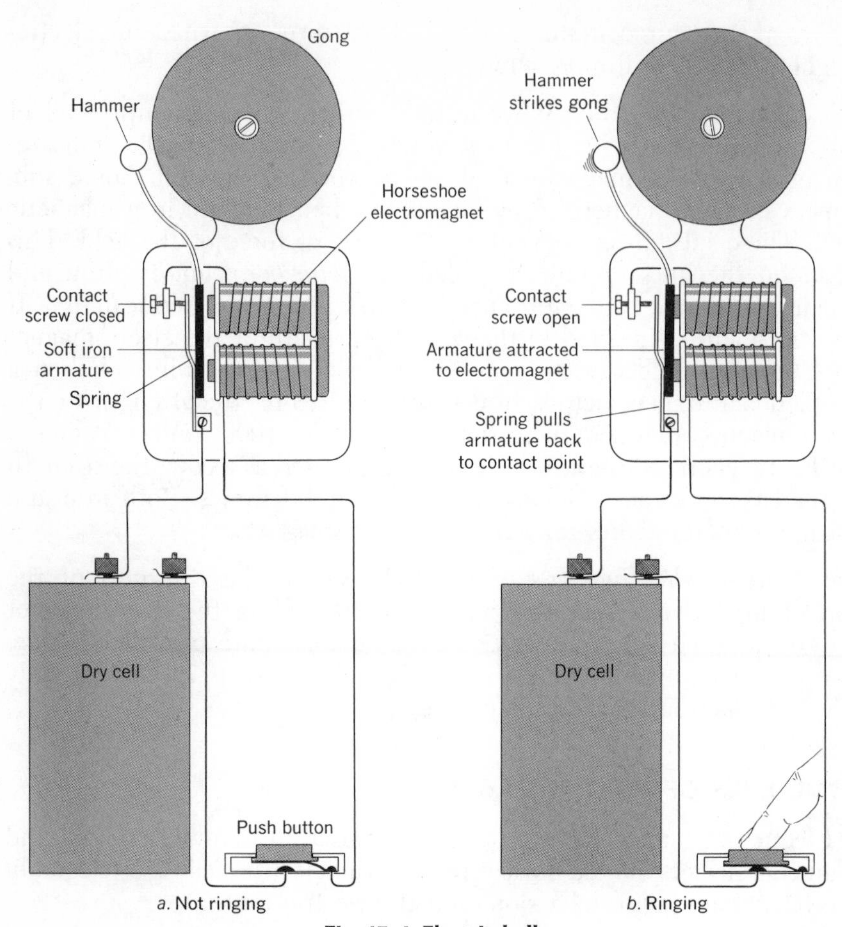

Fig. 17–4. Electric bell.

with the contact screw, completing the circuit. The electromagnet again attracts the armature, and the cycle repeats itself over and over, as long as the circuit is closed (the button is pushed). When the button is released, the circuit is opened, the flow of electrons stops, and the bell stops ringing.

Buzzers operate like bells. However, since a buzzer lacks a gong and a hammer on the armature, the sound you hear is the buzz of the vibrating armature.

The Telegraph

Electromagnets play an important part in the operation of the communications instrument known as the telegraph. Each telegraph unit, or station, consists of a switch, a *key*, and a *sounder*. The key opens and closes an electrical circuit, thereby controlling the flow of electrons to the sounder. The sounder consists of an electromagnet, a soft iron armature, and an anvil. Fig. 17–5 shows a simple telegraph circuit in which two stations are connected by a wire and through the ground. When one person sends a message, the switch on his key is open, whereas the switch on the key of the receiver is closed.

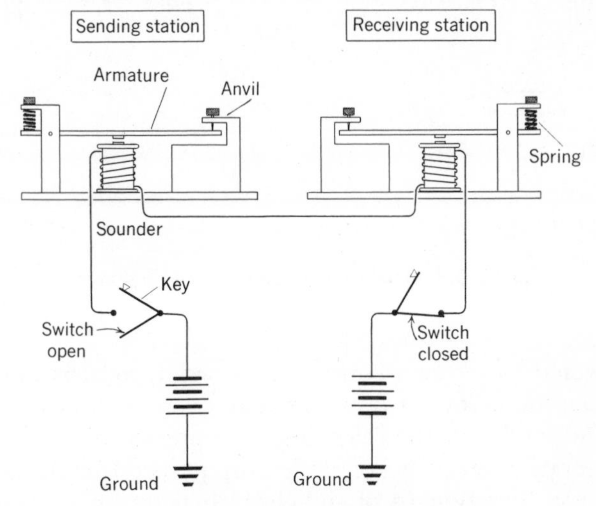

Fig. 17–5. A simple telegraph circuit.

When the sender's key is pressed, the circuit is completed, and electrons flow through wires to the electromagnet of each sounder. Here the current in each coil causes the iron cores to become electromagnets, which then attract the soft iron armatures of the sounders. The armatures strike the anvils and produce a click. When the key is released, the circuit is open, and springs cause the armatures to return to the upper part of the anvils, producing a second click.

Operators can communicate with each other by using a code composed of clicks with short intervals between them (dots), and clicks with longer intervals between them (dashes). This code, known as the *International Morse Code*, has been in use since the middle of the nineteenth century.

A problem arises when sending messages by telegraph over long distances. Long wires are required; this, we recall, means increased resistance to the flow of electrons. Thus, the current that passes through the long wire may be so weak that the sounder in the long-distance *main line* cannot be heard.

A device known as a *relay*, shown in Fig. 17–6, page 302, is used in the main line to strengthen the signal. The relay is, in effect, another

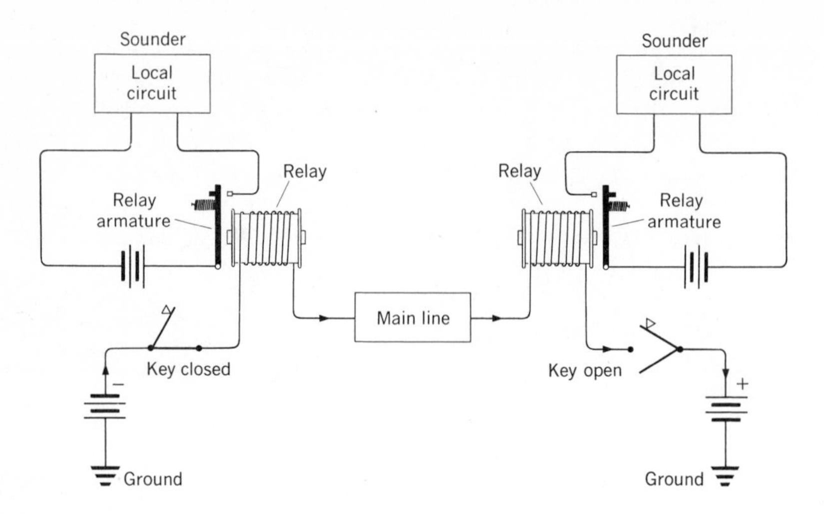

Fig. 17–6. A simple telegraph circuit with relays.

sounder powered by its own batteries. The relay consists of an electromagnet containing many turns of wire and a very light armature. When the key of the sender in the main line is depressed, the relay armature responds to even a very weak electric current because the many turns of wire increase the strength of the electromagnet. The relay armature moves and acts as an electromagnetic switch to open and close the sounder of the local circuit. The opening and closing of this circuit corresponds to the action of the armature in the relay. In this way, the weak signals in the main line become audible signals in the local circuit. In modern telegraph systems, electronic devices are beginning to replace electrical relays for strengthening the signals in the local circuit.

The Telephone

The telephone, perhaps our most widely used communications device, also uses electromagnets. As shown in Fig. 17–7, the telephone circuit consists of a *transmitter* at one end of the line, a *receiver* at the other end of the line, and a source of electricity.

The transmitter of any telephone is the mouthpiece into which we speak. The mouthpiece contains a box of carbon granules to which a circular metal disk is attached. The disk and a flexible diaphragm to which the disk is attached vibrate back and forth according to the sound waves that reach the mouthpiece. The receiver is the earphone of the telephone. The receiver reproduces the sounds entering the transmitter. The receiver is a horseshoe electromagnet in which a permanent horseshoe magnet acts as the core. A diaphragm

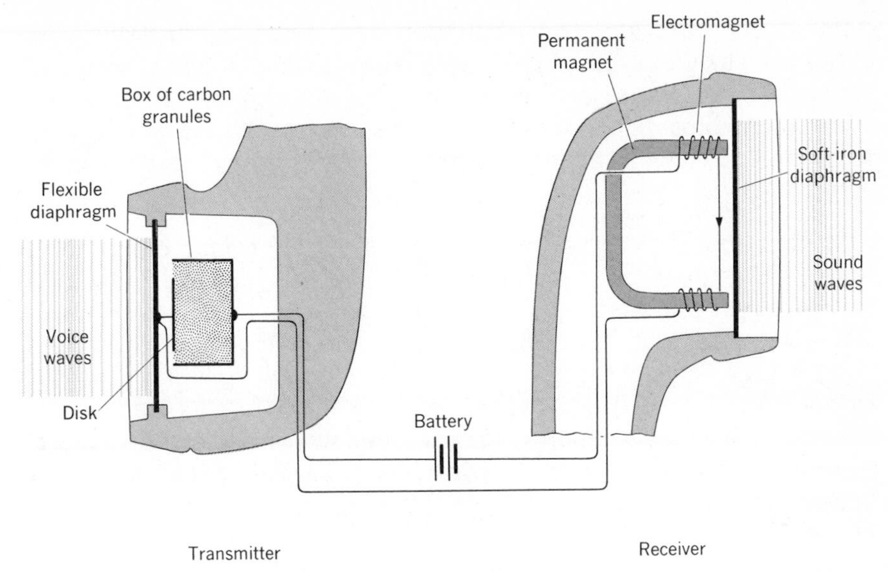

Fig. 17–7. A telephone circuit.

made of a thin sheet of soft iron is set close to the poles of the electromagnet.

How does the receiver reproduce the sounds that enter the transmitter? Sounds cause the diaphragm of the transmitter to vibrate. This, in turn, increases or decreases the compression of the carbon granules. Increasing the compression of these granules can be likened to increasing the thickness of a wire. This compression decreases the resistance of the carbon granules to the flow of electrons and permits more electrons to flow. In the same manner, decreasing the compression of the granules can be likened to decreasing the thickness of a wire. With little compression of the carbon granules, the resistance to the current is strongest, and little electricity flows. Thus, when sounds enter the transmitter, a current that varies in strength passes through the circuit. At the receiving end of the telephone circuit, this varying current changes the strength of the electromagnet, increasing and decreasing the attraction of the electromagnet for the diaphragm. This produces vibrations of the diaphragm, corresponding to the vibrations of the diaphragm of the transmitter. In this manner, the sound waves that enter the transmitter are reproduced in the receiver.

Radio

Electromagnets are present in the speakers of radios and in some types of microphones used in radio stations. In telephone communication, sound waves are changed in the mouthpiece to varying electric currents, which are then sent over wires to the receiver. In radio communication, wires are absent, but the microphone acts like the mouthpiece of a telephone, while the speaker acts like a telephone receiver. The steps in radio transmission (broadcasting) and reception are as follows:

1. *Formation of electrical waves.* How is a signal from a radio station sent to a radio receiver without wires? Suppose someone in a radio station sings a low-pitched (low-frequency) note. The sound waves from this note cause the diaphragm in the microphone to vibrate. This, in turn, changes the flow of electrons in the microphone circuit and causes a varying current, or *electrical voice wave,* to pass through the circuit. If a high-pitched note is sung, a sound wave of different frequency is formed, and the electrical voice wave formed is different from before. Thus, a high-pitched note produces an electrical voice wave of higher frequency than does a low-pitched note (Fig. 17–8).

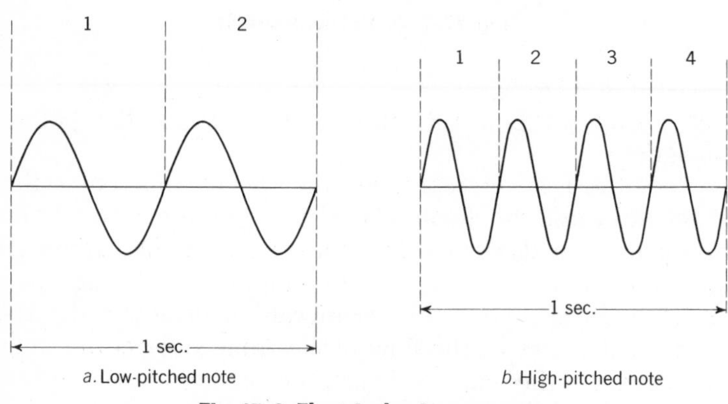

a. Low-pitched note

b. High-pitched note

Fig. 17–8. Electrical voice waves.

2. *Broadcasting radio programs.* To send, or *broadcast,* electrical voice waves from one place to another, the voice waves are made to ride "piggyback" on another type of electrical wave called a *radio wave,* or *carrier wave* (Fig. 17–9). The carrier wave is produced in a special circuit by a device called a *transmitter.* The two types of electrical waves are then mixed together and strengthened, or *amplified,* by transistors and vacuum tubes. The mixed wave, consisting of the electrical voice wave from the microphone and the carrier wave from the transmitter (Fig. 17–10), is then sent into space by means of a towerlike *antenna,* or aerial, which is located near the transmitter.

3. *How AM radio differs from FM.* You probably have a radio that

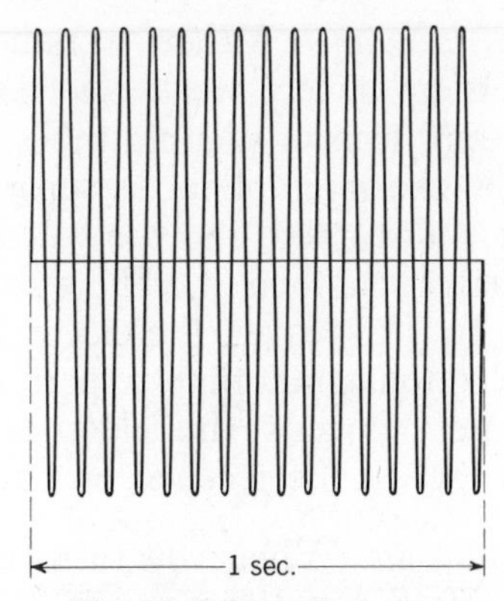

Fig. 17–9. A carrier wave.

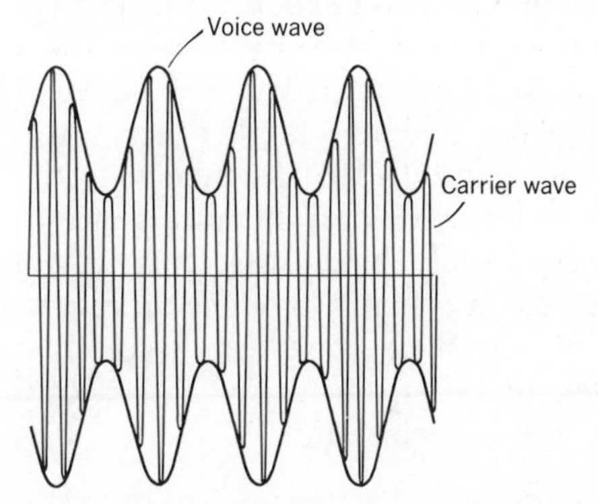

Fig. 17–10. Voice wave and carrier wave mixed (AM).

can receive either AM or FM broadcasts. In the case of AM, the voice wave changes the amplitude (height) of the carrier wave sent out from the antenna (Fig. 17–10). Thus, AM stands for *amplitude modulation.* In the case of FM, the voice wave changes the frequency of the carrier wave (Fig. 17–11). Thus, FM stands for *frequency modulation.*

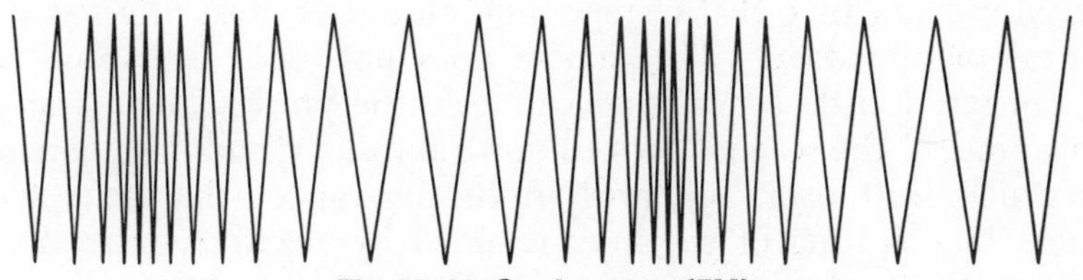

Fig. 17–11. Carrier wave (FM).

4. *Receiving radio programs.* When a radio wave reaches your radio set, the wave sets up a very weak electrical signal in the set's antenna. By means of transistors or vacuum tubes, the original electrical voice wave produced by the microphone is separated from the carrier wave. The carrier wave is discarded, and the voice wave is sent through tubes or transistors that strengthen it. The strengthened voice wave is fed into the speaker. In the speaker, the electrical voice wave changes the strength of the electromagnet that is part of the speaker. As a result, the electromagnet converts the electrical voice wave into a sound wave, just as it does in the receiver of a telephone.

5. *Tuning in radio stations.* When you turn on your radio, why do you not hear all the different stations at the same time? Each radio station is assigned a certain frequency for its carrier wave by the government. Every radio receiver has built into it a *tuner*, which is a device that can select different frequencies, one at a time. When you turn the station knob on your set, you are turning the tuner. Thus, when you turn the knob to frequency 1010 AM or 96.3 FM, the tuner selects only that frequency and rejects all others. As a result, you hear only the program sent out with that frequency.

AM radios can receive only broadcasts from AM transmitters. FM radios can receive only broadcasts from FM transmitters. Lightning discharges and electric sparks produce waves that closely resemble AM radio waves. When these waves are received by AM sets, the waves produce noises, or static. Since FM radios cannot receive AM waves, these sets are free of such static.

Television

In broadcasting television programs, the sound part is transmitted by FM radio waves; the picture part is transmitted by AM radio waves. Electromagnets are important in transmitting the picture as well as the sound. The steps in television transmission and reception are as follows:

1. *Transmitting television programs.* A television camera contains a special vacuum tube that changes light and dark areas of a scene into electrical picture waves. The camera does not "see" the scene all at once but sees a little bit of it at a time in the process called *scanning.* In this process, the scene is broken down into light and dark horizontal lines which shift back and forth from the top of the scene to the bottom. The shifting of the lines is aided by electromagnets. During scanning, electrical picture waves are formed, one after the other,

for each line. These waves are sent out over wires to the transmitting station and antenna. As with radio voice waves, electrical picture waves are mixed with a carrier wave and are sent out piggyback on them. The carrier wave for sound is sent out at the same time, so that both sound and picture arrive at your television set together.

2. *Receiving television programs.* A home television set contains two separate receivers. One receives the sound part of the program, and the other receives the picture part. When the broadcast waves reach your television antenna (as in radio), weak electrical waves reach your set and are separated from the carrier waves. Then, after being strengthened, the remaining electrical picture and voice waves reach your picture tube and speaker. With the aid of electromagnets, the picture tube converts the picture waves into light and dark lines that follow one another rapidly on the screen of the television tube. The lines are produced so rapidly—32,500 lines every second—that your eyes combine them into a complete picture without your being aware of it.

Recording Sound

A phonograph record is a disk containing grooves which were originally scratched on a master disk and then copied in plastic. The grooves are made with the aid of a microphone, an amplifier, a turntable, and a very fine needle, called a *stylus.* These devices convert the sound waves into electrical signals—as in the telephone and radio—and then into wavy scratches. The scratches correspond in pitch and amplitude to the sounds recorded.

When you play a plastic disk, the recording procedure is reversed. As the record turns, the stylus of the record player produces vibrations that correspond to the vibrations of the original sound. The vibrations are amplified and fed into a loudspeaker or earphones.

Stereophonic records are made similarly, but with two microphones that pick up sound from more than one direction. Double scratches are made on the record. When the record is played, the sound is fed into two separated speakers. What you hear is sound that appears to come from all directions and thus seems more realistic.

An important advance in sound recording is the use of a magnetic tape in place of a record. During recording, the sound is converted into electrical signals that correspond to the pitch and amplitude of the original sound. These signals, in turn, produce variations in the magnetic domains of the tape. On playing the tape, the procedure is reversed. The magnetic tape is fed into a reproducer which contains an electromagnet. The magnetic variations stored in the tape produce corresponding changes in the electromagnet. The outgoing electrical signals, which correspond to the characteristics of the original sound, are amplified and passed into a loudspeaker.

Recording Pictures

Pictures, like sound, may also be recorded on tape. Just as in TV, light is converted into electrical signals. The signals are fed onto magnetic tape. When the tape is played on proper TV equipment in the TV studio or in the home, the procedure is reversed. What was stored on the tape becomes a picture.

The Electric Motor

Electromagnets are important to electric motors, which, in turn, are used to power trains, elevators, and many household devices such as vacuum cleaners and electric drills.

An electric motor is composed of a *field magnet*, an *armature*, a *commutator*, and *brushes*. The field magnet may be a permanent horseshoe magnet or a horseshoe electromagnet as shown in Fig. 17–12. The armature is a bar electromagnet mounted on a shaft or axle that is

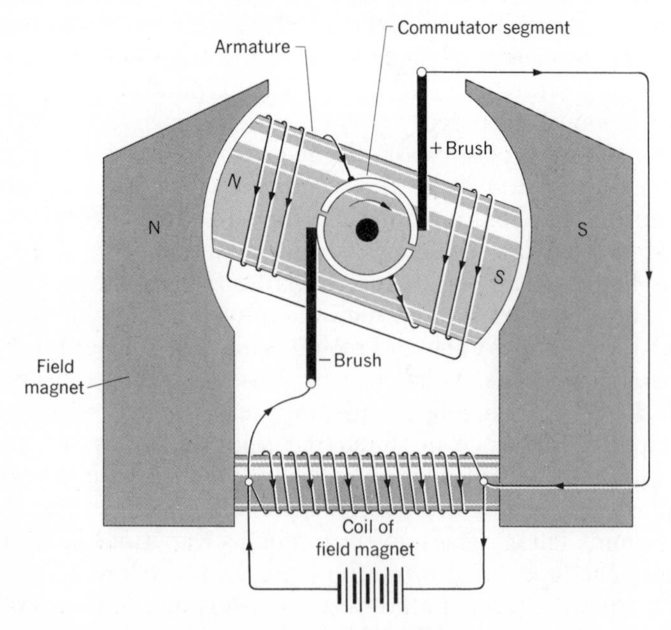

Fig. 17–12. An electric motor.

free to rotate between the poles of the field magnet. The commutator, located on the shaft of the armature, is a metal ring split into two halves. Each half is insulated from the other. The same current that enters the coil of the horseshoe electromagnet is brought to the commutator by brushes. The brushes are so mounted that each brush is always in contact with one of the commutator segments. From the commutator, wires lead to the coil of the armature.

In a complete circuit containing a motor, the electricity flows from the coil of the field magnet to the brushes, into one segment of the commutator, and into the coil of the armature. As a result, the armature coil is magnetized. When one pole of the armature becomes a north pole, the north pole of the field magnet repels it, and the armature rotates, making a half-turn. As the armature rotates, each brush makes contact with a different commutator segment. This reverses the direction of the electron flow through the armature coil. According to the left-hand rule, the poles of the electromagnet of the armature are also reversed. Like poles again face each other, and the armature makes another half-turn. As the commutator continues to reverse the direction of the flow of electrons, the armature continues to rotate. When a mechanical device is connected to the shaft of the armature, the device operates. Thus, electrical energy is transformed into mechanical energy.

ELECTRIC METERS

Recall (Chapter 16, pages 280–282) that Ohm's law describes the relationship between amperage, voltage, and resistance. We will now see how each of these characteristics of a circuit can be measured using electric meters.

In its simplest form, an electric meter of any type resembles an electric motor. Both devices contain an armature (moving coil) free to rotate on its axle between the poles of a magnet. (In the electric meter, this is usually a permanent horseshoe magnet.) In an electric motor, because of the action of the commutator, the armature makes complete rotations. In an electric meter, however, the armature makes only a partial turn. When current enters the coil of a meter, the coil becomes magnetized. Since no commutator is present, the attraction and repulsion between the poles of the coil and the poles of the horseshoe magnet cause the coil to make a partial turn. The greater the current, the greater is the turn. A needle attached to the coil points to a scale designed to give the proper reading. When the circuit is broken, a spring pulls the needle back to its original position.

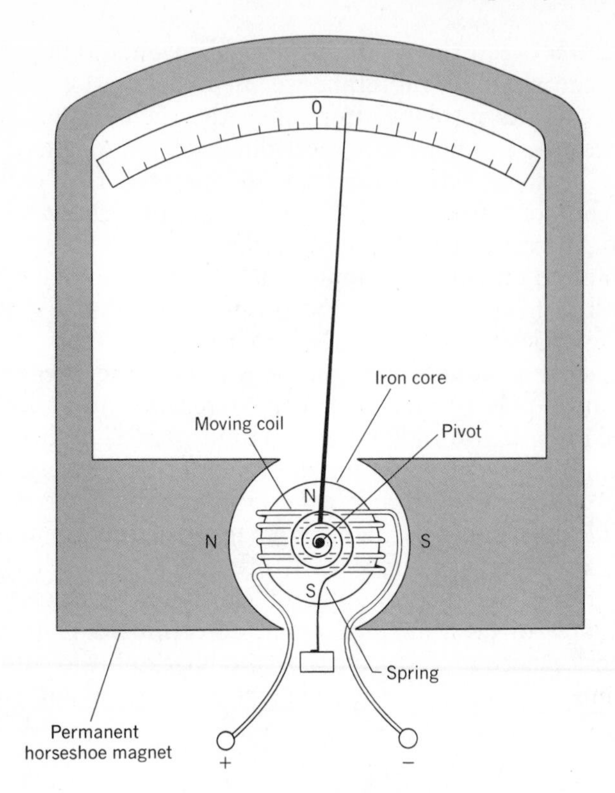

Fig. 17–13. A galvanometer.

Tiny electric currents are measured by a *galvanometer* (Fig. 17–13). Note that the zero (0) position on this meter is in the center of the scale. This permits a galvanometer to detect the direction of the current (polarity). Larger electric currents are measured with an *ammeter* (Fig. 17–14). To protect the windings of the delicate coil in the ammeter from burning out, a bar of metal called a *shunt* is connected in parallel with the coil. The shunt offers very low resistance to the flow of electrons. Remember that the current in a parallel circuit divides and that most of the current enters the lower resistance. This means that, in the ammeter, very little current enters the coil. Thus, the shunt allows the ammeter to measure large currents without damage to the meter. Since an ammeter measures electrons flowing through a circuit, it is always connected in series with the circuit.

Voltage is measured by a *voltmeter*, which is really a high-resistance galvanometer (Fig. 17–15, page 312). Hence, only a very small amount of current enters the voltmeter itself, thus protecting the delicate coil in the voltmeter. Changes in the voltage will determine the deflection of

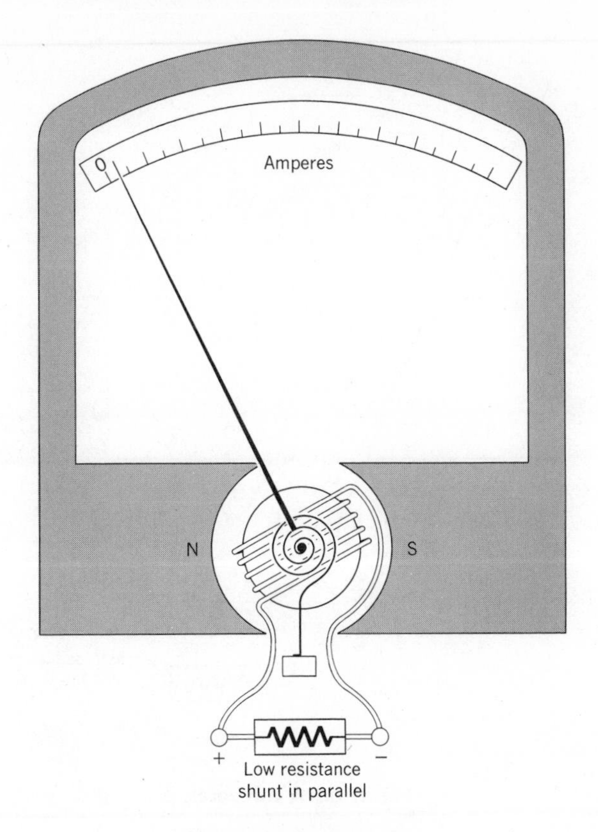

Fig. 17–14. An ammeter.

the needle. Since a voltmeter measures the voltage across two points in a circuit, it is always connected in parallel with the circuit.

The resistance of an electrical circuit is measured with the aid of a special meter called an *ohmmeter*. However, if we measure the amperage and the voltage in a circuit, we can use Ohm's law to calculate the resistance ($R = \frac{V}{I}$). In the circuit shown in Fig. 17–16, page 312, the resistance (R) can be found by dividing the ammeter reading (A), which is the same as (I), into the voltmeter reading (V).

GENERATING ELECTRICITY WITH MAGNETS

As you know, Oersted discovered that an electric current passing through a wire produces a magnetic field around the wire. This discovery is the basis of all modern inventions containing electromagnets.

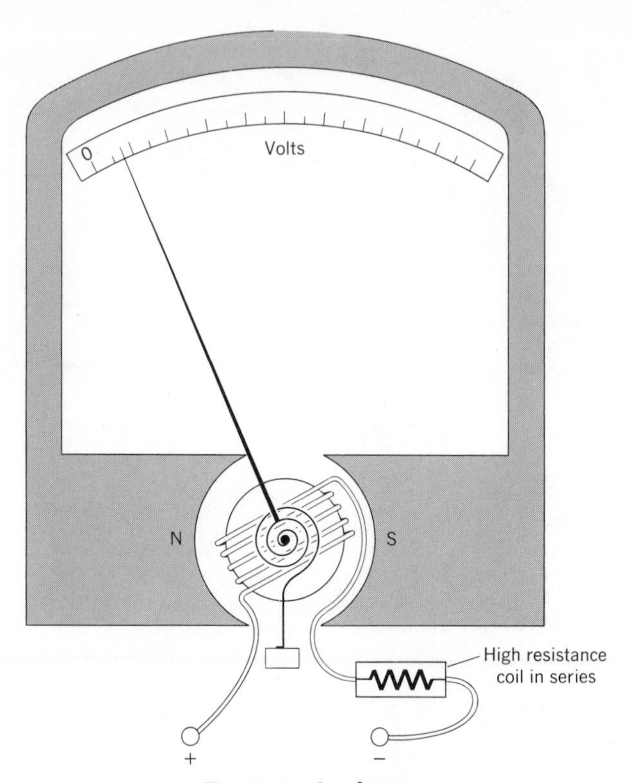

Fig. 17–15. A voltmeter.

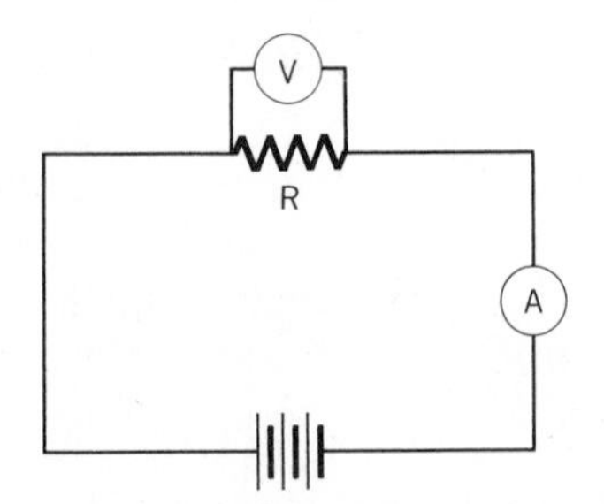

Fig. 17–16. Measuring resistance.

In 1831, *Michael Faraday*, an English scientist, showed that it was possible to produce the reverse effect—that is, he discovered how to obtain electricity from magnetism. Faraday placed a permanent magnet in a coil. A galvanometer connected to the ends of the coil indicated that no electricity was flowing. Upon moving the magnet out of the coil, Faraday noted that the galvanometer needle moved, indicating the presence of current (Fig. 17–17). When he placed the magnet

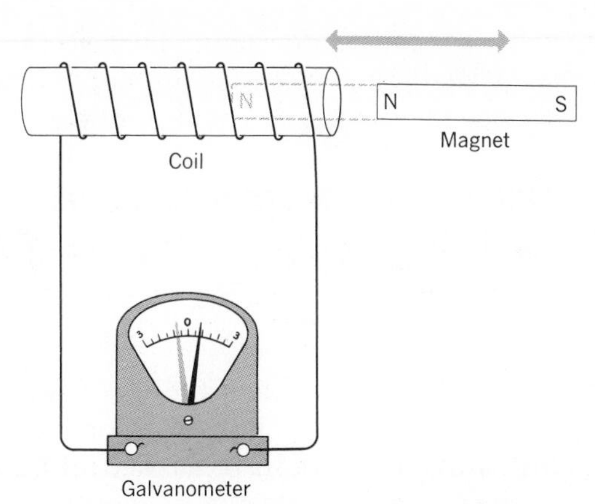

Fig. 17–17. Generating an electric current.

back into the coil again, the needle of the meter moved—but in the opposite direction.

Note that Faraday succeeded in producing an electric current only when he *moved* the magnet into or out of the coil of wire. He also found that he could produce a current in a coil by holding the magnet still and moving the coil back and forth. In this case, the direction in which the needle of the meter moves depends on the direction in which the coil is moved. Producing an electric current by moving a magnet through a coil of wire (or by moving the coil of wire back and forth) is called *electromagnetic induction.* It does not matter whether the coil moves or the magnet moves. We say that electromagnetic induction takes place whenever a coil of wire cuts the lines of force of a magnet.

If the ends of the coil are not connected to a complete circuit, electrons will not flow; instead, an induced electromotive force or voltage is produced between the ends of the wire in the coil. When the circuit is complete, however, the induced voltage will produce an induced current. Thus, electrons will flow through the circuit as long as the coil cuts the lines of force of the magnet.

How do we account for electromagnetic induction? Recall that a magnet is surrounded by a field composed of lines of force that spread out from the magnet. Recall also that a conducting wire is metallic and is composed of atoms that contain electrons. When a magnet is moved in and out of a coil of wire, the lines of force of the magnet are cut by the wire. When a conductor cuts the lines of force of a magnet, electrons pile up at one end of the conductor. As this occurs, the other end of the wire becomes deficient in electrons. Accordingly, when the two ends of the wire are connected to a galvanometer, electrons flow from the end of the wire where they are in excess to the end of the wire where they are deficient. The electrons continue to flow as long as the magnetic lines of force are cut by the wire, that is, as long as either the magnet or the coil is in motion.

VARYING THE STRENGTH OF AN INDUCED CURRENT

Recall that the strength of an electromagnet can be varied in many ways. Somewhat similar methods are used to vary the strength of an induced current.

1. *Varying the speed of motion.* When the speed of motion of either the coil or the magnet is increased, the strength of the induced current increases. To confirm this, slowly push a magnet into a coil connected to a galvanometer, and note how far the needle moves. Remove the magnet, and now push it rapidly into the coil. Note that the galvanometer needle deflects to a much greater extent. This indicates that the amount of current induced in the coil has increased. The same results are obtained regardless of whether the magnet or the coil is moving. Thus, it appears that the strength of an induced current is related to the speed with which the coil of wire cuts the lines of force of the magnet.

2. *Varying the strength of the magnet.* Push a bar magnet into a coil connected to a galvanometer. Note how far the needle moves. Then place two magnets side by side, with similar poles together, and push them into the coil, moving at the same speed as before. The galvanometer connected to the coil registers a larger movement of the needle than when the single magnet was pushed into the same coil. A stronger single magnet produces the same effect as the two individual magnets. Since stronger magnets have stronger magnetic fields, the coil cuts more lines of force in a given time. Thus, the strength of the induced current increases as more lines of force are cut by a coil.

3. *Varying the number of turns.* When the speed of motion and the strength of the magnet remain the same, the amount of current induced in a coil is increased by increasing the number of loops in the coil. Thus, it appears that when more turns of wire cut the magnetic lines of force, more electrons in the coil are disturbed. As a result, the amount of induced current is increased.

ALTERNATING AND DIRECT CURRENT

When a current is induced by plunging a magnet into a coil of wire connected to a galvanometer, the needle of the galvanometer deflects in a particular direction. As we have noted, when the magnet is withdrawn from the coil, the galvanometer needle deflects in the opposite direction. This shows that the direction of current depends on the direction in which the magnet is moved.

An electric current that reverses its direction at regular intervals is known as an *alternating current,* or AC. When the electrons make one complete trip back and forth in the circuit, we say that two alternations have occurred, and the electrons are said to have completed one *cycle.* Most homes in this country are supplied with 60-cycle alternating current, that is, current that changes its direction approximately 120 times every second.

A flow of electrons traveling in one direction in a circuit is known as a *direct current,* or DC. Batteries are common sources of direct current. Both alternating current and direct current circuits are useful in the home and for commercial and industrial needs. However, most power companies supply only alternating current for these purposes because alternating current, as we will see later, is transmitted from generating stations to the user more economically than direct current.

ELECTRIC GENERATORS

Electric generators resemble electric motors. In an electric motor, a flow of electrons through the windings of a coil causes a continuous rotation of the armature. In a generator, on the other hand, the rotation of the armature between the poles of a magnet induces voltage in the armature. The voltage, in turn, induces current. The mechanical energy required to drive the armature of a generator may be derived directly or indirectly from falling water, from coal, or from atomic energy.

AC Generators

An *alternating-current generator* consists of an armature coil mounted on a shaft between the poles of either a permanent magnet, as shown in Fig. 17–18, page 316, or an electromagnet. A half-turn of the armature causes a flow of electrons in the coil in one direction. Completing the rotation of the armature with another half-turn means motion through the magnetic field in the opposite direction. This causes a flow of electrons in the coil in the opposite direction. To complete the circuit, the alternating current passes to two metal rings, called *slip rings,* which are mounted on the same shaft as the armature. From the slip rings, brushes lead the alternating current to the load (lamps) or to the user.

DC Generators

In some generators, a commutator, such as the one used in the electric motor, is mounted on the shaft in place of the slip rings (Fig.

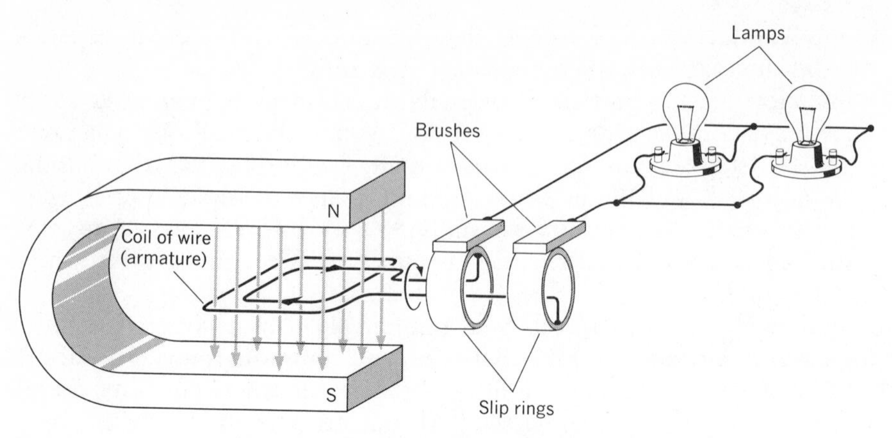

Fig. 17–18. An alternating-current generator.

17–19). Recall that the commutator reverses the direction of electron flow in the motor. In the same way, each half of the commutator in this type of generator changes from one brush to another at the exact instant that the direction of electron flow in each half of the commutator is reversed. This produces a flow of electrons in one direction only, and such a generator is called a *direct-current generator*.

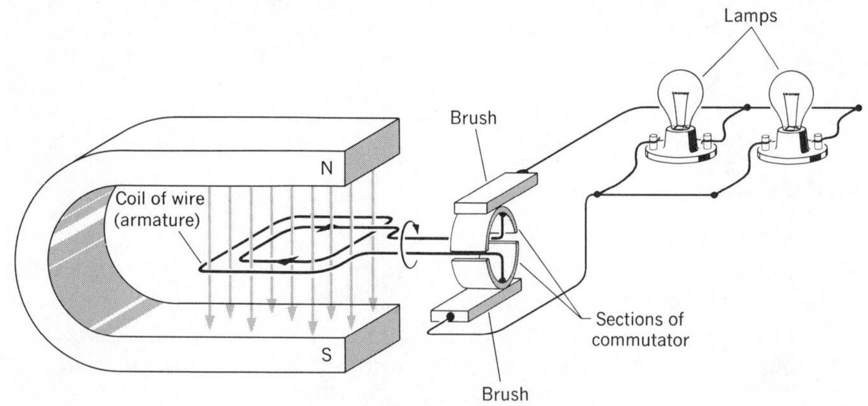

Fig. 17–19. A direct-current generator.

TRANSFORMERS

It is impossible to transmit electricity over long distances without some loss of power. These losses generally occur as heat. Wires carrying electric current generate heat, and the quantity of heat is roughly dependent upon the amperage. The larger the amperage, that is, the greater is the heat produced. It is therefore more economical to transmit low-amperage electricity.

Transformers are devices designed to change the voltage produced by power companies for use in the home and in industry. For many home uses, the voltage supplied must be reduced, or *stepped down.* For many industrial uses, the voltage must be increased, or *stepped up.*

Basically, a transformer is an electromagnet consisting of two coils, a *primary coil* and a *secondary coil,* both wound on the same core (Fig. 17–20). When alternating current enters the primary coil, the coil becomes magnetized, and the poles change many times a second as the alternating current changes direction. The effect of the alternating current is to make and break a magnetic field very often. This has the same effect as moving a magnet into and out of a coil very rapidly. Thus, in a transformer, magnetic lines of force are cut in the same manner as they would be cut by a moving magnet or coil.

When the alternating current in the primary coil of a transformer magnetizes the coil, lines of force spring up first in one direction and then in the other. Since the primary and secondary coils are on the same core, when the primary becomes an alternating electromagnet, the lines of force of the primary induce a corresponding alternating voltage in the secondary coil.

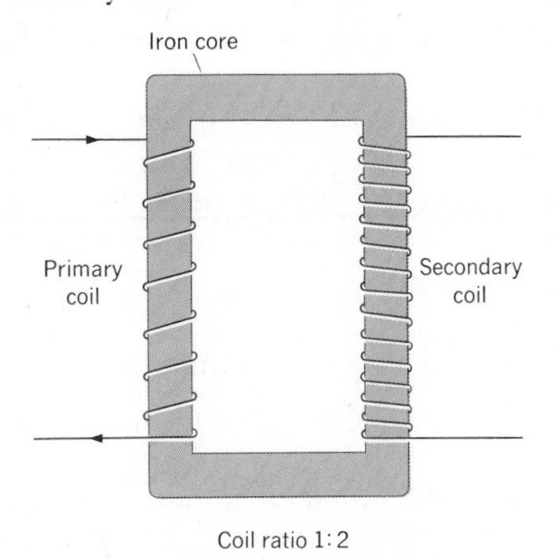

Fig. 17–20. A transformer.

Step-Up Transformer

When the number of turns in the secondary coil is greater than that in the primary coil, the voltage induced in the secondary is greater than that in the primary. Such a device is called a *step-up transformer.*

It would appear that, in the transformer, we are getting something for nothing—which violates the law of conservation of energy. But we know that the total electrical energy is roughly equal to the product of the voltage and the current. Thus, as the induced voltage increases, the induced current drops proportionately, and the total amount of electrical energy remains unchanged. Before an alternating voltage is transmitted over long distances, it is sent through the primary coil of a step-up transformer. The secondary coil then supplies a much higher voltage but a smaller current. In this way, heat losses in transmission are minimized.

Step-Down Transformer

When the number of turns of wire in the secondary coil is less than the number of turns in the primary coil, the voltage in the secondary is less than the voltage in the primary. The current in the secondary is proportionately higher, which keeps the total amount of electrical energy unchanged. This type of transformer is called a *step-down transformer.*

Calculating the Voltage of a Transformer

When the secondary coil has twice as many turns of wire as the primary coil, the voltage induced in the secondary is twice that in the primary. Accordingly, we conclude that the ratio of the number of turns in the primary to the number of turns in the secondary determines the ratio of the voltages between the primary and the secondary coils. Thus, when we know the number of turns of wire in the primary and secondary coils, as well as the voltage in one of the coils, we can find the voltage in the other by using the formula

$$\frac{\text{primary voltage}}{\text{secondary voltage}} = \frac{\text{turns in primary}}{\text{turns in secondary}}$$

For example, suppose the primary is wound with 300 turns of wire and the secondary with 600 turns. If the voltage of the primary is 115 volts, what is the voltage of the secondary?

$$\frac{\text{primary voltage}}{\text{secondary voltage}} = \frac{\text{turns in primary}}{\text{turns in secondary}}$$

$$\text{or, } \frac{\text{secondary voltage}}{\text{primary voltage}} = \frac{\text{turns in secondary}}{\text{turns in primary}}$$

$$\text{secondary voltage} = \text{primary voltage} \times \frac{\text{turns in secondary}}{\text{turns in primary}}$$

Now, substituting from the problem,

$$\text{secondary voltage} = 115 \text{ volts} \times \frac{600 \text{ turns}}{300 \text{ turns}}$$

(Note that the numbers $\frac{600}{300} = \frac{2}{1}$, and that the units $\frac{\text{turns}}{\text{turns}} = 1$.)

$$\text{secondary voltage} = \frac{115 \text{ volts} \times 2}{1} = 230 \text{ volts}$$

The use of step-up transformers in generating stations permits power companies to use thin wires to carry high-voltage, low-current electricity to transformer stations near the user's home. By using step-down transformers installed near the user, the high voltages can be reduced to 220 or 110 volts, which are the voltages usually required by electrical devices in our homes.

Looking Back

With very few exceptions, the electrical devices used in homes, factories, and transportation depend upon electromagnets. Such devices are used in communication, radio, television, and in electric motors.

Looking Ahead

A large part of the electrical energy we use is produced by the burning of fuels. Our continuing use of increasing amounts of electricity leads to the use of increasing amounts of fuels. This is the basis of our modern energy crisis. Nuclear energy is a possible solution to the energy crisis. We will study nuclear energy next.

Multiple-Choice Questions

1. The advantage of FM radio transmission over AM transmission is that FM
   a. is cheaper
   b. cuts out static noises
   c. can be sent over greater distances
   d. can transmit pictures

2. When the number of turns of wire around the core of an electromagnet is increased, the strength of the electromagnet
   a. increases
   b. remains the same
   c. decreases
   d. increases then decreases
3. A decrease in the amount of current supplied to an electromagnet causes the strength of the electromagnet to
   a. increase
   b. decrease
   c. remain the same
   d. first decrease then increase
4. Which of the following substances, used as the core of an electromagnet, produces the strongest magnet?
   a. copper b. cobalt c. wood d. soft iron
5. In general, when the thickness of the core of an electromagnet is increased, the strength of the electromagnet
   a. increases
   b. decreases
   c. remains the same
   d. first increases then decreases
6. In an electric bell, the circuit is completed when the hammer touches the
   a. armature b. electromagnet c. contact screw d. core
7. A telegraph consists of a switch, a key, and
   a. an anvil b. an armature c. a relay d. a sounder
8. A device that strengthens a telegraph signal traveling long distances is the
   a. armature b. key c. relay d. sounder
9. A telephone transmitter contains a box containing granules of
   a. carbon b. sulfur c. cobalt d. silicon
10. A telephone receiver contains a
    a. relay b. diaphragm c. commutator d. set of brushes
11. In an electric motor, the split metal ring is called the
    a. armature b. brushes c. field magnet d. commutator
12. A tiny electric current can be measured with
    a. a voltmeter b. an ohmmeter c. a galvanometer d. a shunt
13. An ammeter is protected from burning out by a
    a. shunt b. coil c. magnet d. galvanometer
14. Large electric currents are best measured with
    a. an ammeter
    b. a galvanometer
    c. a voltmeter
    d. an ohmmeter
15. Electromotive force in a circuit is measured with
    a. a galvanometer
    b. a voltmeter
    c. an ammeter
    d. an ohmmeter
16. That electricity can be produced from magnetism was first proposed by
    a. Oersted b. Ampère c. Volta d. Faraday
17. As the motion of a magnet in a coil of wire increases, the voltage induced in the coil
    a. decreases
    b. remains the same
    c. increases
    d. decreases then increases
18. When a strong magnet moving in a coil is replaced by a weaker magnet, the voltage induced in the coil
    a. decreases
    b. increases
    c. remains the same
    d. decreases then increases

19. An electric current that reverses its direction frequently is known as
    a. a direct current
    b. a reversing current
    c. an alternating current
    d. a steady current
20. A device that produces an electric current by means of electromagnetic induction is called
    a. a meter b. a generator c. a transformer d. an amplifier
21. In an alternating-current generator, the current produced is carried to the load by the
    a. magnet b. transformer c. commutator d. brushes
22. A transformer in which the number of turns of wire in the secondary coil is greater than the number of turns of wire in the primary coil
    a. increases the voltage
    b. decreases the voltage
    c. increases the current
    d. decreases the voltage and the current
23. In a step-up transformer, as the induced voltage increases, the induced current
    a. remains the same
    b. increases
    c. increases then decreases
    d. decreases
24. When the secondary coil of a transformer has twice as many turns of wire as the primary coil, the induced voltage in the secondary coil is
    a. half as great as in the primary
    b. the same as in the primary
    c. twice that in the primary
    d. four times that in the primary
25. Radio waves that carry voice waves are called
    a. transmitters b. detectors c. carriers d. amplifiers
26. A television wave consists of
    a. an FM wave only
    b. an AM wave only
    c. an AM wave and an FM wave
    d. two FM waves

Modified True-False Questions

1. Objects that permit magnetic lines of force to pass through them have the property of *magnetism.*
2. An electromagnet is *a permanent* magnet.
3. In an electric bell, the electromagnet attracts the *armature and hammer.*
4. Messages are sent by telegraph using the *International Morse Code.*
5. A transmitter and receiver are parts of *a generator.*
6. In an electric motor, current is brought to the commutator by *a slip ring.*
7. In a circuit, a voltmeter is always connected in *series.*
8. A magnet moving in a coil produces a voltage by *electromagnetic induction.*
9. A flow of electrons traveling in one direction in a circuit is known as *alternating current.*
10. When electrons make one back-and-forth trip in an alternating current, they have completed one *cycle.*
11. In a motor, the direction of voltage flow is reversed by the *armature.*

12. A device used to change the voltage entering it is called *a generator*.
13. The input voltage of *a step-down transformer* is less than the output voltage.
14. Electrical resistance is measured by *an ammeter*.
15. As the number of turns of wire on a coil is increased, the voltage induced by a magnet moving in this coil *increases*.
16. A carrier wave is produced by *an antenna*.
17. Different frequencies in a radio are selected by *a tuner*.
18. The sound portion of a television program is transmitted by *AM* radio waves.

Thought Questions

1. Describe four methods that we can use to increase the strength of an electromagnet.
2. Describe how a telephone operates.
3. Describe how electricity is produced from magnetism.
4. Discuss three methods by which the strength of an induced current can be increased.
5. What is the difference between alternating and direct current?
6. a. The number of turns of wire in the primary of a step-up transformer is 200. The secondary contains 800 turns of wire. What is the voltage produced by the secondary coil if 120 volts enters the primary coil?
   b. In a step-down transformer, the primary has 1000 turns of wire, whereas the secondary has 500 turns of wire. What voltage is produced by the secondary if the primary is supplied with 120 volts?
7. Explain how it is possible for your television set to have a picture but *no* sound.

CHAPTER 18

WHAT IS THE SOURCE OF NUCLEAR ENERGY?

When you have completed this chapter, you should be able to:

1. *Relate* the atomic structure of elements to the development of our knowledge of radioactivity.
2. *Describe* the properties of the different particles emitted from radioactive elements.
3. *Explain* the devices used to detect radiation.
4. *Discuss* some of the peaceful applications of radioactivity.
5. *Appreciate* the dangers and safety precautions in using radioactive materials.
6. *Define* transmutation, half-life, chain reaction.
7. *Distinguish* between (*a*) isotope and radioisotope (*b*) electrons, protons, and neutrons (*c*) nuclear fission and nuclear fusion.

In the laboratory experience that follows, you will construct and use a device to detect radiation.

Laboratory Experience

HOW IS RADIATION DETECTED?

A. For this experiment, you will need a glass jar that has been especially prepared, a small amount of alcohol, a piece of dry ice, a flashlight, and a metal tray.

   The glass jar should have a clear bottom. Do not use a jar with a rippled or frosted bottom. Line the inside of the jar with black cloth or dull black paper. The black cloth or paper should cover the sides of the jar except for a strip 2 centimeters wide at the top of the jar. The inside of the lid should be painted dull black. See Fig. 18–1, page 324.

B. Your teacher will provide the alcohol and a source of radioactivity.

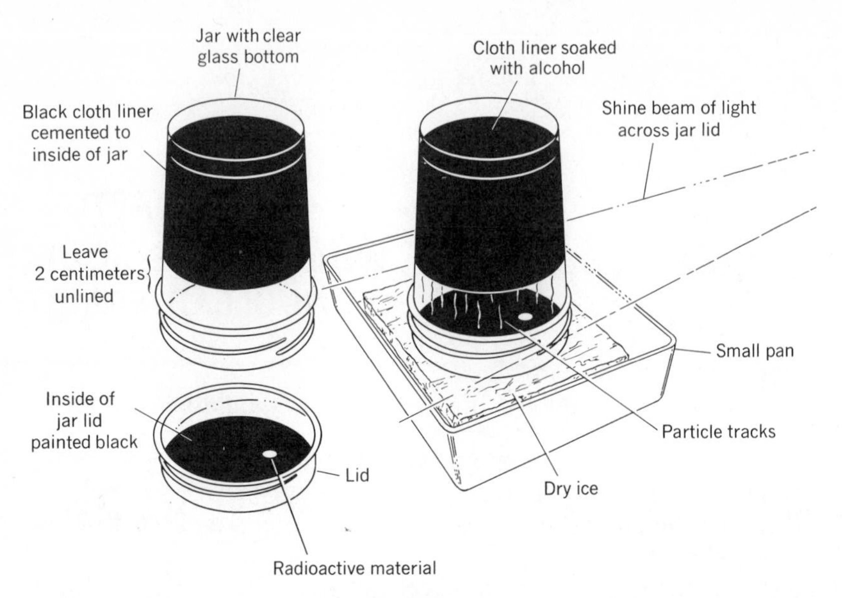

Fig. 18–1.

Lay the lid of the jar upside-down on the table. Place the radioactive source inside the lid. Soak the black lining with the alcohol and screw the jar into the lid, which should remain upside-down on the table.

CAUTION: Dry ice can cause serious burns. Do not handle the dry ice with your bare hands.

C. Using a pair of tongs or a cloth towel, place a flat piece of dry ice in the metal tray. Place the jar, still upside-down, on the piece of dry ice.

1. Describe what you see inside the jar.

D. Allow the jar to cool for 15 minutes. Turn out the lights in the room. Shine a flashlight into the jar, just above the lid, so that the beam of light passes completely through the jar, as shown in Fig. 18–1.

2. Describe the appearance of any particles or tracks that you may see inside the jar.

3. How do you account for the presence of these particles or tracks?

E. Remove the jar from the dry ice, unscrew the lid (making sure the jar is still upside-down), and place the lid on the table. Hold a Geiger-counter probe 15 centimeters from the radioactive source. Note how rapidly the clicks occur.

4. Cover the lid with a sheet of cardboard. Is there any change in how rapidly the clicks occur? Explain.
5. Cover the lid with a sheet of lead. Is there any change in how rapidly the clicks occur? Explain.
6. If the rate of clicking between the cardboard and the lead is different, how do you account for the difference?
7. Which substance, cardboard or lead, do you believe offers greater protection against harmful radiation? Explain.

Introduction

In the preceding chapters of this unit, we have discussed the various forms of energy that we need and use in our civilized environment. Much of this energy is derived from some type of fuel such as wood, coal, natural gas, and petroleum (oil). These fuels are exhaustible resources. If we continue to use these resources at the current rate, we may exhaust them in a few generations. Without these fuels, our advanced civilization would come to a standstill.

Energy is derived from coal and petroleum by burning. The smoke and gases produced by burning pollute the air and sometimes make it unbreathable. Until the day comes when we can use the sun's energy on a large scale, we must look for other energy sources.

An immediate, possible answer to the energy problem appears to be *nuclear energy*—the energy locked in the nuclei of atoms. Generators that convert nuclear energy to heat and electrical energy are available and are in use to a limited extent. Although generators of this type have many advantages over those that use ordinary fuels, generators using nuclear energy usually produce different types of pollutants. In this chapter, we will discuss the source of nuclear energy, its uses, and its dangers.

RADIOACTIVITY

Our understanding of nuclear energy began with the discovery of radioactivity. In 1896, *Antoine Henri Becquerel*, a French physicist, conducted experiments with crystals of a uranium compound. By accident, he stored these crystals in a drawer containing a photographic plate that was wrapped securely in black, lightproof paper. When Becquerel used this plate in a camera and developed it, he noticed that, in addition to the picture, there were black streaks on the plate. Puzzled as to how the streaks were formed, he placed a fresh photographic plate in the same drawer, but this time he removed the uranium crystals. Later, when he developed this plate, he found that there were no black streaks on it.

He reasoned that the uranium compound must have emitted invisible rays that possessed enough energy to affect the chemicals in a covered photographic plate.

At the request of Becquerel, the French physicists *Marie* and *Pierre Curie* investigated the mysterious rays coming from the uranium compound. As a source of the uranium compound, they used an ore of uranium called *pitchblende*. In 1898, they succeeded in isolating from pitchblende two elements that release even more energy than uranium—radium and polonium.

Today, we speak of this type of energy as atomic energy, or nuclear energy, because we know that this kind of energy comes from the nuclei (centers) of atoms. Elements containing such atoms are said to be *radioactive*, or to have the property of *radioactivity*. In order to understand radioactivity and its relation to energy, therefore, we must first review some basic ideas about atoms.

SOME ELEMENTS ARE RADIOACTIVE

All matter is composed of tiny particles called atoms. An atom is the smallest part of an element that still has the properties of the element. There are 105 known elements. In a particular element, the atoms generally have the same properties. In different elements, the atoms have different properties.

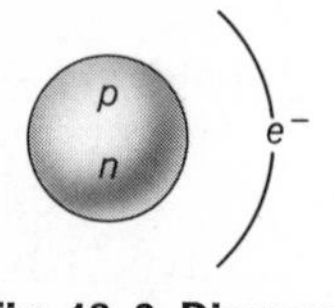

Fig. 18–2. Diagram of an atom.

An atom of any element consists mainly of three types of tinier particles: electrons, protons, and neutrons. Protons (p) and neutrons (n) are found in the center, or nucleus (plural, nuclei), of an atom. The electrons (e^-) are found outside the nucleus (Fig. 18–2).

An electron carries a negative electrical charge. A proton carries a positive electrical charge equal in strength to the negative charge of the electron. A neutron has no electrical charge—it is neutral.

In any atom, the number of electrons around the nucleus equals the number of protons in the nucleus. Thus, the number of positive and negative charges is counterbalanced, making the electrical charge on the atom as a whole equal to zero (neutral). The number of protons, or the number of electrons, in an atom is called the *atomic number* of the element. Each of the 105 elements has a different atomic number ranging from 1 to 105. When atoms react with each other, as in a chemical change, the atoms either transfer electrons or share electrons. Sufficient electrons are transferred or shared between atoms so that the new matter formed is electrically neutral.

Protons and neutrons inside the nucleus make up the greatest part of the weight of an atom. The weight of one atom relative to the weight of a carbon atom, used as a standard, is called *atomic weight* (also *atomic mass*). Protons and neutrons have about the same weight. Since each proton or neutron is about 1840 times heavier than an electron, the weight (or mass) of an atom is concentrated in the nucleus. That is, the weight (mass) of an atom is the weight (mass) of its protons and neutrons. The atoms of a particular element differ in atomic weight from the atoms of other elements because no two elements have the same number of protons and the same number of neutrons in the nuclei of their atoms. (Since the weight of electrons is so small, we usually omit their weights when atomic weights are considered.)

The same element may exist in different forms. Each form has the same number of electrons (and protons) in its atoms, but each form has a slightly different atomic weight. This difference means that each form of the element has a different number of neutrons in its atomic nucleus. These varieties of the same element are called *isotopes*. For example, the element carbon (atomic number 6) has several isotopes. Among these are the isotope having an atomic weight of 12 and another of atomic weight 14. Common carbon (coal, diamond, black deposits on spark plugs) is composed largely of atoms of atomic weight 12. Any other isotopes in such examples of carbon are present in extremely small quantities. Carbon of atomic weight 12 (carbon-12) is not radioactive. Therefore, it is said to be a stable isotope of carbon. On the other hand, carbon of atomic weight 14 (carbon-14) is radioactive and is said to be unstable.

All the elements from atomic number 1 through 83 exist as both stable (nonradioactive) and unstable (radioactive) isotopes. Unstable isotopes are also called *radioisotopes*. All the elements beyond atomic number 83, whether natural or artificial, are radioactive.

An example of an element that has stable and unstable isotopes is hydrogen (atomic number 1). This element has three isotopes, all of which have 1 electron outside the nucleus. Usually, when representing the isotopes of elements, the atomic number is written as a subscript to the left of the symbol; the atomic weight (number of protons and neutrons) is written as a superscript to the left of the symbol. Common hydrogen, also called *protium*, which has 1 proton in its nucleus but has no neutrons, is written ${}^{1}_{1}H$. *Deuterium*, another isotope of hydrogen, has 1 proton and 1 neutron in its nucleus. Since the atomic weight is 2, deuterium is written ${}^{2}_{1}H$. Deuterium, often called *heavy hydrogen*, is not radioactive. Water containing heavy hydrogen is called *heavy water*. The third isotope of hydrogen, *tritium*, has 1 proton and 2 neutrons in its nucleus. Tritium, written ${}^{3}_{1}H$, is heavier than deuterium and is radioactive.

An example of an element that has only unstable isotopes is uranium. This element, and others like it, will be discussed later in this chapter.

RADIOACTIVE ISOTOPES DISINTEGRATE AND EMIT RAYS

When an unstable isotope emits radiation, the isotope changes to another element that is lighter in atomic weight and often different in atomic number. Such a change in an unstable element is called *radioactive decay* or *disintegration*. For example, when atoms of carbon-14 emit radiation, their nuclei emit electrons. (The electrons are thought to come from the breakdown of a neutron into a proton and an electron.) As a result, the nuclei are left with a greater positive charge than before. Such nuclei are no longer those of carbon but instead are nuclei of the element nitrogen. This change is shown in a special equation called a *nuclear equation:*

$$\text{carbon} \rightarrow \text{nitrogen} + \text{electron}$$
$$^{14}_{6}\text{C} \rightarrow {}^{14}_{7}\text{N} + {}^{0}_{-1}e$$

Each superscript represents the number of protons and neutrons in the nucleus (atomic weight), and each subscript represents the number of protons in the nucleus or of electrons outside the nucleus (atomic number). Note that the superscripts on both sides of the nuclear equation are balanced: $14 = 14 + 0$. Similarly, the subscripts are also balanced: $6 = 7 + (-1)$.

All the radioactive elements undergo radioactive decay and, in so doing, change to other elements. In this process, energy is released. When the element that is formed is a stable one, the decay process stops, and no more energy is released.

TYPES OF RAYS EMITTED BY ATOMS

In 1903, *Ernest Rutherford* investigated the nature of the radiations emitted from pitchblende. He placed a sample of the ore in a lead box open on one side (Fig. 18–3). By allowing the radiations to pass through the opening and then between a positively charged plate and a negatively charged plate, he identified three types of radiation.

Alpha Particles

As Fig. 18–3 shows, one component of the beam of radiation veers toward the negatively charged plate. According to the law of electric charges, opposite charges attract each other. Therefore, the rays or particles that are attracted to the negative plate must be positively charged. These rays are called *alpha rays*, or *alpha particles*.

Many experiments have shown that alpha particles are actually the

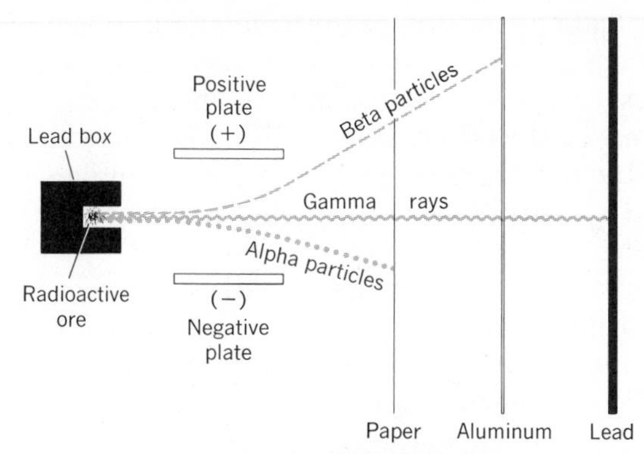

Fig. 18–3. Rutherford's experiment.

nuclei of helium atoms; that is, they are composed of 2 protons and 2 neutrons. Therefore, an alpha particle has an atomic weight of 4 and a charge of +2. The abbreviation for an alpha particle is ${}_2^4He$.

The speed at which alpha particles travel is approximately one-tenth the speed of light. Traveling at this relatively slow speed, these relatively heavy particles can pass through a thin sheet of paper. However, they can be stopped by a barrier of greater thickness.

Beta Particles

Fig. 18–3 also shows that one component of the beam turns sharply toward the positive plate and, therefore, must be negatively charged. This component of the beam consists of electrons which, in this case, are called *beta rays*, or *beta particles*. These particles turn toward the positive plate to a far greater extent than the alpha particles turn toward the negative plate. The angles to which the alpha and beta particles are turned (deflected) show that alpha particles are more massive, or heavier, than beta particles.

These observations, and other experiments, indicate that beta particles are high-speed electrons emitted from the nuclei of atoms. The abbreviation for this kind of beta particle is the same as the symbol for an electron, ${}_{-1}^{0}e$. These electrons travel at a speed close to that of light. Beta particles can pass through paper because of their great speed. However, they cannot pass through a thin sheet of aluminum.

Gamma Rays

The third component of the beam of radiation shown in Fig. 18–3 is not deflected from the path between the oppositely charged plates. Therefore, we know that this component must be electrically neutral.

This type of radiation is called *gamma radiation*, or *gamma rays*. These rays are high-frequency electromagnetic waves (similar to X rays).

Gamma rays have no mass but possess high energy. They are the most penetrating of the rays emitted from radioactive elements and are, consequently, the most dangerous. Gamma rays can pass through paper, aluminum, and living tissue. They can be stopped only by thick sheets of lead or concrete.

When any one of the three types of radiation collides with an atom, electrons are stripped from the atom. As a result, the atom becomes electrically charged, or *ionized*. For this reason, alpha, beta, and gamma rays are described as *ionizing rays*.

DETECTING RADIATION

The ionizing ability of alpha, beta, and gamma rays makes it possible to detect their presence. This is accomplished by means of devices that tell us when ionization takes place. Some of these are briefly described in the following sections.

Film Badges

Remember that radiations from radioactive substances were first discovered by their effect on a photographic plate. Although invisible, the radiations ionize the photographic chemicals in film and change them. Buttons containing film, called *film badges*, are worn by people working near radioactive materials. At the end of each work day, the film is developed and examined for black streaks to determine the extent of a worker's exposure to radiation.

The Electroscope

In Chapter 15 we learned that the electroscope is used to detect a static electric charge. This device can also be used to detect radioactivity. When a charged electroscope, which has its leaves separated, is placed near a radioactive source, the radiations ionize the air molecules near the electroscope. The ionized air molecules neutralize the charge of the electroscope and cause its leaves to collapse. The rate at which the leaves of the electroscope collapse is a measure of the amount of radioactivity present; that is, the faster the rate of collapse of the leaves, the greater is the amount of radiation present.

The Geiger-Müller Counter

A *Geiger-Müller counter*, or *Geiger counter*, is composed of a gas-filled tube (Geiger-Müller tube), shown in Fig. 18–4, and a signaling

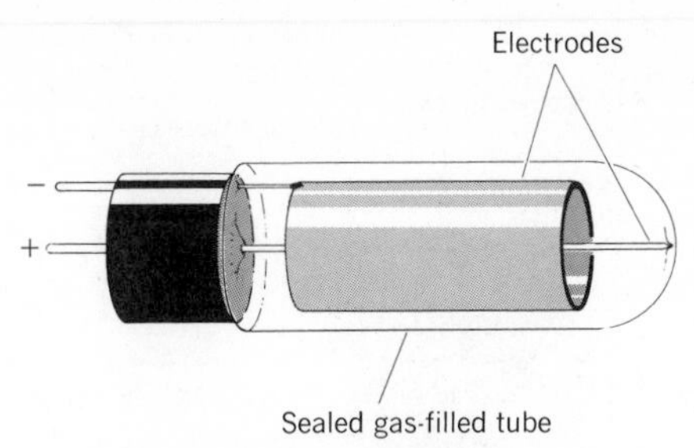

Fig. 18–4. The Geiger-Müller tube.

device such as a lamp or a sounder. The tube contains argon gas under low pressure and two electrodes that are separated by the gas. The electrodes are part of an electric circuit that connects them to the signaling device. When charged particles or gamma rays pass into the tube, the gas inside becomes ionized for a split second. The ionized gas conducts an electric current to the signaling device, which then produces a flash of light or a clicking sound. The greater the number of signals per second, the greater is the degree of radioactivity of the substance being studied.

The Cloud Chamber

In 1911, *C. T. R. Wilson,* a Scottish physicist, designed an apparatus in which radioactive particles could be tracked and studied. This device, called a *cloud chamber,* consists of a reservoir and a rubber bulb (Fig. 18–5, page 332). Water containing a black dye is placed in the reservoir, and the material to be studied is placed on a little shelf above the water. In a short time, the air above the water becomes saturated with water vapor. Then the rubber bulb is squeezed, thereby compressing the saturated air. As the bulb is released, the air expands and cools and becomes super-saturated with water vapor. Alpha particles (or any other ionizing material) striking the air molecules cause these molecules to become ionized. The ions act as centers around which the water vapor can condense. As water vapor condenses on the ions, the path of the ions becomes visible.

Our laboratory experience employed a variation of Wilson's cloud chamber. We account for the bright streaks coming from the radioactive sources as follows: The alcohol evaporates into the air of the jar, which is cooled by the dry ice. When an ionizing particle passes through the cold vapor, condensation takes place along the path of the particle, making the track visible. Using a Geiger-counter probe, you also observed how certain solids stop radioactive particles, such as alpha particles.

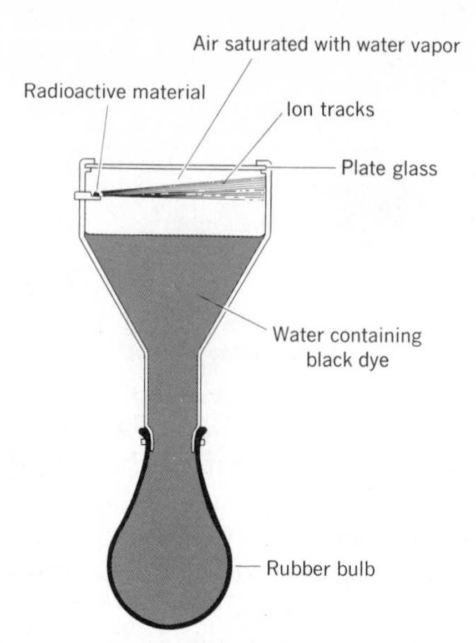

Fig. 18–5. The Wilson cloud chamber.

The Bubble Chamber

The *bubble chamber,* a highly specialized piece of equipment, is used to observe the tracks of particles that move too rapidly for observation in a cloud chamber. In one type of bubble chamber, liquid hydrogen is heated under pressure to a temperature slightly above its normal boiling point. The liquid becomes superheated, but does not boil. When high-energy particles enter the chamber, they create a trail of ions. These ions, in turn, pass through the liquid and cause the liquid to boil, producing a track of small bubbles. The properties of the track of bubbles make it possible to identify the type of particle producing it.

HOW NUCLEAR ENERGY IS RELEASED

All radioactive elements undergo radioactive decay. For example, when carbon-14 decays and emits radiation, the carbon is transformed into another element—nitrogen. Such a transformation of one element into another is called *transmutation.*

The natural decay of uranium to a stable element involves several transmutations. Each transmutation is accompanied by the release of energy. When an atom of uranium-238 ($^{238}_{92}U$) decays, it emits an alpha particle (helium nucleus, $^{4}_{2}He$). Accordingly, the atomic weight of the atom decreases by 4 weight units (2 protons + 2 neutrons), and its atomic number decreases by 2. These changes result in an atomic nucleus of 234 weight units and an atomic number of 90. This is the nucleus of the element thorium. Thus, the decay of uranium results in nuclei of two different atoms—helium and thorium. These changes can be summarized as follows:

$$\text{uranium} \rightarrow \text{thorium} + \text{alpha particle} + \text{energy}$$
$$^{238}_{92}\text{U} \rightarrow {}^{234}_{90}\text{Th} + {}^{4}_{2}\text{He} + \text{energy}$$

Note that the atomic weights (superscripts) balance. $238 = 234 + 4$. The atomic numbers (subscripts) also balance: $92 = 90 + 2$.

Like uranium, thorium is radioactive and decays as follows:

$$\text{thorium} \rightarrow \text{protactinium} + \text{beta particle} + \text{energy}$$
$$^{234}_{90}\text{Th} \rightarrow {}^{234}_{91}\text{Pa} + {}^{0}_{-1}e + \text{energy}$$

The atomic weights balance: $234 = 234 + 0$; the atomic numbers balance: $90 = 91 + (-1)$.

Protactinium is also radioactive and decays. This decay results in another element which, in turn, also decays. This process continues for several more such radioactive transmutations, each of which is accompanied by the release of energy. The final stable element that results after 14 transmutations is an isotope of lead, $^{206}_{82}\text{Pb}$.

The transmutation of uranium and other radioactive isotopes to lead is a natural process that has been going on since the earth came into being. Artificial transmutation, however, has been utilized only since 1919. At that time, Ernest Rutherford bombarded the nuclei of nitrogen atoms with alpha particles and produced an isotope of oxygen and common hydrogen, as shown in the following equation:

$$\text{nitrogen} + \text{alpha particle} \rightarrow \text{oxygen} + \text{hydrogen}$$
$$^{14}_{7}\text{N} + {}^{4}_{2}\text{He} \rightarrow {}^{17}_{8}\text{O} + {}^{1}_{1}\text{H}$$

HALF-LIFE OF RADIOISOTOPES

The rate at which a radioactive element decays is expressed as the *half-life* of the element. The half-life of a radioactive element is the time it takes for one-half of a given amount of the element to undergo change into another element. For example, the half-life of radium is 1620 years. Thus, if a sample of 10 grams of radium existed 1620 years ago, only 5 grams of the radium would exist today. The other 5 grams would be a stable form of lead. This sample would decrease to 2.5 grams of radium, and the amount of lead would increase by the same quantity, over the next 1620 years. The rest of the sample would continue to decay at the same rate. The process never stops, since some small quantity of radioactive material is always formed.

As we will learn later in this chapter, the knowledge of the half-lives of some elements is useful in determining the age of materials containing radioactive elements. Table 18–1 shows the half-lives of some radioactive elements.

Table 18–1. The Half-Lives of Some Radioactive Elements

Isotope	*Symbol*	*Half-Life*
Carbon-14	$^{14}_{6}C$	5700 years
Cobalt-60	$^{60}_{27}Co$	5.25 years
Iodine-131	$^{131}_{53}I$	8.04 days
Iron-53	$^{53}_{26}Fe$	8.9 minutes
Phosphorus-32	$^{32}_{15}P$	14.3 days
Polonium-210	$^{210}_{84}Po$	138 days
Radium-226	$^{226}_{88}Ra$	1620 years
Sodium-24	$^{24}_{11}Na$	14.9 hours
Uranium-238	$^{238}_{92}U$	4.5 billion years

USING ENERGY FROM RADIOACTIVE ISOTOPES

In 1905, *Albert Einstein*, the renowned German-American physicist, proposed his famous equation $E = mc^2$, which indicates the amount of energy released when matter disintegrates. When this occurs, the matter is converted to energy. In the Einstein equation, E represents energy, m represents mass, and c^2 represents the square of the speed of light. According to this equation, one gram of matter can produce 25 million kilowatt-hours of energy—the amount of energy that can be released by burning about 4000 metric tons of coal.

The energy released by the decay of the naturally radioactive elements is seldom useful because these elements are relatively scarce. Since the discovery of how to convert matter to energy by means of *nuclear fission* and *nuclear fusion*, however, certain atoms have become an important source of power for our everyday needs.

Nuclear Fission and the Chain Reaction

In 1939, three European scientists, *Otto Hahn, Fritz Strassman,* and *Lise Meitner* confirmed the idea that a uranium nucleus can be split by a neutron. When the isotope uranium-235 ($^{235}_{92}U$) is bombarded with neutrons, its nucleus suddenly splits into two fragments as a burst of energy is released. As shown in the following equation, the uranium nucleus accepts a neutron, becomes unstable, and then splits, forming an atom of barium (Ba) and an atom of krypton (Kr). As this occurs, both nuclear energy and three neutrons are released.

$$\text{uranium} + \text{neutron} \rightarrow \text{barium} + \text{krypton} + 3\ \text{neutrons} + \text{energy}$$
$$^{235}_{92}U + {}^{1}_{0}n \rightarrow {}^{138}_{56}Ba + {}^{95}_{36}Kr + 3\,{}^{1}_{0}n + \text{energy}$$

The splitting of a nucleus with the release of nuclear energy into two fragments of approximately equal size is called nuclear fission. As shown in Fig. 18–6, page 336, the three neutrons released during the fission of the first uranium atom can cause the fission of three other uranium atoms, thereby releasing nine additional neutrons. These neutrons, in turn, can cause the fission of nine other uranium atoms, and so on. Such a self-continuing fission reaction is called a *chain reaction.* If the chain reaction is allowed to continue, more uranium undergoes fission, and increasing amounts of nuclear energy become available.

When a chain reaction is uncontrolled, vast quantities of nuclear energy are released instantaneously. It is this type of chain reaction that is responsible for the destructiveness of an atomic bomb.

Nuclear Fusion

Nuclear fission is important because it can release enormous amounts of energy. Nuclear fusion is the process in which the nuclei of two light atoms combine to produce a nucleus of a heavier atom. For example, when four hydrogen atoms fuse, one helium atom is formed, and two *positrons* (positively charged particles similar in size to electrons) and nuclear energy are released:

$$4\ \text{hydrogen atoms} \xrightarrow{\text{fusion}} \text{helium atom} + 2\ \text{positrons} + \text{energy}$$
$$4\,{}^{1}_{1}H \xrightarrow{\text{fusion}} {}^{4}_{2}He + 2\,{}^{0}_{+1}e + \text{energy}$$

This type of reaction is capable of releasing even larger amounts of energy than nuclear fission. Fusion reactions, also called *thermonuclear reactions,* appear to be the source of the energy released by the sun as

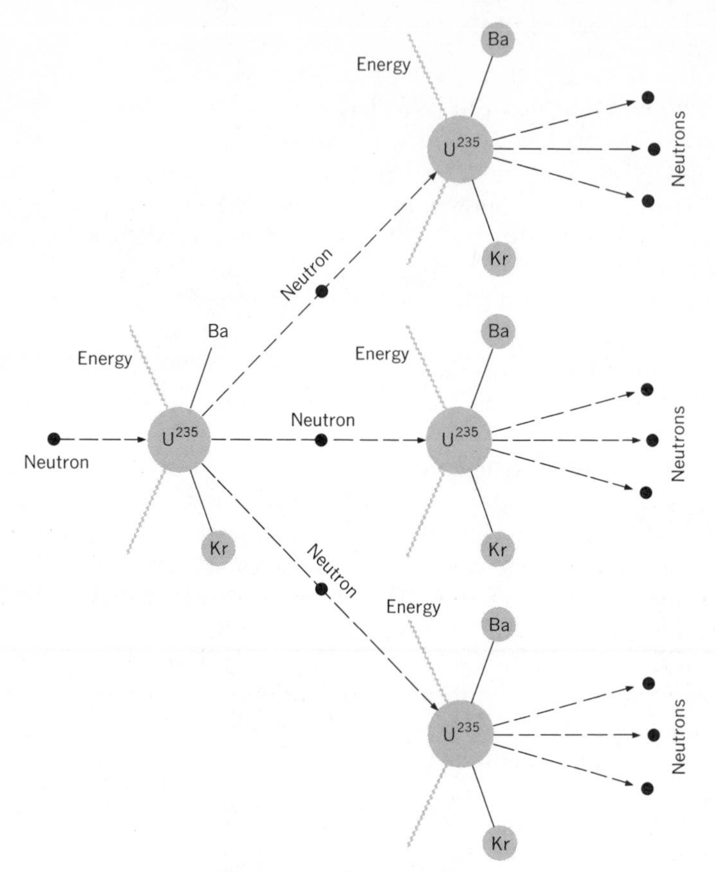

Fig. 18–6. A chain reaction.

we discussed in Chapter 7. The enormous destructiveness of the hydrogen bomb is the result of a fusion reaction.

How a Nuclear Reactor Provides Useful Energy

When a chain reaction is controlled, the energy released can be regulated and used for many peaceful purposes. Nuclear chain reactions can be controlled in the device called the *nuclear reactor*. As shown in Fig. 18–7, there are five main parts of a nuclear reactor:

1. The *fuel element* is a substance capable of undergoing nuclear fission. Such substances as uranium-235 and plutonium are often used as fuels for the nuclear reactor.

2. The *moderator* slows down the neutrons released by the nuclear fission of the fuel element. This makes the fissioning process more effi-

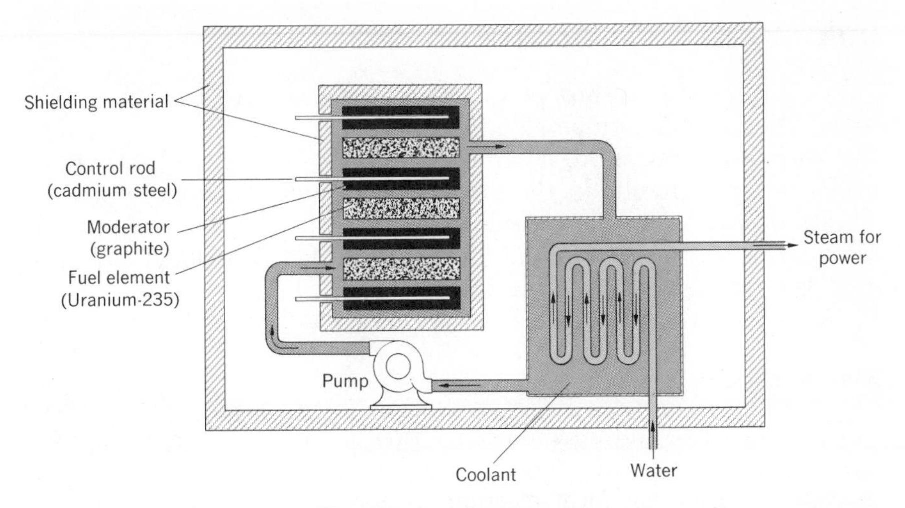

Fig. 18–7. A nuclear reactor.

cient. Pure graphite (carbon) is generally used as the moderator in a nuclear reactor.

3. The *control rods* absorb neutrons readily. Such rods are composed of cadmium steel or boron. When the control rods are withdrawn from the reactor, the chain reaction begins, as neutrons are permitted to bombard the fuel element. To stop the chain reaction, the control rods are pushed back into the reactor. Since they absorb neutrons, they stop the chain reaction.

4. The *pump* circulates a fluid, called a *coolant,* inside the shielded chamber in which fission is occurring. The coolant conducts away the heat released by fission to a heat exchanger. In the heat exchanger, water in the coil is converted to steam, which is drawn off and used to run electrical generators. Some common coolants used in reactors are heavy water or liquid sodium.

5. The *shielding* prevents the leakage of radiation. The danger of radiation produced by a nuclear reactor is lessened by proper shielding. The shielding material usually consists of concrete and thick blocks of lead.

The heat energy provided by nuclear reactors has been put to use in powering submarines, aircraft carriers, and other seagoing vessels. Nuclear reactors are used increasingly by large utility companies to produce electricity for our daily needs. One such reactor is located in the Con Edison nuclear plant at Indian Point, New York. It produces a good portion of the electrical energy consumed by New York City.

OTHER USES OF RADIOACTIVE ISOTOPES

In addition to providing power, nuclear reactors are used to prepare some artificial radioisotopes. For this purpose, an element is placed in the reactor and exposed to neutrons. The absorption of neutrons by the nuclei of atoms results in the production of radioactive elements. Examples of such elements include cobalt-60, which is used in treating some forms of cancer, and plutonium (an artificial element), which is used as a fuel element in some reactors.

Radioisotopes As Tracers

The radioactive and nonradioactive isotopes of any element have the same chemical properties. Consequently, either type of isotope may be used in a specific chemical reaction. When a radioisotope is used, its chemical pathway can be followed with one of the types of radioactivity detectors. Radioisotopes used in this way are called *tracers*. Although small quantities of radioisotopes are not useful as sources of energy, they are useful as tracers. Many of the valuable applications of radioactivity depend upon tracers. When radioisotopes are properly used, they are valuable in medical treatment, industry, and research.

Medical Uses of Radioisotopes

Phosphorus-32, one of the radioisotopes of phosphorus, is sometimes used to find certain types of cancer deep inside the body. If the cancerous tissue is a kind that ordinarily absorbs phosphorus, the absorption of phosphorus-32 by the tissue makes it possible to locate the cancer by means of one of the radioactivity detectors. Since the half-life of P-32 is about 14 days, it does not accumulate in the body.

Iodine-131, one of the radioisotopes of iodine, is used to treat an overactive thyroid gland. This gland normally absorbs iodine. When iodine-131 is given to a patient in an "atomic cocktail," the iodine-131 is absorbed by the gland. There, the radiation from the iodine-131 destroys the excess thyroid tissue. Since the half-life of iodine-131 is about 8 days, the dose can be adjusted in order to prevent damage to other tissues of the body.

Cobalt-60, a radioactive isotope that has become widely available as a result of its manufacture in nuclear reactors, is a strong emitter of gamma rays. Gamma rays have properties similar to those of X rays. Accordingly, cobalt-60 is used in X-ray photography and in treating cancers.

Radioactive salts of iron or sodium are used to trace the circulation of blood in various parts of the body. After injecting a salt containing an isotope, a doctor can follow its course in the body by means of a Geiger counter.

Industrial Uses of Radioisotopes

Radioisotopes are used as tracers in following the flow of oil through pipelines. Since these pipes transport samples of different kinds of oil one after the other, it is important to know where one kind of oil begins and another ends. If a small quantity of a radioisotope is placed into the pipeline at the point of entry of a batch of oil, workers at the receiving end of the pipeline can use a Geiger counter to identify the point of separation between two types of oil.

Radioisotopes are also used to measure the uniformity of thickness of sheets of paper, plastic, glass, or metal as they are being manufactured. The radiation from cobalt-60 is allowed to penetrate the sheet and is then detected by a Geiger counter. When differences in thickness cause the Geiger counter reading to change, it is a signal to a worker to adjust the manufacturing process.

Research Uses of Radioisotopes

Carbon-14 has been used as a tracer in the study of photosynthesis, the process by which green plants make food. As a result, the chemistry of this process is better understood.

Radioisotopes that have long half-lives may be used to determine the age of an ancient object, which usually contains radioactive material. In this process, called *radioactive dating,* the proportion of a radioactive element remaining in the object to that of the element into which it has changed is first determined. Then, the knowledge of the half-life of the radioactive element enables us to calculate how long it took for the transmutation of the radioactive element to a stable one. For example, the half-life of uranium-238 is approximately 4.5 billion years. Thus, by comparing the proportion of uranium-238 to lead-206 (the last stable element formed in the decay of uranium-238) in rocks, the age of the rocks can be determined. Using such methods, scientists believe the age of the oldest rocks on earth to be close to 5 billion years.

Carbon-14 has a half-life of about 5700 years. By calculations similar to those used for uranium and lead, the age of the remains of some living things can be found. In this type of research, the proportion studied is that of carbon-14 to carbon-12.

DANGERS OF RADIOACTIVITY

The rays emitted by radioactive substances and other sources can penetrate the body without being immediately felt. Prolonged exposure to penetrating radiation can seriously injure the body to the point of death. Radiation can damage or destroy both surface and internal tissues. Not only can radiation cause burns, but radiation can also damage the genes within cells and thereby cause *mutations*. Mutations are changes in heredity and are generally harmful. As we have learned earlier in this chapter, proper shielding can prevent excess exposure to radiation.

When a nuclear device (atomic or hydrogen bomb) is exploded in the atmosphere, radioactive materials are released, polluting the atmosphere. In time, these materials fall to the ground and continue to emit radiation. Such materials that fall to the ground any time after a nuclear explosion are called *fallout*. Frequently, fallout contains radioisotopes that have long half-lives. When these isotopes are inhaled, or when they land on food materials and are eaten, they can inflict radiation damage for a long period of time afterward. It is for these reasons that every nation is interested in taking steps to limit future tests of nuclear explosions to underground regions or to abolish all nuclear tests.

Looking Back

In this unit, we have studied the effects and uses of the various forms of energy in our environment. Nuclear energy is difficult to produce and to use safely because it carries with it the danger of long-lasting damage to ourselves and to our environment. However, if nuclear energy is produced and used with proper precautions, it will become a major source of energy in the future.

Looking Ahead

The forms of energy are as much a part of our environment as are the many kinds of matter. Both these parts of our environment are constantly changing. In Unit IV, we will learn how living things adjust to these changes.

Multiple-Choice Questions

1. Invisible rays, emitted from uranium crystals, that affect a photographic plate were discovered by
   a. Curie b. Becquerel c. Wilson d. Einstein
2. Pierre and Marie Curie succeeded in isolating
   a. polonium and radium
   b. radium and uranium
   c. polonium and uranium
   d. radium and plutonium
3. Elements that have the same atomic numbers but different atomic weights are called
   a. ions b. nonmetals c. metalloids d. isotopes
4. A radioactive isotope of carbon is
   a. C-4 b. C-12 c. C-14 d. C-6
5. A radioactive isotope of hydrogen is
   a. common hydrogen b. deuterium c. radium d. tritium
6. When a radioactive element emits radiation and changes to a different element, it is said to undergo
   a. a physical change
   b. radioactive decay
   c. a chemical change
   d. atomic fusion
7. An alpha particle is a
   a. helium nucleus
   b. hydrogen nucleus
   c. helium atom
   d. hydrogen atom
8. High-speed electrons emitted from the nuclei of atoms are called
   a. beta particles
   b. gamma rays
   c. alpha particles
   d. ions
9. A sheet of aluminum can stop
   a. gamma rays
   b. gamma rays and alpha particles
   c. alpha particles and beta particles
   d. beta particles and gamma rays
10. Gamma rays are most similar to
    a. radio waves
    b. visible light waves
    c. sound waves
    d. X rays
11. When an atom is subjected to radiation, the atom is
    a. destroyed b. disintegrated c. ionized d. split
12. Scientists who work with radioactive materials determine the amount of radiation to which they have been exposed by using a device called
    a. a film badge
    b. an electroscope
    c. a Geiger counter
    d. an ammeter
13. A device used to track and study radioactive particles is
    a. an electroscope
    b. a cyclotron
    c. a Geiger counter
    d. a cloud chamber
14. When a uranium-238 atom decays, it emits an alpha particle. The atomic weight of the new atom formed is
    a. decreased by 2
    b. increased by 4
    c. decreased by 4
    d. increased by 2

15. The final stable element formed from the radioactive decay of uranium is
    a. thorium b. lead c. plutonium d. silver
16. When an atom of nitrogen emits an alpha particle,
    a. the atom disintegrates
    b. atomic fission takes place
    c. carbon is formed
    d. oxygen is formed
17. The half-life of radium is approximately
    a. 1620 years b. 5700 years c. 5 years d. 10,000 years
18. If an original sample of carbon-14 weighs 10 grams and the half-life of carbon-14 is 5700 years, then at the end of 5700 years the amount of carbon-14 remaining would be
    a. 2.5 grams b. 5 grams c. 10 grams d. 8 grams
19. The equation $E = mc^2$ was proposed by
    a. Curie b. Becquerel c. Rutherford d. Einstein
20. When an atom of uranium undergoes fission, one of the elements produced is
    a. argon b. neon c. krypton d. xenon
21. In a nuclear reactor, neutrons are slowed down by the
    a. moderator b. control rods c. fuel element d. shielding
22. In nuclear fusion, when 4 atoms of hydrogen fuse,
    a. one atom of nitrogen is formed
    b. one atom of helium is formed
    c. a chemical change takes place
    d. a physical change takes place
23. Radioisotopes that are used to track a chemical pathway are called
    a. ions b. tracers c. atomic cocktails d. radiators
24. Of the following, the radioisotope used to treat a thyroid gland is
    a. cobalt-60 b. carbon-14 c. iodine-131 d. phosphorus-32
25. Changes in heredity that may be produced by radiation are called
    a. transformations
    b. chemical changes
    c. mutations
    d. physical changes

Modified True-False Questions

1. An element that emits rays is said to be *contaminated.*
2. Unstable isotopes of elements are called *radioisotopes.*
3. Gamma rays can be stopped by *aluminum.*
4. A clicking device used to detect radiation is *an electroscope.*
5. A device used to observe the tracks of particles that move too rapidly for a cloud chamber is *a bubble chamber.*
6. The change of an atom into a new element is called *a chemical change.*
7. The first artificial transmutation was performed by *Albert Einstein.*
8. The rate at which a radioactive element decays is known as the *half-life.*
9. The splitting of an atom into two fragments of approximately equal size is called *nuclear fusion.*
10. The self-continuation of nuclear fission is called *a chain reaction.*
11. A device used to control a nuclear chain reaction is *a bubble chamber.*

Thought Questions

1. Define each of the following terms:
   a. radioactivity
   b. isotope
   c. alpha particle
   d. transmutation
   e. half-life
2. Describe each of the following types of radiation:
   a. alpha particles b. beta particles c. gamma rays
3. List five devices that can be used to detect radiation.
4. Complete each of the following equations:

   a. ${}^{14}_{7}N + {}^{4}_{2}He \longrightarrow$

   b. ${}^{235}_{92}U + {}^{1}_{0}n \longrightarrow$

   c. $4\,{}^{1}_{1}H \xrightarrow{\text{fusion}}$
5. Determine the age of each of the following specimens:
   a. Scientists have discovered that only 2.5 grams of carbon-14 remain in a sample that originally contained 10 grams.
   b. From 10 grams of radium-226, 5 grams remain. The rest of the radium has changed to lead.
6. Complete the table, entering the function of each of the parts of a nuclear reactor.

Part	*Function*
Fuel element	
Moderator	
Control rod	
Shielding	

UNIT IV
How Living Things Adjust to the Environment

Overview

To a living thing, the environment consists of both nonliving and living parts, or factors. The *nonliving factors* include energy, such as light energy and heat energy, and substances, such as oxygen and water. The *living factors* include other living things such as plants, agents of disease, animal enemies, and living things belonging to the same species.

Normally, both the nonliving and living factors in the environment are constantly changing. If a living thing is to stay alive in its environment, the living thing must adjust to these changing conditions. Thus, the living thing must adjust to changes from light to dark, from warmth to cold, from silence to sound, from dryness to wetness, from plenty of food to lack of food, and to the presence of organisms that might either harm it or help it.

The property of *irritability* (or *sensitivity*) enables a living thing to detect and react to changes in its environment and to changes that take place within its own body. These changes are called *stimuli*, and the reactions are called *responses*.

An organism is affected by many stimuli. Some stimuli can harm the organism; others can be beneficial to it. Stimuli that start outside the body are called *external stimuli*. Among important external stimuli are light, heat, water, and the presence of other organisms. Stimuli that start inside the body are called *internal stimuli*. Among important internal stimuli are the presence of food in the stomach, the accumulation of carbon dioxide in the blood, and the products of various glands.

An organism can adjust to changes that might harm it only if it can detect such changes and then react to them. We shall concentrate on the human organism, which has two special systems that enable the body to adjust to changes. These are the *nervous system* and the *chemical control*, or *endocrine*, *system*, which is a system of ductless glands. The nervous system is sensitive to both external and internal stimuli and controls the responses of the body to both types of stimuli. For example, the stimulus of pain—from a burn or stomach ache—leads a person to react in ways that protect the body against further injury. The chemical control system responds mainly to internal stimuli. These stimuli come in part from the nervous system and in part from changes in the quantities of certain chemicals within the body. In Chapter 19 we will study the human nervous system. The chemical control system will be studied separately in Chapter 20.

CHAPTER 19
HOW DOES THE NERVOUS SYSTEM HELP US ADJUST TO THE ENVIRONMENT?

When you have completed this chapter, you should be able to:

1. *State* the functions of the nervous system and of each of its major structures.
2. *Distinguish* between (*a*) stimulus and impulse (*b*) sensory and motor nerves (*c*) nerve and nerve cell.
3. *Define* synapse, axon, ganglion.
4. *Describe* the major parts of the brain and the functions of each.
5. *Discuss* how each sense organ makes us aware of the environment.
6. *Explain* how some types of defective vision are corrected.

In the laboratory experience that follows, you will work with a frog to study the functions of some parts of its nervous system.

Laboratory Experience

HOW DOES A FROG WITHOUT A BRAIN REACT?

Note: Your teacher will either demonstrate this experience with two frogs or allow you to carry it out yourself.

A. Place a frog in a battery jar, and cover it with a piece of wire screening. Slowly turn the battery jar from right to left and then back again. Slowly turn the battery jar upside down and then back again to the normal position. Gently touch one of the frog's eyes with a pencil. With forceps, gently pinch one of the frog's toes. Copy the following table into your notebook, and record your observations of the frog's reactions.
B. The second frog has had its brain destroyed. Follow the same steps with this frog as you did with the normal frog. Record your observations in the table.

Changes in Frog's Environment	*Reactions of Normal Frog*	*Reactions of Frog With Brain Destroyed*
Turning jar		
Inverting jar		
Touching eye		
Pinching toe		

1. What conclusions do you draw from the reactions of the two frogs?
2. What part of a frog's nervous system controls each of the reactions that you tested? Give a reason for each of your answers.

Introduction

Many electrical circuits present in complicated appliances such as computers and air conditioners have thermostats and similar control devices wired into the circuits. The control devices automatically regulate the appliances. The human nervous system resembles such circuits in many ways.

The major structures that make up the nervous system are the *brain*, the *spinal cord*, *nerves*, *ganglions*, and parts of the *sense organs*. All of these structures are composed mainly of *nerve tissue*.

NERVE CELLS

The basic unit, or building block, of all living things is the *cell*, which consists of *protoplasm*. A cell contains a *nucleus* surrounded by *cytoplasm* and a *cell membrane*.

The basic unit of nerve tissue, and hence of the nervous system, is the *nerve cell* (or *neuron*). The protoplasm of this cell is more sensitive than that of any other type of cell. Some nerve cells detect stimuli; others send along *impulses*, or signals, from one part of the body to another.

Parts of a Nerve Cell

As shown in Fig. 19–1, a nerve cell has the following specialized parts:

1. The *cell body* (or *cyton*) includes the nucleus of the cell and the cytoplasm that immediately surrounds it.

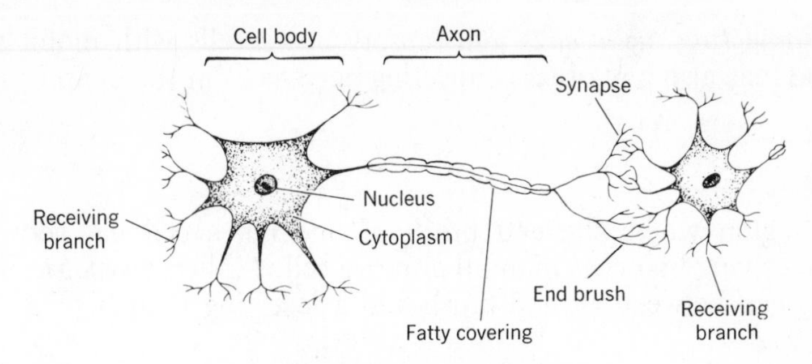

Fig. 19–1. Parts of a nerve cell.

2. The *receiving branches* are the numerous branched structures projecting from the cell body.

3. The *axon* is the single long projection from the cell body. The axon usually extends in a direction opposite to that of the receiving branches.

4. The *end brush* consists of numerous tiny branches from the end of the axon.

5. The *fatty covering* is a layer of fatlike material around the axon. The fatty material is enclosed by a delicate membrane. Some axons lack the fatty material but have the delicate membrane around them.

The receiving branches of a nerve cell pick up impulses and pass them to the cell body which, in turn, leads the impulse to the axon. The axon then leads the impulse away from the cyton to the end brush. The end brush passes the impulse to another nerve cell or to a muscle or a gland.

Types of Nerve Cells

There are four main types of nerve cells. Each type carries on a different specific activity.

1. *Receptor nerve cells,* which are present in sense organs (or *receptors*), receive stimuli from the environment. When a change in the environment occurs, impulses begin in the receptor nerve cells and continue inward into the nervous system.

2. *Sensory nerve cells* pick up impulses from sense organs and pass the impulses to the brain or spinal cord. In these organs, the sensory nerve cells make contact with many other nerve cells.

3. *Motor nerve cells* carry impulses to muscles or glands. Since these organs then respond—that is, they become active and bring about an effect—muscles and glands are called *effectors.*

4. *Connecting nerve cells* join sensory nerve cells with motor nerve cells and may also join other connecting nerve cells in the brain or spinal cord.

Synapse

The region where the end brush of one nerve cell lies very close to the receiving branches of another nerve cell is called a *synapse*. There is a tiny gap between an end brush and a receiving branch (Fig. 19–1, page 349).

Nerve Impulse

The impulse that passes along a nerve cell is a movement of chemical and electrical particles. These move from the receiving branches to the cell body, and then to the axon, end brush, and synapse. As the impulse travels, the nerve cell releases certain compounds. These substances aid in getting the impulse across the gap of the synapse.

Nerves and Ganglions

A nerve consists of a bundle of axons of several nerve cells that lie side by side. A covering of connective tissue encloses the bundle. The cell bodies of the nerve cells of some nerves lie within the brain or spinal cord. The cell bodies of the nerve cells of other nerves are located in enlargements of the nerves, called ganglions (Fig. 19–2). Ganglions are located in the trunk and neck on either side of the spinal cord, and in the head, below the brain.

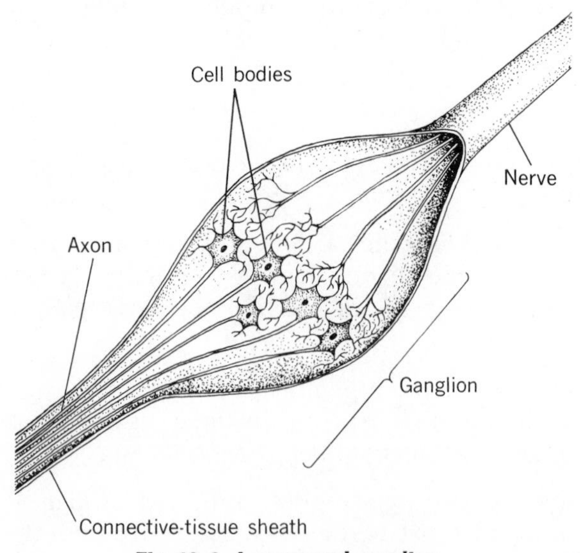

Fig. 19–2. A nerve and ganglion.

THE BRAIN

Three membranes, called *meninges,* and the bones of the skull protect the large mass of delicate nerve cells that make up the brain. (Inflammation of the meninges of the brain or spinal cord is called *meningitis,* a serious disease.) There are three main sections to the brain: the *cerebrum,* the *cerebellum,* and the *medulla oblongata* (Fig. 19–3).

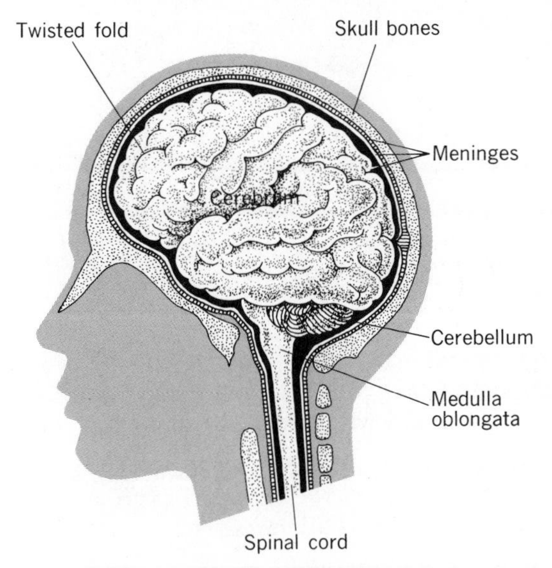

Fig. 19–3. The brain and its protections.

Cerebrum

The cerebrum is the largest section of the brain. It consists of two halves, called *cerebral hemispheres,* the bottoms of which are joined. There are two layers in the cerebrum. The outer layer consists mostly of cell bodies and synapses. This layer is often referred to as "*gray matter*" because of the grayish color of the cell bodies. The outer layer of the cerebrum has many twisted folds, which increase its surface area. The inner layer of the cerebrum, consisting mainly of axons, is referred to as "*white matter*" because of the whitish color of the fatty covering around the axons. The cerebrum carries on three major activities:

1. The cerebrum interprets the impulses, or sensations, received from the sense organs. Nerves from the sense organs reach particular portions of the cerebrum, where the impulses register as sound, light, or other sensation (Fig. 19–4, page 352).

2. The cerebrum is the center of awareness (consciousness) and

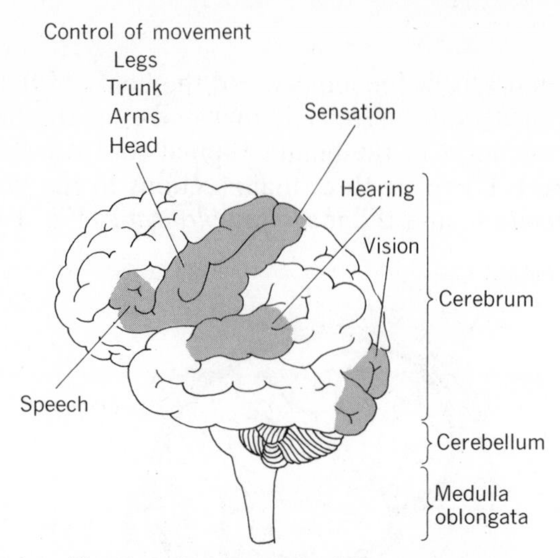

Fig. 19–4. Activity areas of the cerebrum.

thinking. Such mental activities as reasoning, deciding, remembering, and learning are associated with special areas of the cerebrum.

3. The cerebrum controls all voluntary (willful) and learned acts.

Cerebellum

The cerebellum is much smaller than the cerebrum, but, like the cerebrum, is composed of two hemispheres and two layers. The cerebellum lies below the rear portion of the cerebrum. The cerebellum carries on two major activities:

1. The cerebellum is the pathway through which impulses from the cerebrum pass on their way to muscles that are under control of the will. The movements of these muscles are coordinated by the cerebellum.

2. The cerebellum, together with the *semicircular canals* of the ear (page 359), helps maintain body balance.

Medulla Oblongata

The medulla oblongata is the smallest section of the brain. It lies below the cerebellum and connects the brain with the spinal cord. The medulla carries on two major activities:

1. The medulla oblongata controls many processes that are necessary

to maintain life. It contains nerve centers that regulate such activities as the breathing rate and the heartbeat.

2. The medulla oblongata regulates such reflex actions as the contraction of the pupil and the secretion of saliva. Reflexes are described in Chapter 21.

THE SPINAL CORD

The spinal cord is the tubelike mass of nerve tissue that extends downward from the medulla. The bones of the spine (the vertebrae) and three membranes, which are continuations of the membranes around the brain, protect the spinal cord. Like the brain, the spinal cord has two layers. But, unlike the brain, the white matter is the outer layer, and the gray matter, the inner. The spinal cord carries on two major activities:

1. The spinal cord connects the brain with branch nerves located in the lower part of the body.

2. The spinal cord controls some reflex acts. That this is so is shown by the reactions of a normal frog and of a frog whose brain has been destroyed. As you observed in your laboratory experience, when a normal frog is placed in a large jar that is slowly turned upside down, the frog tries to keep its original position. When one of the frog's eyes is touched, the frog withdraws the eye. When one of the toes of a hind leg is pinched, the frog withdraws the toe. When a frog whose brain has been destroyed is treated in the same way, this frog fails to react to changes in position and to the touching of its eye. However, when the toe of the frog whose brain has been destroyed is pinched, this frog withdraws its leg, as the normal frog does. Experiments of this type make it clear that such reflex acts as the withdrawal of the leg are not controlled by the brain, but by the spinal cord.

THE SELF-ACTING PART OF THE NERVOUS SYSTEM

Two chains of nerves and ganglions lie on either side of the spinal cord. Some connecting nerves join these nerves and ganglions to the spinal cord and brain. Other nerves connect all of these structures to groups of large ganglions called *plexuses*. The plexus located near the heart is called the *cardiac plexus*; the one near the stomach, the *solar plexus*. There are other plexuses near other organs inside the body. The chains of nerves, ganglions, plexuses, and the medulla oblongata make up the *autonomic* (self-acting) *nervous system* (Fig. 19–5, page 354).

The medulla oblongata is the coordinating center of the autonomic

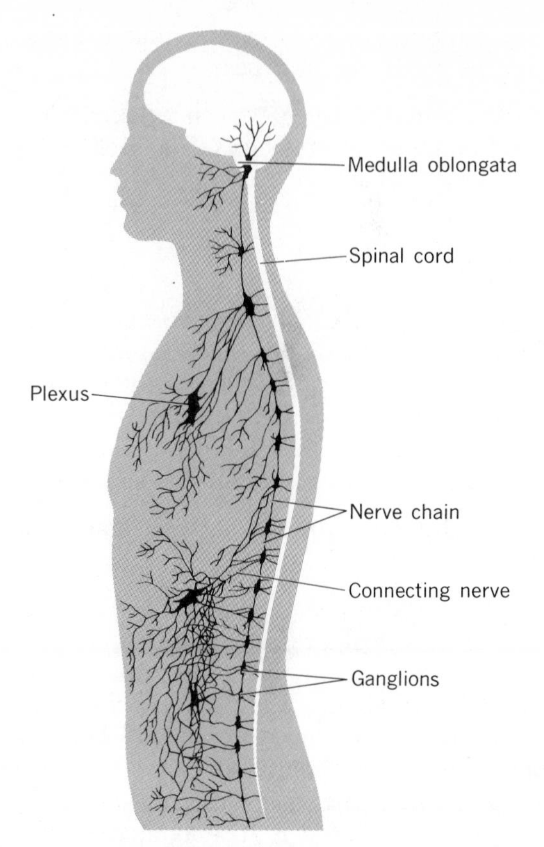

Fig. 19–5. Major parts of the autonomic nervous system.

nervous system. This system regulates many involuntary activities that are essential to our existence and of which we are seldom aware. Examples of such activities are production of juices by the glands, contraction of the small intestine, and contraction of heart muscle.

THE SENSE ORGANS

The organs that are especially sensitive to stimuli are the sense organs, or receptors. Five well-known sense organs are the eyes, ears, nose, tongue, and skin. In addition to these, there are others that receive stimuli from inside the body. Among these internal sense organs are the nerve endings in the stomach that make us aware of hunger and those in the throat that make us aware of thirst.

Each sense organ can detect only one type of stimulus—light, or sound, or chemicals, and so on. When a sense organ detects a stimulus, a nerve impulse passes over the sensory nerve from the sense organ to the special region in the cerebrum. Then, the cerebrum sends impulses over motor neurons to muscles or glands. These organs carry out the responses that help the body adjust to changes in the environment. For example, extreme heat may be harmful to the body. When heat stimuli are received by the skin, impulses eventually reach the sweat glands, which then produce increased quantities of perspiration. The general effect of this reaction is to cool the body.

EYES

The eyes are nearly spherical in shape (Fig. 19–6). Muscles are attached to the eyes and to bony sockets in the skull. These muscles enable the eyes to be moved in all directions.

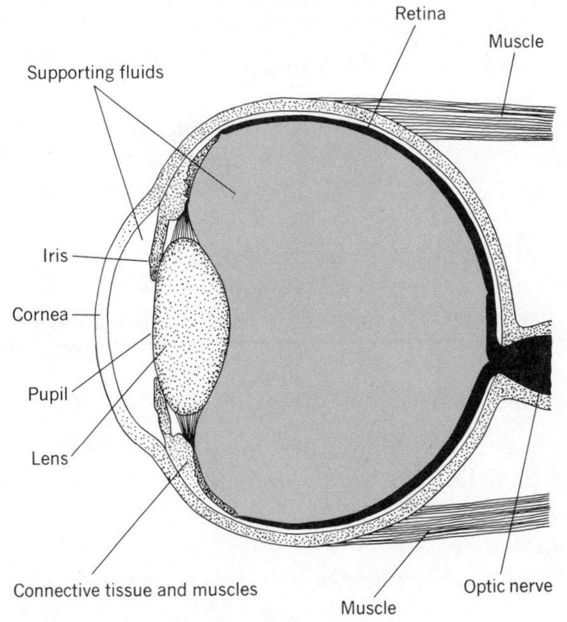

Fig. 19–6. Parts of the eye.

The center of the front of the eye is clear and colorless. This part of the eye is called the *cornea*. A short distance behind the cornea is a circular, colored band, the *iris*. In the center of the iris is a circular opening, the *pupil*. Immediately behind the iris and pupil is a clear, elastic structure, the *convex lens*. Muscle tissue and a tissue composed of fibers hold the lens in place. The *retina* is a thin layer of nerve cells that coats almost all the inner surface of the eyeball. The nerve cells of the retina are especially sensitive to light. Some of them help us distinguish light from dark. Others are sensitive to light of different colors. The retina is connected to the *optic nerve,* which in turn is connected to the cerebrum. Clear fluids fill the internal chambers of the eye and help maintain its shape.

Vision

Light rays coming from an object pass through the cornea, enter the pupil, and reach the lens. The lens bends the light rays, which then form an image on the retina. This image is formed in the same way that a camera lens forms an image on film. The image on the retina produces impulses that reach the brain by way of the optic nerve. When the impulse arrives at the special area of the cerebrum that controls vision, we become aware that we see something.

The iris, which is composed of two sets of smooth muscles, regulates the amount of light that reaches the lens and retina. One set of muscles is arranged in a ring around the pupil. In bright light, this set contracts as the second set relaxes. These actions decrease the size of the pupil. The second set of muscles is arranged around the pupil like the spokes of a wheel. In dim light, this set of muscles contracts at the same time that the ringlike set relaxes. These actions enlarge the size of the pupil.

The muscle attached to the lens can change the shape of the lens. When we look at a nearby or distant object, this muscle automatically changes the thickness of the lens and focuses a clear image on the retina.

Common Defects in Vision

When an image comes to a sharp focus on the retina (Fig. 19–7*a*), vision is clear. People who have certain defects in the shape of parts of the eye cannot see sharp images without the aid of eyeglass lenses that correct these defects.

Nearsightedness usually occurs when the eyeball is longer than normal. In such cases, a sharp image is produced in front of the retina instead of on its surface. Nearsighted people can see only nearby objects clearly. Concave lenses, which spread light, help correct this condition (Fig. 19–7*b*).

Farsightedness usually occurs when the eyeball is shorter than normal. In such cases, a sharp image cannot be produced on the retina. Farsighted people can see only distant objects clearly. Convex lenses, which gather light rays to a point, help correct this condition (Fig. 19–7*c*).

Astigmatism occurs when either the cornea or the lens is unevenly curved. In this condition a hazy image is formed on the retina. Eyeglass lenses with curves that make up for the uneven curves of the cornea or the lens are used to correct astigmatism (Fig. 19–7*d*).

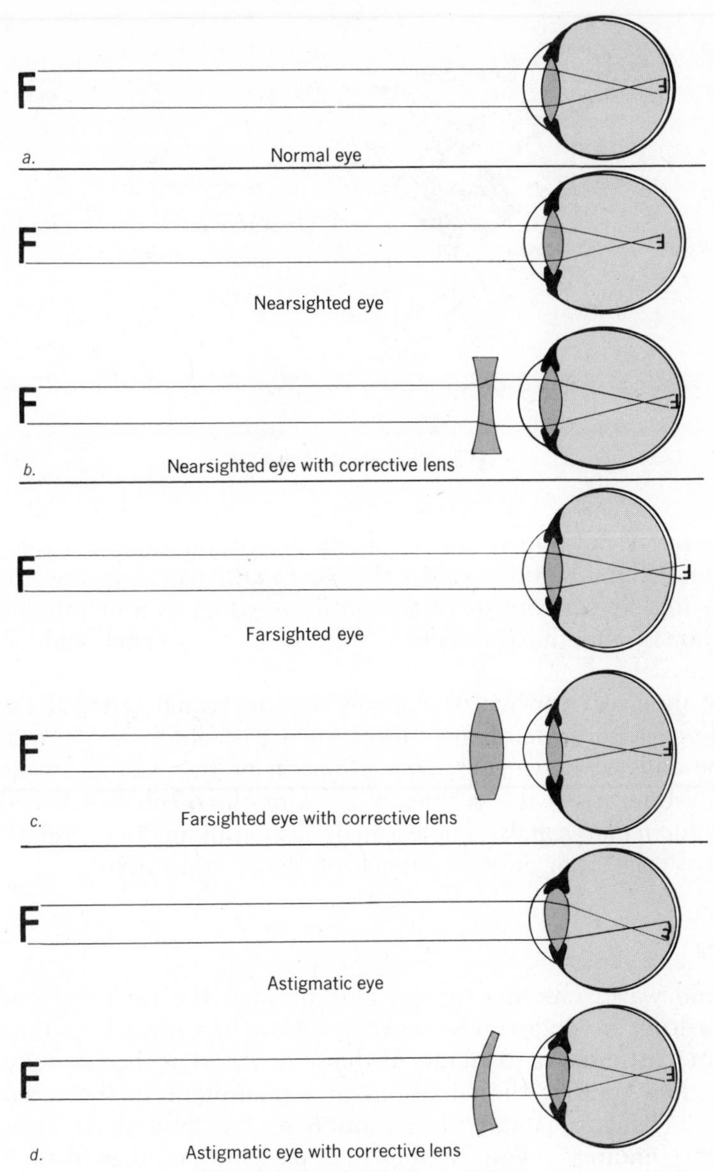

Fig. 19–7. Correcting poor vision.

EARS

In Chapter 12, we learned that each ear is divided into three regions: the outer ear, the middle ear, and the inner ear. Both the middle and the inner ear are located within a hollow portion of the skull bones (Fig. 19–8, page 358).

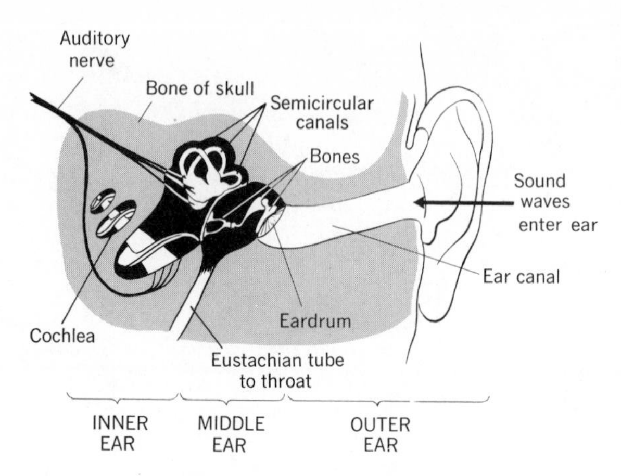

Fig. 19–8. Parts of the ear.

The outer ear consists of the fleshy projection from the side of the head and a hollow tube, called the *ear canal*, that leads inward.

The middle ear consists of the *eardrum*, which is a membrane; three little bones; and the *Eustachian tube*, which is a canal leading to the throat.

The inner ear consists of a snail-like, bony canal called the *cochlea*. It is lined with a membrane and is filled with fluid. In the membrane are the ends of nerve cells from a branch of the hearing, or *auditory*, nerve. Attached to the cochlea is a set of three tubelike loops, called the *semicircular canals*. These canals also contain fluid and the ends of nerve cells from another branch of the hearing nerve.

Hearing

Sound waves entering the ear pass through the ear canal and cause the eardrum to vibrate. The movements of the eardrum, in turn, cause the three little bones to vibrate at the same speed as the eardrum. These bones then transfer the vibrations to a membrane in the cochlea and cause its fluid to vibrate. The motion of the fluid starts impulses in the nerve endings. These endings then pass the impulses to the hearing area of the cerebrum by way of the hearing nerve. When the impulse reaches the hearing area of the cerebrum, we become aware of the sound.

The Eustachian tube acts as a channel that equalizes the air pressure inside the middle ear cavity with the air pressure in the ear canal. Unequal air pressure interferes with hearing. When the eardrum is torn or the three little bones cannot move, hearing may be lost. This can occur even though there is no damage to the hearing nerve.

Maintaining Balance

Changes in the position of the head are detected by the semicircular canals. Bending or turning the trunk or head causes the fluid within these canals to move. This motion starts impulses in the nerve endings present in the canals. When these impulses reach the brain, return impulses may be sent to the muscles that can restore the body to its normal position.

SKIN

Most people think of the skin as a protective covering and as the part of the body that produces perspiration, or sweat. Few people think of the skin as a sense organ possessing several different senses.

The skin consists of two major layers of tissue (Fig. 19–9). The outer layer is called the *epidermis* and the inner layer, the *dermis*. The epidermis contains many microscopic openings, the *pores*. Each pore leads to a tiny tube that ends in a *sweat gland* located in the dermis. Also scattered in the dermis are nerve endings of different types. Each type of nerve ending can detect a different stimulus. Thus, one type of nerve ending is sensitive to heat, another to cold, and others to pressure, pain, and touch. Although these nerve endings are present all over the body, there are more of them in the fingertips than elsewhere.

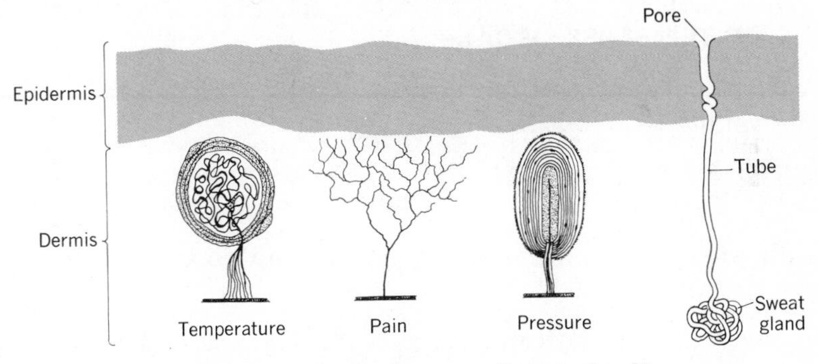

Fig. 19–9. Some kinds of nerve endings in the skin.

NOSE

Nerve endings located in the membrane that lines the upper region of the nasal passages can detect odors. These nerve endings are connected to the cerebrum by way of the nerves of smell.

TONGUE

The sense organs for taste, called *taste buds*, are located on the surface of the tongue. There are several types of taste buds, one of

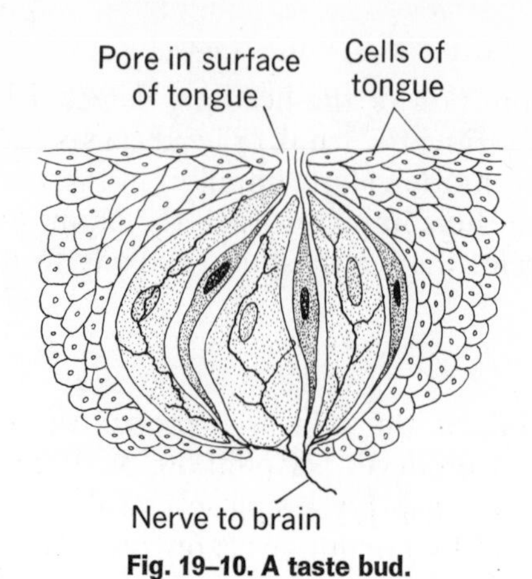

Fig. 19–10. A taste bud.

which is shown in Fig. 19–10. Each type of taste bud can detect a different taste sensation.

Taste buds for different taste sensations occur in groups in different areas of the tongue: sweetness at the tip; sourness on the sides; bitterness at the back; and saltiness on the sides and tip.

CARE OF THE SENSE ORGANS

A few simple measures can help to maintain the proper functioning of our various sense organs.

Eyes

1. Prevent eyestrain by avoiding glare and by working and reading in places that are well lighted.

2. To rest the eyes, stare into the distance. This relaxes the lens muscles.

3. Avoid staring into the sun because ultraviolet rays destroy the delicate nerve cells in the retina.

4. Keep the eyes clean to avoid irritation and infection.

5. Have your vision checked regularly.

6. Prevent nightblindness by including vitamin A in your diet.

Ears

1. Clean the ears with a washcloth. Avoid using sharp objects that can puncture the eardrum.

2. Keep both mouth and nostrils open when blowing your nose. This will prevent forcing mucus into the Eustachian tubes.

Skin

1. Wash regularly in order to keep the skin clear and free of infection.

2. Avoid excessive exposure to ultraviolet rays because they burn and destroy tissue.

Nose

1. Nasal disorders should be promptly treated because obstruction of the nasal passages interferes with breathing and smelling.

2. Avoid the prolonged use of nose drops and similar medications because they injure the membrane lining the nose.

Tongue

1. Since extremes of temperature injure taste buds, avoid eating excessively hot or excessively cold foods.

2. Avoid the excessive use of alcohol and tobacco because these substances dull the sensitivity of the taste buds.

Looking Back

The human nervous system is composed of highly sensitive nerve tissue. This tissue is organized as nerves, the brain, and the spinal cord. As the environment changes, nerves from the sense organs carry rapid signals to the brain and spinal cord which relay them to muscles and glands. The actions of the muscles and glands finally result in the bodily changes that help us adjust to the changed environment.

Looking Ahead

In adjusting the body to the environment, the nervous system is aided by the chemical control, or endocrine, system. This system is the subject of Chapter 20.

Multiple-Choice Questions

1. The nervous system is specialized
   a. only to detect changes in the environment
   b. to detect changes in the environment and to adjust the body to them
   c. only to adjust to changes in stimuli
   d. to detect and adjust to responses
2. A change in the environment of a cat is called a
   a. stimulus b. response c. food chain d. prey
3. The unit of which the nervous system is composed is the
   a. axon b. cell body c. nerve cell d. impulse
4. The nucleus of a nerve cell is located in the part of the cell called the
   a. axon b. cell body c. neuron d. end brush
5. The axon of a nerve cell
   a. receives impulses from nearby nerves
   b. is a long continuation of the cell body
   c. sends impulses to the cell body
   d. receives impulses from the end brush
6. Impulses pass over the gap of a synapse with the aid of
   a. plexuses c. ganglions
   b. electric sparks d. special chemical substances
7. Nerve cells that carry impulses from sense organs to the brain are of the type called
   a. sensory b. motor c. connecting d. effectors
8. Which type of nerve cell causes glands to produce sweat?
   a. sensory b. connecting c. motor d. receptor
9. Synapses occur between
   a. cell bodies and receiving branches
   b. cell bodies and axons
   c. end brushes and receiving branches
   d. cytons and end brushes
10. A fatty sheath covers the part of a nerve cell called the
    a. end brush b. dendrites c. axon d. cyton
11. Clusters of cell bodies that are attached to nerves are called
    a. ganglions b. cytons c. axons d. synapses
12. Into how many parts is the human cerebrum divided?
    a. two parts b. three parts c. four parts d. five parts
13. If the cerebellum of a pigeon were destroyed, the bird would live but would not be able to
    a. fly b. breathe c. digest food d. excrete
14. A nerve impulse that leaves the eye is eventually interpreted by the
    a. optic nerve b. cerebrum c. cerebellum d. spinal cord
15. The nerve center that controls the breathing rate of humans is located in the part of the brain called the
    a. cerebrum b. cerebellum
    c. gray matter d. medulla oblongata
16. The outer layer of the cerebrum is composed mostly of
    a. white matter b. axons c. gaps d. cell bodies

17. Which organs of the body can detect changes in the environment?
    a. plexuses b. sense organs c. ganglions d. nerves
18. An animal whose entire brain has been destroyed can still move its legs because the part of its nervous system than can still act for a short time is the
    a. cerebrum c. spinal cord
    b. cerebellum d. medulla oblongata
19. The group that includes only sense organs is
    a. medulla, cerebrum, optic nerve c. lens, iris, cyton
    b. nose, tongue, skin d. axon, cyton, ganglion
20. The spinal cord is made up of the tissue called
    a. bone b. vertebrae c. connective d. nerve
21. When light enters the eye, the first part of the eye that the light passes through is the
    a. retina b. pupil c. cornea d. lens
22. As you read, an image of the print is formed in the eye on the
    a. optic nerve b. retina c. lens d. cerebrum
23. Some automatic balancing movements of the body depend upon sense organs in
    a. the bones b. the tongue c. the skin d. the ear
24. The eye structure that regulates the amount of light that reaches the retina is the
    a. iris b. pupil c. cornea d. lens
25. The Eustachian tubes
    a. help in balance
    b. balance the air pressure on the diaphragm
    c. balance the air pressure on the eardrum
    d. connect the cochlea to the auditory nerve

Modified True-False Questions

1. The retina is connected to the brain by means of the *auditory* nerve.
2. In dim light, the size of the *cornea* of the eye increases.
3. The inner end of the ear canal is covered by a membrane called the *Eustachian tube.*
4. The hearing nerve ends in the part of the ear called the *cochlea.*
5. We know that we have heard a sound when impulses from the ear reach the *cerebellum.*
6. Hearing depends on the ability of three little bones in the ear to *vibrate.*
7. The ability to sense heat, cold, and pressure on the surface of the body depends upon different nerve endings in the *nose.*
8. Nerve endings that enable us to taste sugar are located at the *tip* of the tongue.
9. Taste buds that enable us to taste lemon are located at the *sides* of the tongue.
10. For good vision in dim light we need *vitamin B.*

Increases—Decreases—Remains the Same

1. When a person lacks vitamin A, his ability to see in dim light
   increases, decreases, remains the same
2. As you learn, the number of activities that your cerebrum controls
   increases, decreases, remains the same
3. As a muscle contracts, the length of the motor nerve attached to it
   increases, decreases, remains the same
4. As you grow older, the number of simple reflex acts you can carry out
   increases, decreases, remains the same
5. When you run, the medulla oblongata causes the heartbeat to
   increase, decrease, remain the same
6. If a farsighted person puts on concave eyeglass lenses, the sharpness of his vision
   increases, decreases, remains the same
7. After a period of silence, music causes the vibrations of the eardrum to
   increase, decrease, remain the same

Thought Questions

1. Tell the difference between the terms in each of the following pairs:
   a. sensory nerve cell and motor nerve cell
   b. nerve and nerve cell
   c. convex lens and concave lens
   d. cerebrum and cerebellum
   e. gray matter and white matter
2. Tell the cause and correction for each of the following eye conditions:
   a. astigmatism b. farsightedness c. nearsightedness
3. Name the three main divisions of the human brain, and give the major activities of each.
4. A person watching a television program is frightened by what she sees. Her heart begins to beat faster. During this time, stimuli are received, and nerve impulses start and move over a definite pathway. Trace the course of the stimulus and impulses by rearranging the following body parts in a proper sequence: lens; cerebrum; pupil; autonomic nervous system; cornea; optic nerve; medulla oblongata; retina; cerebellum; heart muscle.
5. Give an explanation for each of the following situations:
   a. The human brain is capable of greater mental accomplishments than that of other animals.
   b. During many brain operations, the patient remains conscious. When the surgeon touches a side of the cerebrum, the patient hears a sound; when he touches the rear of the cerebrum, the patient sees a flash of light.
   c. The heart of a frog whose cerebrum has been destroyed continues beating.
   d. A salt tablet placed on the back of the tongue and then swallowed is not tasted.

CHAPTER 20
HOW DOES THE CHEMICAL CONTROL SYSTEM HELP US ADJUST TO THE ENVIRONMENT?

When you have completed this chapter, you should be able to:

1. *Distinguish* between duct and ductless glands and their products.
2. *Discuss* the thyroid gland, indicating its hormone and normal function and the conditions that may occur when its functioning is impaired (damaged).
3. *Describe* the parts and functions of the adrenal glands.
4. *Compare* the secretions of the duct and ductless portions of the pancreas.
5. *Identify* the hormone secreted by each of the following ductless glands and the function of each hormone: pituitary, lining of the small intestine, sex glands.
6. *Explain* how a hormone helps plants adjust to a change in environment.

In the laboratory experience that follows, you will determine how a plant adjusts to changes in illumination and position.

Laboratory Experience

HOW DOES A PLANT ADJUST TO ITS ENVIRONMENT?

A. In each of four paper cups, or other containers, plant three radish seeds. Place all of these plantings in a dark closet, and water them regularly. When the seedlings have reached a height of about 3 centimeters, remove them from the closet.
   1. Describe the appearance of the seedlings immediately after removal from the closet.

B. Place one container near a one-sided source of light. Set another container in a place where the seedlings will be illuminated evenly from all sides. Place the third container on its side, making sure that these seedlings also will be illuminated evenly from all sides. Place the fourth container on its side in a dark closet. (See Fig. 20–1.) Continue to water the plants as necessary, and observe them for any changes in the direction of their growth.

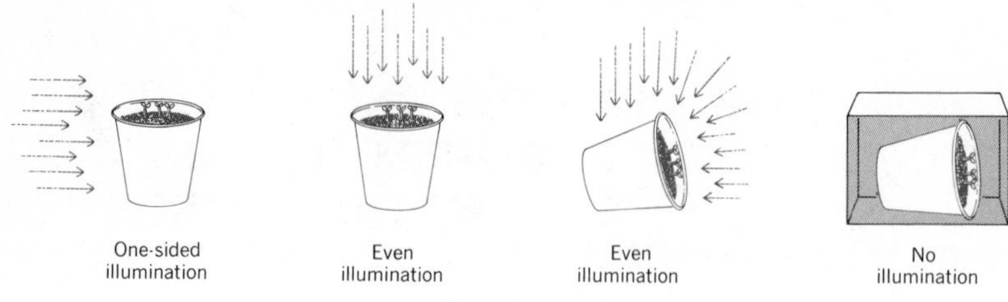

Fig. 20–1.

2. Describe the growth of the plants in each of the following conditions, naming the stimulus (or stimuli) to which the plants responded:
   a. After exposure to one-sided illumination.
   b. After exposure to uniform illumination.
   c. After having been placed on a side and exposed to uniform illumination.
   d. After having been placed on a side in a dark closet.
3. In this laboratory experience, to what stimuli did the radish stems respond?

Introduction

Although plants and many simple organisms lack a nervous system, they do detect stimuli, respond to them, and thereby adjust to many changes in their environment. Since the responses of these organisms are automatic and usually beneficial, it is apparent that some control system exists.

The control system of plants depends upon certain chemicals, called *hormones*, which are produced within the cells. Plant hormones control such activities as the production of flowers and the dropping of leaves. In humans, some activities are controlled by hormones, and some both by hormones and by the nervous system.

HORMONES AND DUCTLESS GLANDS

A gland, such as the liver, that secretes a juice into a tube leading to another organ is called a *duct gland*. In addition to this type of gland, the body has numerous glands that have no tubes (Fig. 20–2). These

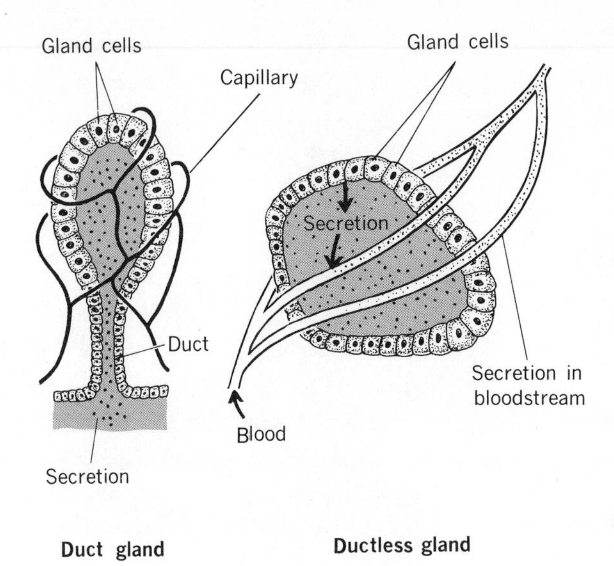

Fig. 20–2. A duct and a ductless gland.

glands are called *ductless*, or *endocrine, glands*. The major ductless glands are shown in Fig. 20–3, page 368. Each of these glands is composed of cells that produce a special hormone. Each hormone passes from its ductless gland directly into the blood, which transports the hormone throughout the body.

A hormone acts on parts of the body that are at some distance from the ductless gland that secretes the hormone. For this reason, hormones are often called "chemical messengers." Hormones help control and coordinate the activities that go on inside the body. The hormones exert their control by speeding up or slowing down the activities of different organs.

Should a ductless gland release too much or too little of a hormone, some organs fail to work normally. Such disturbances of these glands often result in disease.

Among the major ductless glands are the *thyroid gland*, the *adrenal glands*, the *pituitary gland*, the *pancreas*, the *parathyroid glands*, certain cells that line the small intestine, and the *sex glands*.

Thyroid Gland

Located in front of the windpipe near the base of the neck is the thyroid gland. This gland is shaped like a bow tie. *Thyroxin* is the major hormone secreted by the thyroid gland. Thyroxin speeds up the oxidation of nutrients in the cells. In this way, the thyroid gland regulates the release of energy in the body.

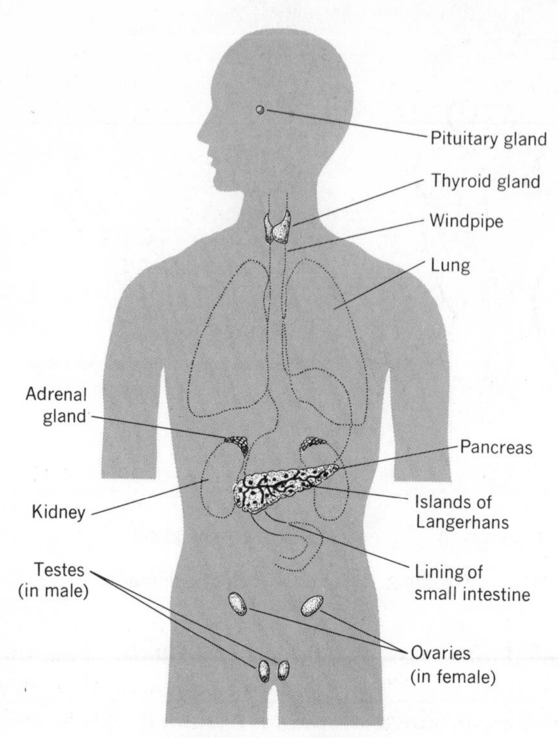

Fig. 20–3. Human ductless glands.

Thyroxin contains iodine, which is supplied to the thyroid gland by the blood. If the diet lacks iodine, or if the thyroid gland does not function properly for other reasons, an abnormal body condition results. Some important diseases of the thyroid gland are:

1. *Simple goiter.* When the body does not receive an adequate supply of iodine, the thyroid gland fails to manufacture a usable form of thyroxin. In time, this results in an enlargement of the thyroid gland, called simple goiter. This disease is easily prevented by eating foods naturally rich in iodine. Among these are seafoods and vegetables that have been grown in seacoast regions. In the absence of such foods, iodized salt can be added to available foods. In some communities, small quantities of iodine are added to the water supply.

2. *Exophthalmic goiter.* When the thyroid gland secretes excessive quantities of thyroxin, the rate of oxidation in the cells increases. This condition is usually accompanied by nervousness, restlessness, and loss of weight. In time, bulging eyes and an enlarged thyroid gland also develop. This type of thyroid enlargement is called exophthalmic goiter. Treatment of this disease involves partial destruction or partial removal

of the thyroid gland by means of surgery or radiation. For radiation, the radioisotope *iodine-131* is often used. Although this form of iodine is radioactive, it is absorbed by the thyroid gland just as the ordinary form of iodine is. Once in the gland, radiation from iodine-131 destroys some of the thyroid cells.

3. *Mental retardation.* Sometimes a baby is born with a defective thyroid gland which does not produce adequate amounts of thyroxin. Such a child develops slowly, both mentally and physically. If medical attention is not provided during the early years of the child's life, the child can become mentally retarded.

Adrenal Glands

These glands are located one on top of each kidney. Each adrenal gland has an inner and an outer region.

1. The *inner region* of an adrenal gland secretes the hormone *adrenin* (or *adrenalin*) when a person is angry, frightened, or excited. When adrenin reaches the liver, the liver releases glucose, which then enters the bloodstream. As a result, extra fuel, in the form of glucose, is available for energy production. Adrenin also increases the breathing rate and causes heart muscle to beat faster and more strongly. Other effects of adrenin include causing muscles attached to the skeleton to contract more strongly, muscles of the digestive tract to stop contracting, and blood to clot more rapidly. Since these changes make the body ready for emergencies, the adrenal glands are called the "glands of combat."

2. The *outer region* of an adrenal gland secretes several hormones, one of which is *cortisone.* Among the activities of the hormones of the outer region of the adrenal gland is regulation of the amounts of mineral salts in the body. Cortisone is best known for its use as a drug that gives relief to those who suffer from rheumatoid arthritis, certain allergies, and inflammations.

Pituitary Gland

Attached to the underside of the brain is a pea-sized gland, the pituitary. Since the pituitary gland secretes numerous hormones, many of which control the activities of other ductless glands, it is called the "master gland." Some of the major hormones of the pituitary gland are listed below.

1. *Growth hormone* regulates bone growth. A child who has too much of this hormone may grow so rapidly that he becomes a giant.

He may reach a height of two and a half meters. A child who lacks this hormone may grow so slowly that he remains very short—a dwarf. He may never grow beyond a height of one meter.

2. *Thyroid-stimulating hormone* controls the activity of the thyroid gland.

3. *Sex-gland-stimulating hormones* control the development of the sex glands.

Pancreas

This gland is located behind and beneath the stomach. The pancreas is a double gland—part of it is a duct gland, and part is a ductless gland. The duct portion of this gland secretes the pancreatic juice that reaches the small intestine by way of the pancreatic duct. The ductless portion consists of numerous scattered groups of cells, called the *islands of Langerhans*, which secrete the hormone *insulin* into nearby blood vessels. Insulin controls the passage of glucose from the blood into liver and other cells. In this manner, insulin regulates the storage of glycogen in the liver and the use of glucose by all cells.

Normally, the secretion of insulin by the islands of Langerhans keeps the amount of glucose in the blood at a fairly constant level. When too little insulin is secreted, the glucose level of the blood becomes so high that life is endangered. This condition is called *diabetes*. In this disease, some of the excess blood sugar is excreted in the urine. Ever since 1922, when *Frederick G. Banting* and *Charles A. Best* extracted insulin from the pancreas of animals, diabetics have been successfully treated by injections of insulin.

Parathyroid Glands

The parathyroid glands are four separate masses of similar tissue imbedded in the rear surface of the thyroid gland. The hormone of these glands helps keep the amount of calcium in the blood at a constant level.

Lining of the Small Intestine

When food enters the small intestine, the lining cells of the first few centimeters of the small intestine produce the hormone called *secretin*. When secretin reaches the duct-gland portion of the pancreas, the secretin causes the cells of the pancreas to release pancreatic juice. Thus, the release of secretin acts as a timing control that releases a digestive juice when food comes into the small intestine.

Sex Glands

Located in or near the abdomen are the *ovaries* in the female and the *testes* in the male. In addition to acting in reproduction, these glands produce sex hormones which influence the development of the body.

HORMONES IN PLANTS

Plants, as well as animals, respond to the stimulus of light. However, plants generally respond much more slowly than animals do. Your laboratory experience showed that the stem of a plant turns toward light. Such slow-growth movements of plants are controlled by growth hormones, called *auxins*. Although no special gland is visible, these hormones are produced near the tip of each branch.

Auxins stimulate cell growth and thereby control the movement of some plant structures. When one side of a plant has a larger quantity of auxin than the other side, the cells grow faster on the side that has more auxin. The resulting rapid, one-sided growth forces the stem tip to curve. Since light somehow reduces the quantity of auxin in cells directly exposed to light, cells in the light grow more slowly than cells in the shade. Then, the more rapid growth of the cells on the shaded side forces the stem tip to bend toward the source of illumination (Fig. 20–4). The growth and turning of roots are also under chemical control similar to that in the stem.

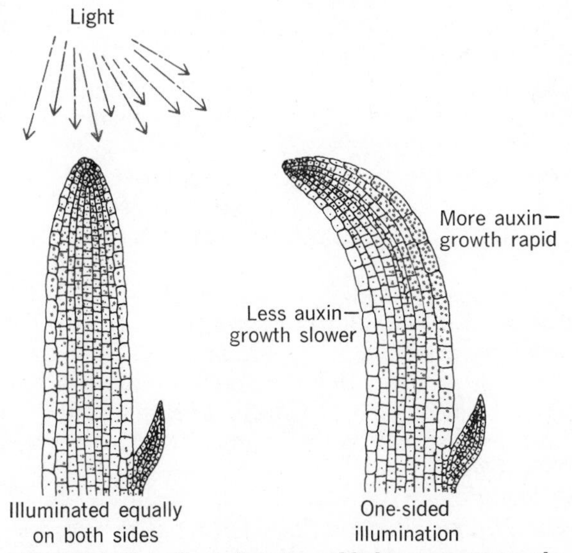

Fig. 20–4. The effect of auxin and light on stem growth.

Looking Back

The ductless glands make up the chemical control system in animals. In this system, signals cause the ductless glands to secrete hormones. A hormone acts as a chemical messenger, or chemical signal, that can affect the activities of the nervous system, muscular system, and other systems. Chemical signals travel more slowly than do nerve signals.

In plants, as well as in animals, a chemical control system brings about responses to stimuli. Since plants lack muscles, they usually move by growth. Thus, the movement reactions of plants are much slower than those of animals.

Looking Ahead

As the control systems adjust an organism to changes in its environment, the organism acts differently from the way it acted before the change. These differences in action are discussed in the next chapter.

Multiple-Choice Questions

1. When the sun rises, most plants
   a. respond in some way to this change in their environment
   b. are inactive
   c. start impulses in their nerve cells
   d. stop oxidizing their food
2. Secretions from ductless glands pass
   a. to duct glands
   b. directly into the blood
   c. out of the body
   d. directly into the stomach
3. A hormone is also called a
   a. chemical messenger
   b. enzyme
   c. catalyst
   d. nerve control
4. An unusual rate of oxidation can be the result of increased secretion by the
   a. lungs b. pineal gland c. thymus gland d. thyroid gland
5. A hormone noted for its value in treating some types of arthritis is
   a. adrenin b. cortisone c. insulin d. thyroxin
6. Dwarfed animals probably lack the hormone that controls
   a. growth b. oxidation c. mental development d. secretions
7. Goiters are usually caused by the improper working of the
   a. parathyroid glands
   b. thyroid gland
   c. sex glands
   d. gastric glands
8. Excess glucose in the blood is characteristic of the disease called
   a. diarrhea b. anemia c. diphtheria d. diabetes

9. The secretion that plays an important part in normal mental development is
   a. thyroxin b. adrenin c. secretin d. insulin
10. Iodine in foods is needed by the body for forming the hormone
    a. adrenin b. insulin c. secretin d. thyroxin
11. Radioactive iodine has been found useful in treating some disturbances of the
    a. adrenal glands
    b. cortex glands
    c. thyroid gland
    d. pancreas
12. The amount of glucose in the cells of the body and in the blood plasma is related to the hormone
    a. secretin b. glycogen c. insulin d. iodine
13. A hormone that a doctor would be likely to inject in a case of heart failure is
    a. insulin b. ACTH c. adrenin d. thyroxin
14. A hormone and a vitamin that affect the amount of calcium in the blood are
    a. the hormone of the pituitary gland and vitamin A
    b. the hormone of the parathyroid glands and vitamin D
    c. the hormone of the pancreas and vitamin D
    d. the hormone of the adrenal glands and vitamin C
15. The small intestine secretes several enzymes and the hormone called
    a. insulin b. cortisone c. glucose d. secretin
16. Auxins are hormones that stimulate the growth of
    a. bone tissue
    b. muscle tissue
    c. plant tissue
    d. gland tissue
17. Secretin is the hormone that stimulates the secretion of
    a. pancreatic juice b. gastric juice c. thyroxin d. insulin
18. The turning of a sunflower as the sun moves is controlled by
    a. the sun
    b. the muscular system of the plant
    c. the receptors of the plant
    d. one or more hormones

Thought Questions

1. Explain the difference between the terms in each of the following pairs:
   a. enzyme and hormone
   b. duct gland and ductless gland
   c. thyroid gland and parathyroid glands
2. Each of the following conditions is abnormal. For each, tell the probable cause and how the condition might either be prevented or treated.
   a. simple goiter
   b. diabetes
   c. a child dwarf
   d. The stem of a geranium plant in a schoolroom grew sideways instead of upright.

3. An experimenter removed the pancreases from several freshly killed rabbits. He ground the pancreases and extracted a juice from them. He then injected the juice into several live rabbits whose pancreases had been removed two weeks before.
   a. By this time the live rabbits probably had the disease called
      (1) dwarfism (2) diabetes (3) cretinism (4) goiter
   b. The hormone that was probably present in the extracted juice is
      (1) insulin
      (2) pancreatic juice
      (3) parathyroxin
      (4) estrogen
   c. The scientists who originally isolated the hormone that the experimenter was seeking were
      (1) Best and Banting
      (2) Banting and Langerhans
      (3) Best and Harvey
      (4) Harvey and Leeuwenhoek
   d. In the experiment described above, the injections probably
      (1) killed the rabbits
      (2) improved their condition
      (3) had no effect
      (4) helped new pancreases to develop
4. For each of the following hormones, name the gland or the part of the organism that produces it, and give the use of the hormone in the organism:
   a. thyroxin
   b. growth hormone
   c. adrenin
   d. cortisone
   e. insulin
   f. secretin
   g. auxin

CHAPTER 21
HOW DOES OUR BEHAVIOR HELP US ADJUST TO THE ENVIRONMENT?

When you have completed this chapter, you should be able to:

1. *Compare* the ways in which the behavior of humans and that of simple organisms helps them adjust to environmental changes.
2. *Distinguish* between (*a*) a tropism, a simple reflex act, a reflex arc, and a conditioned response (*b*) a voluntary act, a habit, and an instinct.
3. *Discuss* the major methods by which a person learns.
4. *Identify* the major drugs that influence normal behavior, and describe some of the dangers associated with each drug.

In the laboratory experience that follows, you will discover how the human eye adjusts to changes in lighting.

Laboratory Experience

HOW DO THE EYES REACT TO CHANGES IN LIGHT?

A. Using a hand mirror, look into your own eyes. Note the size of the pupil of one eye. Shine the beam of a small flashlight into the eye, and continue to observe the size of the pupil.
   1. Describe what happens to your pupil.

B. Repeat what you have done with the flashlight, but now observe what happens to the pupil as you switch off the light.
   2. Describe what happens to your pupil.

C. Repeat each of the preceding steps, but now try to keep your pupil from changing size.
   3. Describe your results.
   4. What conclusions can you draw about the behavior of your pupil?

Introduction

The variety of responses that an organism makes to different stimuli is called the *behavior* of the organism. The stimuli may originate outside or inside the organism's body. The way in which an organism behaves shows how the organism adjusts to changes in its environment. Behavior is controlled by chemicals (hormones) or a nervous system, or both.

HOW SIMPLE ORGANISMS ADJUST

Although they lack a nervous system, plants such as the radish and animals such as the paramecium automatically respond to changes in their environment. The type of behavior shown by simple organisms that lack a nervous system is called a *tropism*. A tropism is the simplest type of automatic behavior, involving only motion toward or away from a stimulus. In general, tropisms favor the survival of the organism. Tropisms are never learned. Instead, this type of behavior is inborn. Chemicals appear to be the controlling factor in most tropisms.

Each tropism is named according to the type of stimulus that causes the response. If the response movement is in the direction toward the stimulus, the tropism is said to be *positive*; if in the direction away from the stimulus, *negative*. Some of the different kinds of tropisms are as follows:

Phototropism is the response to light. The leaves of an ivy plant turn toward light, showing positive phototropism. The paramecium moves away from bright light, showing negative phototropism (Fig. 21–1).

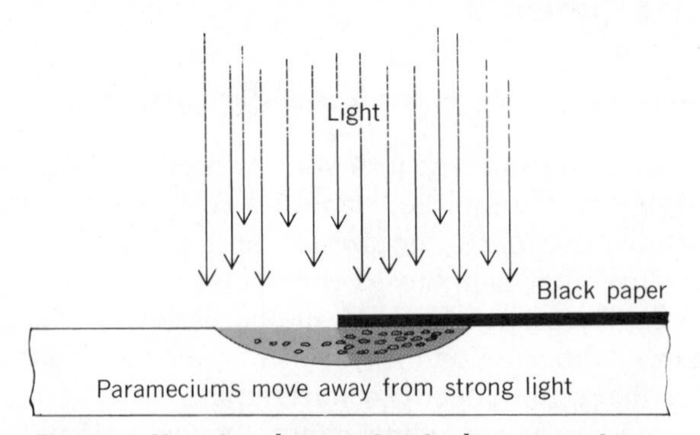

Fig. 21–1. Negative phototropism in the paramecium.

Geotropism is the response to the pull of gravity. The roots of most plants grow downward, showing positive geotropism. Most stems grow upward, showing negative geotropism (Fig. 21–2).

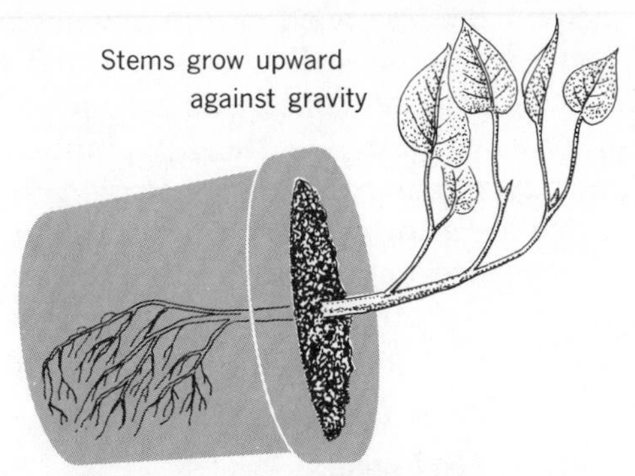

Fig. 21–2. Negative geotropism of a plant.

Other tropisms include *thermotropism*, the response to heat; *chemotropism*, the response to chemicals; *hydrotropism*, the response to water; and *thigmotropism*, the response to contact with a solid object.

HOW HUMANS ADJUST

Since simple organisms respond to a stimulus only by moving toward or away from it, their behavior is fairly well understood. On the other hand, humans can respond to a particular stimulus in so many different ways that many types of human behavior are not well understood. Human behavior varies from the relatively simple inborn type that is carried out from birth, to complex types that cannot be carried out unless a great deal of effort has been used in learning them. The major human behavior types include the *simple reflex act*, the *conditioned response*, and the *voluntary act*.

SIMPLE REFLEX ACT

A simple reflex act is a beneficial, rapid, direct response to a stimulus. Reflex behavior is inborn. The response, which is either the contraction of a muscle or the secretion by a gland, never varies. It is automatically carried out without thought when a particular stimulus is present.

The change in the size of the pupil of the eye in response to varying light conditions, which you observed in your laboratory experience, is a type of simple reflex act. When you shine the beam of a flashlight into an eye as you look into a mirror, you see the pupil becoming smaller than it was. When you switch off the beam, you see the pupil enlarging to its former size. No matter how hard you try, you cannot control the iris muscles around the pupil and voluntarily change the size of the pupil. The behavior of the pupil is called the *pupillary reflex*.

This behavior is helpful because good vision depends upon the proper amount of light entering the eye. The pupillary reflex, like all other simple reflexes, is unlearned, automatic, and not under control of your will. Examples of other reflexes are sneezing, blinking, the flow of gastric juice in the stomach, and the knee kick.

A *reflex arc* is a nerve pathway over which an impulse passes when a simple reflex act is carried out. If, for example, your finger accidentally touches a sharp pinpoint and, without thinking about it, you rapidly withdraw your hand, the impulse travels over a reflex pathway, as shown in Fig. 21–3.

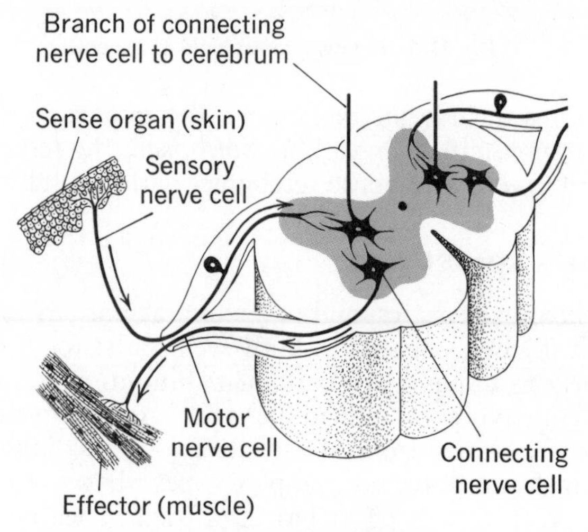

Fig. 21–3. A reflex pathway.

The sense organ, which in this case is a branch of a nerve cell ending in the skin, receives the stimulus and starts a nerve impulse.

The sensory nerve cell passes the impulse to the spinal cord.

The connecting nerve cell in the spinal cord relays the impulse to the motor nerve cell and also to the cerebrum. The cerebrum is not part of the reflex arc, but it makes you aware of what is happening.

The motor nerve cell passes the impulse to an effector, which may be either a muscle or a gland.

The effector, which in this case is a muscle of the arm, responds by contracting and pulling the arm away from the harmful stimulus.

An *instinct* is inborn behavior consisting of a chain of reflex acts. The completion of the first reflex act becomes the stimulus that starts the second reflex act. This in turn becomes the stimulus for the next reflex act in the chain. Eventually the act is completed. Examples of instincts are nest-building by birds and web-spinning by spiders. It is doubtful whether humans are born with instincts.

CONDITIONED RESPONSE

A conditioned response is learned when the nervous system links together two events that occur at nearly the same time. When a conditioned response has been formed, the response that would ordinarily have been the reaction to one stimulus becomes the reaction to a second stimulus. The second stimulus becomes a substitute for the first one. Although forming a conditioned response usually requires repetition of the two stimuli, it does not necessarily require that one be conscious of what is going on.

Ivan Pavlov, a Russian scientist, experimenting with the behavior of dogs, showed that the dogs could be taught to change their behavior —that is, their behavior could be conditioned. He observed that when a dog ate food, its mouth watered. This was a simple reflex act in which saliva was secreted in response to the presence in the mouth of food, which was the stimulus. Then, just before presenting a hungry dog with food, Pavlov rang a bell. Pavlov repeated this procedure many times. At first, every time the bell was rung, the dog lifted its head and raised its ears. When the dog ate food, its saliva flowed. In time, the dog's mouth watered shortly after the bell-ringing, even though it was not given any food (Fig. 21–4). Pavlov concluded that the ringing of the bell had become linked in the dog's brain with the presence of food. In other words, the dog responded to the new stimulus (the ringing of the bell) just as it had responded to the original stimulus (the presence of food in the mouth).

Examples of conditioned responses in humans are: likes, dislikes, fears, mouth-watering when thinking of a favorite food, and the linking of words with their meanings.

The *conditioned-response pathway* is the nerve pathway that is

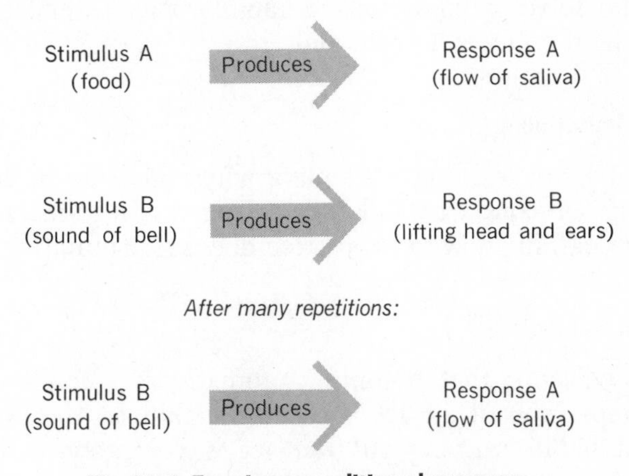

Fig. 21–4. Forming a conditioned response.

established when conditioning occurs. Each reflex act has a separate reflex arc in the nervous system. From each reflex arc, connecting nerve cells reach the cerebrum. Here an impulse can pass from one reflex arc to a second reflex arc. Then the impulse can pass along the motor nerve cell of the second reflex arc. Thus, in the dogs of Pavlov's experiment, connecting nerve cells in the cerebrum made it possible for the impulses from the sensory nerve cells of the ears to cross over to the motor nerve cells leading to the salivary glands.

VOLUNTARY ACT

When an act is controlled by the will, the behavior is called voluntary. The stimuli that produce voluntary responses often begin within the cerebrum. Such behavior is conscious behavior. This type of behavior is very complex, involving many nerve pathways and many connecting nerve cells in the cerebrum. Examples of voluntary behavior include imagining, reasoning, making decisions, and remembering. Voluntary behavior makes it possible for humans to adjust to a greater variety of conditions than other organisms can.

Voluntary behavior can often be changed. Undesirable behavior patterns, such as eating with dirty hands, can be improved. Desirable behavior, such as speaking a foreign language, can be acquired, or learned. Among the major methods of learning are *trial and error, imitation,* and forming *habits.*

Trial and Error

One type of learning takes place when one tries an act, makes mistakes, tries again, and repeats the process until the act is learned. A child who solves a jigsaw puzzle rapidly after several attempts has learned to fit the pieces by trial and error.

Learning by Imitation

Another type of learning takes place when one tries to do something by watching someone else and then trying to do it the same way. A child who is learning how to write often does so by imitating the teacher.

Formation of Habits

Learned behavior that becomes automatic as a result of continual voluntary repetition of an act is called a habit. In the early stages of acquiring a habit, carrying out the act is voluntary, conscious, and, usually, difficult and slow. After practicing, the act becomes involuntary, unconscious, easier, more rapid, and more skillful. Examples of habits are obeying traffic signals, penmanship, spelling, and fingering the strings of a guitar.

The *habit pathway*, like that of a conditioned response, must be established. When we decide to make an act habitual, the stimulus starts in the cerebrum. The nerve impulse then passes over pathways from the cerebrum, through the cerebellum, the medulla oblongata, the spinal cord, the motor nerves, and to the proper muscles. During its passage, the impulse crosses numerous synapses. If these synapses are used for the first time, the nerve impulse has difficulty in crossing them. With repeated use of the new pathway, the impulse crosses the synapses more easily. In time, voluntary control lessens, and the act is performed unconsciously and smoothly. Thus, after repeating a complicated new dance step many times, it becomes easy to do.

Because habits are basically voluntary acts, good habits can be formed and bad ones broken. Establishment of good habits gives us time to think and to accomplish more worthwhile tasks. Thus, a beginning driver must concentrate on each of the movements necessary to operate an automobile. However, when these movements have become habitual, the driver has more time to think of safety and of the route to be followed.

Forming a useful habit is assisted by following these four steps:

1. Make up your mind that you wish to establish a new worthwhile habit. A strong desire and firm decision somehow make it easier for the nerve impulse to pass along the new nerve pathways that will be used.

2. Concentrate on the act as you practice it. Try to do a perfect job at each practice session. Concentration and practice make it easier for the nerve impulse to pass across the synapses.

3. Do not be satisfied with an imperfect job. Do not allow yourself any exceptions.

4. Be proud of what you are doing. The feeling of pride that accompanies success encourages you to keep on improving.

Breaking a bad habit is assisted by following these five steps:

1. Decide why breaking the bad habit would be beneficial to you.

2. Replace the old habit with a new beneficial activity.

3. Keep your thoughts on practicing the new activity. As you practice the new activity and abandon the old one, it becomes harder for the nerve impulse to pass over the nerve pathway of the old activity.

4. Do not allow yourself even one exception. Keep from doing the old act. Keep on doing the new one.

5. Be proud of your willpower in ridding yourself of the bad habit.

DRUGS INTERFERE WITH ADJUSTMENT

Drugs that are helpful to sick people are extremely dangerous to healthy people when the drugs are repeatedly used without a doctor's advice. Especially dangerous are those drugs that act by speeding up or slowing down the nervous and chemical control systems. Such drugs often interfere with these systems to the extent that one's behavior becomes abnormal and dangerous to one's self and others. Very often, a person who is under the influence of drugs does not adjust properly to his or her environment. The most dangerous drugs that influence behavior are listed here.

Marijuana can cause a person to become intoxicated and lose his or her sense of time and of distance. Thus, it can seriously impair one's ability to relate and react properly to the environment.

LSD (or *lysergic acid diethylamide*) causes hallucinations, that is, the user sees things that do not exist. Hallucinations brought on by LSD can be so frightening that users have been known to commit suicide.

Cocaine, with repeated use, causes nervousness, sleeplessness, and loss of appetite. Users of cocaine neglect eating, lose weight, and usually become seriously ill.

Nicotine interferes with normal heart action, digestion, and respiration. As a result of smoking, nicotine and other substances in smoke may cause such conditions as high blood pressure, ulcers, and asthma to become worse. Smoking has also been linked to lung cancer and other serious diseases.

Alcohol decreases the control of the cerebrum over behavior. It can dangerously impair the ability to react to environmental stimuli. In large amounts, alcohol stops the activities of the brain and thereby causes death.

Opium and drugs derived from it (heroin, morphine, and codeine) slow down the nervous system and, consequently, the entire body. Heroin is so dangerous that its manufacture has been prohibited by law.

In large doses, many of these drugs can be fatal. The use of a drug in small, repeated doses becomes habitual. In time, one becomes addicted to some drugs and then has great difficulty in overcoming the habit. The body cells become so dependent upon the drug that they cannot work normally. Lacking the drug, one suffers uncontrollable craving and great pain. Avoiding addiction is much easier than overcoming it.

SOME STEPS TO INSURE NORMAL ADJUSTMENT

Taking proper care of your body—including the nervous and chemical control systems—can help insure normal adjustment to the environment.

1. *Eat properly*. For the nervous and chemical control systems to work normally, they require a balanced, varied diet that includes mineral elements such as iodine, potassium, and sodium, and vitamins such as thiamin.

2. *Get ample rest*. When the body is not active, wastes are removed from nerve cells, as they are from all body cells.

3. *Engage in some recreational activity*. Changing from work to play or to a hobby relieves mental strains that interfere with normal nerve activities.

4. *Avoid taking drugs without medical advice*. Improperly used, drugs are a menace to health and life.

5. *Consult a physician regularly*. The early discovery and treatment of disturbances of the nervous system can prevent physical and mental damage.

Looking Back

The way in which an organism behaves as it adjusts to its environment is the result of the activities of the nervous system and the chemical control system. Behavior is visible in actions such as tropisms, reflexes, instincts, and voluntary acts. Normal behavior may be seriously affected by the abuse of drugs.

Looking Ahead

Usually, when organisms adjust to the environment, they survive. Often, however, some type of disease interferes with adjustment and survival. The causes and effects of different types of diseases are discussed in Chapter 22.

Multiple-Choice Questions

1. Although lacking a nervous system, plants such as Venus's flytrap catch insects by the type of behavior called
   a. an instinct
   b. a conditioned response
   c. an intelligent response
   d. a tropism

2. Roots of a grass plant grow downward. This is an example of
   a. positive geotropism
   b. negative geotropism
   c. positive thermotropism
   d. negative thermotropism
3. Withdrawing the hand from a hot stove is an example of
   a. a reflex
   b. a conditioned response
   c. a voluntary act
   d. an instinct
4. Fear of mice in humans is an example of a
   a. voluntary response
   b. voluntary act
   c. conditioned response
   d. habit
5. The nerve pathway carrying an impulse that causes a reflex act is called
   a. voluntary arc b. synapse c. reflex arc d. instinct
6. Which is an example of instinctive behavior?
   a. a robin brings a worm to its nest
   b. the pupillary reflex
   c. breathing faster when running
   d. the solving of a maze by a mouse
7. A type of behavior that results from the linking in the brain of impulses from two different stimuli is called
   a. instinct
   b. conditioned response
   c. stimulated response
   d. simple response
8. A frog without a cerebrum can scratch itself. This ability illustrates
   a. an instinct
   b. a voluntary act
   c. a simple reflex
   d. a conditioned reflex
9. The organ in which conditioned responses are established is the
   a. spinal cord b. cerebrum c. medulla d. ganglion
10. Which group contains only voluntary acts?
    a. mouth-watering, fear of snakes, blinking
    b. iris movement, sneezing, coughing
    c. breathing, coughing, blinking
    d. reasoning, remembering, deciding
11. Although bees seem to act cleverly, their responses do not appear to involve
    a. instincts b. reflexes c. sense organs d. thought
12. Acts controlled by the will start with impulses in the
    a. cerebellum b. cerebrum c. medulla d. spinal cord
13. The ability of a circus seal to balance a ball is an example of
    a. learning b. a reflex c. an autonomic response d. instinct
14. The activity that is often learned by imitation is
    a. multiplication b. silent reading c. writing d. breathing
15. Habits are
    a. acquired automatic acts
    b. inborn reflexes
    c. autonomic acts
    d. acts of willpower only
16. The term that includes all the others is
    a. instinct b. automatic c. habit d. inborn
17. The decision to form a good habit starts a nerve impulse in the
    a. nerve cell of a ganglion
    b. cerebellum
    c. medulla
    d. cerebrum

18. In forming habits that lead to good penmanship, it is most necessary to
    a. practice good penmanship
    b. think about good penmanship
    c. exert trial and error
    d. have good instincts
19. One's control over one's behavior decreases as one takes in increasing quantities of
    a. protein b. salt c. alcohol d. carbohydrate
20. Cough medicine may contain drugs, such as codeine, that can be addicting if taken for prolonged periods. When a cough persists, the best procedure is to
    a. use any advertised remedy
    b. consult a doctor
    c. ask a neighbor
    d. stay in bed and wait until the condition improves

Modified True-False Questions

1. When a bird escapes from a cat that has almost caught it, the bird's adjustment to its enemy is an example of *behavior*.
2. All tropisms are *inborn.*
3. The turning of the leaves of a geranium plant to light is an example of *negative* phototropism.
4. Pride in one's appearance helps to overcome the habit of *nail-biting.*
5. The flow of gastric juice is the result of *a voluntary* act.
6. A child born in China usually speaks Chinese without difficulty because speaking this language is *an inherited* type of behavior.
7. Once the spelling of a word has become *an instinct,* spelling the word thereafter is easy.
8. Both *habits* and reflexes leave a person more time for other activities.
9. The first step in forming the habit of studying daily is to make the *decision* to do it.
10. The ability to sneeze is *a learned* reflex act.

Matching Questions

Column A	Column B
1. tropism	a. one stimulus substitutes for another
2. voluntary, conscious act	b. muscle or gland
3. reflex act	c. simplest behavior under chemical control
4. motor nerve cell	d. simplest behavior under nerve control
5. skin and ears	e. connects to a muscle or a gland
6. habit	f. passes impulse to the spinal cord
7. conditioned response	g. sense organs
8. effector	h. learning to write
9. sensory nerve cell	i. controlled by cerebellum
10. reflex arc	j. a nerve pathway
	k. consciously learned, becomes automatic

Thought Questions

1. In two or three sentences, and using examples, show that you understand the difference between the terms in each of the following pairs:
   a. thigmotropism and thermotropism
   b. positive tropism and negative tropism
   c. reflex and instinct
   d. habit and simple reflex
   e. reflex arc and reflex act
2. In what ways are reflex, habit, and conditioned response alike? different?
3. a. Give three examples of human reflex acts.
   b. Give at least three characteristics common to all reflex acts.
4. Describe the harmful effects of each of the following drugs on the body or the personality:
   a. heroin b. LSD c. alcohol d. nicotine e. marijuana
5. Many young children are afraid of dogs. Such fear is usually the result of conditioning. Outline a plan by which you might condition such children to liking dogs instead of fearing them.
6. Describe how you would apply the four steps in habit formation to becoming a skillful typist.
7. A friend of yours habitually bites her fingernails. What advice regarding breaking this habit can you give her?

CHAPTER 22
HOW DO GERMS IN THE ENVIRONMENT AFFECT US?

When you have completed this chapter, you should be able to:

1. *Discuss* different ways in which germ diseases are spread and prevented.
2. *Describe*, with examples, the damage that germs can do to the body.
3. *Explain* how the body defends itself against germs.
4. *List* the major causes of infectious and noninfectious diseases.
5. *Identify* the major methods of fighting infectious and noninfectious diseases.
6. *Compare* the uses of antiseptics, antitoxins, antibiotics, toxoids, and vaccines.
7. *Contrast* natural and acquired immunity.
8. *Indicate* the part pollution plays in disease.
9. *Define* sickle-cell anemia and emphysema.

In the laboratory experience that follows, you will compare how well different antiseptics fight bacteria.

Laboratory Experience

HOW CAN WE COMPARE THE EFFECTIVENESS OF ANTISEPTICS?

Your team will be provided with four different antiseptics, such as hydrogen peroxide, tincture of iodine, tincture of merthiolate, mercurochrome, boric acid, or others. You will also receive two petri dishes containing nutrient agar mixed with sour milk. The sour milk contains millions of harmless bacteria. The nutrient agar is a convenient food-containing material on which bacteria grow well.

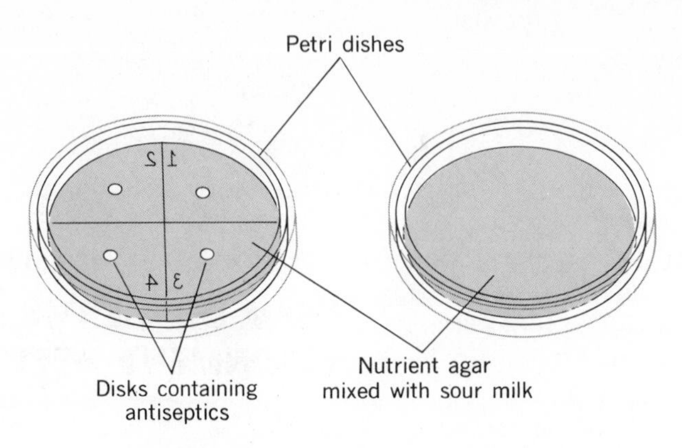

Fig. 22–1. Appearance of dishes before incubation.

A. With a glass-marking pencil, draw lines on the underside of one petri dish, dividing the dish into four equal sections (Fig. 22–1). Number each section. Copy the table below into your notebook.

Section Number	*Antiseptic*	*Change*
1		
2		
3		
4		
Untreated dish	XXX	

Out of blotting paper or filter paper, cut four disks of equal size. Holding a disk with forceps, dip the disk into one of the antiseptics. After draining off the excess antiseptic from the disk, open the petri dish and set the disk on the agar in section 1. Record the name of the antiseptic for section 1 in your table. Proceed similarly with each of the other antiseptics. Promptly close the dish. Do not open or put anything into the second petri dish.

Set both dishes into an incubator for 2 or 3 days.

1. Explain why it was necessary to keep the second dish closed, without adding an antiseptic to it.

B. Draw the two dishes (as in Fig. 22–1). After incubation, shade your drawing to show the changes that have occurred in each dish.

2. Describe the changes that occurred during incubation in the untreated dish and in each section of your treated dish. Record your description in the table.

3. What are your conclusions?

Introduction

A disease is a body condition in which the normal body structures or activities of an organism are disturbed. When a person suffers from a disease, the body does not behave normally and, usually, the person cannot adjust properly to changes in the environment.

Many diseases that attack living things have their origin in the environment. In one type of disease, some living or nonliving factor of the environment may penetrate the body and harm it. In another type of disease, some factor essential to health may be missing from the materials normally taken into the body from the environment. Both situations can be made worse by pollutants present in the environment.

In this chapter, we will become familiar with diseases caused by living organisms and other factors in the environment. Microscopic organisms that cause disease are called *germs*. The antiseptics you used in your laboratory experience are chemicals that have been found to slow the growth of germs. (You have no doubt found from your laboratory work that all antiseptics do not work equally well.) We shall also become familiar with some important diseases, how they are spread, how they can be prevented, and how they are treated. You should make special note of how proper care of the environment can promote good health.

CONQUERORS OF DISEASE

Through the research of scientists, we have learned the causes of many diseases and the ways to treat and prevent them. As a result, we have conquered a number of diseases that once resulted in early death. In this conquest, the use of antiseptics by *Joseph Lister* (1827–1912) has been very important, as have been contributions by Pasteur and Koch.

Louis Pasteur (1822–1895) proved that some diseases were caused by microscopic organisms (germs) that entered the body. Pasteur developed vaccines for *anthrax* and *rabies*. Anthrax is a disease of sheep and humans. Rabies is a disease of dogs and other mammals, including humans.

Robert Koch (1843–1910) developed a reliable method for finding the germs that cause particular diseases. He discovered the bacterium that causes *tuberculosis*.

Diseases can be classified into two main groups—*infectious* and *non-infectious*.

INFECTIOUS DISEASE

An infectious disease is one that is caused by a particular organism—a germ. Most infectious diseases are contagious (or "catching") and are called *communicable diseases.* Examples are diphtheria and the common cold.

WAYS IN WHICH GERMS SPREAD

Germs from an infected (diseased) individual are spread to others in several ways:

1. Germs can be transferred from one individual to another when the individuals touch—*direct contact.* For example, tuberculosis can be spread by kissing.

2. A person can pick up germs by using objects that have been in contact with an infected individual—*indirect contact.* For example, athlete's foot can be caught by wearing the shoes of a person who has the disease.

3. By inhaling the *droplets* (tiny drops) that spray out of the nose of an infected person, another person can acquire the same disease. For example, the droplets discharged by the sneeze of an influenza patient can infect several people.

4. Certain healthy animals—*animal carriers*—can transfer germs from one individual to another. For example, the tsetse fly carries the germ of African sleeping sickness from one person to another.

5. Certain healthy people—*human carriers*—may have germs in their bodies which do not harm them. However, these people can spread the germs to other people whom the germs can harm. "Typhoid Mary," a cook who had recovered from typhoid fever, carried the germs of typhoid fever and spread them to many people.

6. Most germs can live only within a person's body. However, some germs can live for a while in water and food. Water and food that have come in contact with the body wastes of sick people usually carry germs and, therefore, are said to be polluted. When such polluted water or food is taken into the body, the germs multiply and make the person ill. For example, dysentery germs that have entered a water supply can cause disease in people who drink that water.

WHAT GERMS DO INSIDE THE BODY

Germs can enter the body by way of such body openings as the mouth and nose, and breaks in the skin. Germs interfere with normal body activities by destroying tissue or by releasing *toxins,* which are chemical compounds that poison the body. For example, the malaria germ destroys red blood cells, and the rabies germ destroys nerve tissue. The tetanus (lockjaw) germ produces a poison that prevents muscles from relaxing.

HOW THE BODY PROTECTS ITSELF AGAINST GERMS

The bodies of humans and of other organisms possess several natural defenses against germs.

1. The nose and windpipe are lined by a *mucous membrane* which secretes a slimy mucus to which inhaled particles stick.

2. In addition to mucus, the linings of the nose and the windpipe have microscopic hairs that always lash back and forth. These hairs, called *cilia*, push the particles trapped in the mucus toward the nostrils and the throat. Sneezing and coughing eventually discharge the particles and the mucus from the body.

3. If it is unbroken, the *skin* cannot be pierced by most germs.

4. Tears, produced by the tear glands of the eyes, and hydrochloric acid, produced by the gastric glands of the stomach, are *body secretions* that are able to destroy some germs.

5. Germs that get into the tissues are often captured and destroyed by certain *white blood cells*.

6. Certain chemical compounds, called *antibodies*, are produced by the body after germs have invaded it. Germs can be dissolved by some antibodies. The toxins produced by germs can be made inactive by other antibodies. Antibodies that dissolve germs are called *lysins;* those that make toxins inactive are called *antitoxins*. Other types of antibodies also exist.

BODY RESISTANCE TO GERMS

Some individuals never get a particular disease, because their bodies are able to resist it. Others are not so fortunate. The ability of a body to resist the effects of germs is called *immunity*.

Some people inherit the ability to resist a particular disease. Immunity which is inherited is called *natural immunity*. For example, some people are born with the ability to resist tuberculosis.

The ability to resist a particular disease can also be developed. Immunity which is developed is called *acquired immunity*. There are two kinds of acquired immunity—*active* and *passive*.

Active Immunity

A body will be able to resist a disease if the body has manufactured its own antibody to that disease. This kind of immunity, known as an active acquired immunity, usually lasts for several years or longer. An active immunity often develops when a person naturally overcomes a disease. Thus, one who has recovered from smallpox is usually immune to this disease forever. The smallpox antibody that has formed will destroy any smallpox germs that may enter the body in the future.

Another method of making a person actively immune to disease is by injecting either a *vaccine* or a *toxoid.* A vaccine is made by using chemical or other means to weaken or kill a germ. A toxoid is usually made by using chemicals to weaken a toxin (poison) released by a germ.

The injection of a vaccine or a toxoid causes the body to manufacture its own antibody against the particular germ or toxin that was injected. Thus, the injection of smallpox vaccine (the procedure called *vaccination*) produces immunity to smallpox. Similarly, injection of tetanus toxoid produces immunity to tetanus. These injections do not usually cause illness. Vaccination against smallpox was first used by *Edward Jenner* in the eighteenth century.

Passive Immunity

A body can also resist a disease if it has received an antibody that was produced by the body of another person or animal. This is known as a passive acquired immunity. Although this type of immunity is rapidly acquired and helps a sick person recover, the immunity lasts only a short time—a few weeks or months. For example, when measles antibody is injected into a measles patient, the patient usually recovers in a short while. However, this antibody injection may not safeguard the person against catching measles again.

FIGHTING GERMS WITH DRUGS

We use certain drugs to fight germs. Among these are *antiseptics, sulfa drugs,* and *antibiotics.* Some of these prevent the growth of germs, others slow their growth, and still others kill germs. With the assistance of these drugs, the body can fight off germs rapidly before they can do much damage.

Antiseptics

Before the middle of the nineteenth century, deaths commonly occurred because surgical and other wounds became infected. Since

Joseph Lister introduced the use of carbolic acid as an antiseptic in surgery, the death rate from surgery has dropped sharply.

Since Lister's time, many antiseptics have been developed and are now in common use. Some familiar antiseptics are hydrogen peroxide, mercurochrome, and boric acid. In your laboratory experience, you tested the effectiveness of a few antiseptics by observing how cultures of known bacteria react to them. Where the antiseptic checked the growth of the bacteria, a clear area appears around the disk. Where the antiseptic had no effect, the area around the disk appears cloudy as a result of the continued growth of the bacteria. The effect of the antiseptic on the bacteria can be judged from the size of the clear area. By means of tests of this type, the effectiveness of many antiseptics has been compared. It has been found, for example, that for cuts, hydrogen peroxide is more effective than boric acid.

Sulfa Drugs

When placed in wounds or when swallowed, the sulfa drugs slow the growth of many germs or kill them. Sulfa drugs are made from coal tar. *Sulfadiazine* is an example of these drugs.

Antibiotics

Like the sulfa drugs, antibiotics slow the growth of certain germs or kill them. Antibiotics are usually obtained from specific mold plants. Examples of antibiotics are *penicillin* (discovered by *Alexander Fleming* in 1929) and *streptomycin* (discovered by *Selman Waksman* in 1944).

The effectiveness of new sulfa and antibiotic drugs is tested in a similar manner to that used for antiseptics. However, since sulfa and antibiotic drugs are often taken internally, they are tested further in order to insure their safety for humans.

KINDS OF ORGANISMS THAT CAUSE DISEASE

Many kinds of organisms may cause disease. Some, such as viruses, are so small that they can be seen only with an electron microscope. Others, such as tapeworms, may be several meters long and are plainly visible. The major disease-causing organisms are listed here.

1. *Viruses* are very small particles that may be on the borderline between living and nonliving matter. A virus reproduces only when inside a living cell. During this process, the virus destroys the cell.

2. *Rickettsias* are organisms smaller than bacteria but larger than viruses. Like viruses, rickettsias destroy cells.

3. Certain *bacteria* harm the body by destroying cells or by producing poisons. However, many bacteria do not cause disease.

4. Like bacteria, certain *animal-like one-celled organisms* related to the ameba invade the body and destroy cells.

5. *Flatworms* and *roundworms* harm the body as they attach themselves to tissues and absorb nourishment from them.

6. *Fungi* harm the body by destroying the tissues from which they obtain nourishment.

SOME IMPORTANT INFECTIOUS DISEASES

Table 22–1 lists several infectious diseases, giving the cause of each disease, the manner in which it is spread, how to prevent it, and the chief measures helpful in overcoming the disease.

Table 22–1. Infectious Diseases

Disease	*Cause*	*How Spread*	*Preventive Measures*	*Helpful Measures*
African sleeping sickness	Animal-like one-celled organism	Bite of infected tsetse fly	Screening; fly destruction; spraying with insecticides	Some drugs containing arsenic
Amebic dysentery	Animal-like one-celled organism	Polluted water; contact with carrier or infected person	Avoiding infected person; control of carriers; good community sanitation	Antibiotics
Athlete's foot	Fungus	Direct and indirect contact	Avoiding infected person; personal cleanliness; wearing shoes in public places	Keeping skin dry; antifungal (against fungus) drugs
Common cold	Virus	Droplets; contact	Avoiding infected person	Rest
Hepatitis	Virus	Droplets; contact; polluted food and water; infected hypodermic needles	Avoiding infected person; good personal and community sanitation; sterilization of hypodermic needles	Rest; special diet

Disease	Cause	How Spread	Preventive Measures	Helpful Measures
Hookworm	Roundworm	Worms in soil containing human wastes enter body through skin, especially sole of foot	Community sanitation; wearing shoes	Antihelminthic (against worm) drugs
Influenza (Asian, swine, or other types of "flu")	Virus	Droplets; contact	Avoiding infected person; vaccine of flu type commonly occurring	Rest
Malaria	Animal-like one-celled organism	Bite of infected female anopheles mosquito	Control of mosquitoes by spraying with insecticides; screening; draining swamps	Atabrine; chloroquine; quinine
Measles	Virus	Droplets; contact	Measles vaccine; avoiding infected person	Measles antibody (from blood of recovered patients)
Pneumonia	Bacterium	Droplet infection, especially when fatigued and body resistance is low	Avoiding infected person	Sulfa drugs; antibiotics
Poliomyelitis (also called polio or infantile paralysis)	Virus	Contact with carrier or polio victim	Salk vaccine (dead virus); Sabin vaccine (weakened virus)	Polio antibody (from blood of recovered patients); rest; hot packs
Rabies (or hydrophobia)	Virus	Bite of infected animal	Avoiding such wild animals as squirrels, bats, and foxes; immunizing pets; Pasteur's antirabies vaccine	If bitten by animal with rabies, use antirabies vaccine
Ringworm	Fungus	Direct and indirect contact	Avoiding infected person; personal cleanliness	Keeping skin dry; antifungal drugs
Rocky Mountain spotted fever	Rickettsia	Bite of infected tick	Spotted-fever vaccine; avoiding tick-infested regions	Antibiotics

Disease	*Cause*	*How Spread*	*Preventive Measures*	*Helpful Measures*
Scarlet fever	Bacterium	Droplets; contact with carrier or infected persons; polluted food	Avoiding infected person; care in food-handling	Scarlet fever antitoxin; sulfa drugs; antibiotics
Smallpox	Virus	Contact	Smallpox vaccine	Rest; nursing care
Tapeworm	Flatworm	Eating insufficiently cooked infected meat	Meat inspection; thorough cooking	Antihelminthic drugs
Tetanus (or lockjaw)	Bacterium	Puncture wounds; cuts that close at their surface	Tetanus toxoid; prompt first aid and medical treatment of deep wounds	Tetanus antitoxin
Trichinosis	Roundworm	Eating insufficiently cooked infected pork	Sanitary feeding of pigs; thorough cooking of pork	No specific effective measures
Tuberculosis	Bacterium	Droplets; close contact; polluted food	Tuberculosis vaccine; avoiding infected person; patch test to detect susceptibility; X rays to detect early cases	Antibiotics and isoniazid; collapse of lung; rest; nursing care
Typhoid fever	Bacterium	Polluted water and food; flies; contact with carrier or infected person	Typhoid vaccine; good personal and community sanitation; water purification; fly control; avoiding infected person; control of carriers	Antibiotics
Typhus fever	Rickettsia	Bite of infected rat fleas and of human lice	Personal cleanliness; dusting with insecticide powder; elimination of rats; typhus fever vaccine	Antibiotics
Yellow fever	Virus	Bite of infected female aëdes mosquito	Yellow fever vaccine; control of mosquitoes by spraying with insecticides; screening; swamp drainage	Rest; nursing care

NONINFECTIOUS DISEASE

A noninfectious disease is one that is usually caused by the presence or absence of some nonliving agent. Some noninfectious diseases are caused by abnormal heredity. Noninfectious diseases are not contagious. The most important types of noninfectious diseases include *allergies, cancer,* many *circulatory diseases,* certain *lung diseases, deficiency diseases,* and *hereditary diseases.*

Allergies

An allergy is a harmful body reaction to some substance, which is usually a protein. The reaction may be one of itching, swelling, or a burning sensation. The tendency to become allergic may be hereditary or may arise from emotional conditions. The substances responsible for allergies may differ in different people. Among such substances are pollen, dust, eggs, polluted air, and various drugs. Hay fever and hives are examples of allergic reactions.

Allergy tests help determine to what substances a person's body reacts abnormally. Once the cause is known, the reactions can be prevented by avoiding contact with the offending substance or by building body resistance to the substance. Resistance can often be built by means of repeated injections of the offending substance.

Cancer

Ordinarily, the division and growth of cells in the body is controlled in some way by the body itself. When this control is lost, cancer may develop. Cancer is an abnormal growth (or *malignant tumor*) that is a result of the rapid, uncontrolled division of cells. One factor that can cause cancer is being exposed for too long a time to strong radiation such as ultraviolet light, X rays, and atomic radiation. Another factor is contact with chemicals in tars and in some kinds of smoke. There seems to be a connection between lung cancer and cigarette smoking. It is possible that air polluted with exhaust fumes from automobiles and chimneys may also be a factor in cancer.

Tests that can detect cancer include X-ray, *biopsy,* and *smear tests.* In a biopsy, a bit of living tissue is examined under the microscope and searched for cancer cells. In a smear test, fluid from the suspected organ is spread on a microscope slide and is similarly examined. If detected early enough, cancer is usually curable by means of radiation, surgery, or chemicals. The best way to prevent cancer is to avoid the factors known to cause the disease.

Seven signs are considered to be danger signals. Each may only be the result of a minor condition that can be readily treated by a physician. Should any one of the signs arise, a physician should be consulted so that, if necessary, proper steps for cure can be started at once. The seven danger signals of cancer are:

1. Sores that do not seem to heal in a reasonable time.

2. A wart or similar condition that starts to grow very rapidly.

3. A permanent lump anywhere on the body.

4. Unexplained, irregular bleeding from any body opening.

5. Coughing or hoarseness that continues without apparent cause.

6. Frequent digestive disturbances.

7. A change in normal bowel or bladder habits that continues for a long period of time.

Circulatory Diseases

Some diseases of the heart and blood vessels are the result of damage caused by certain bacteria, such as the streptococci. Other diseases of these organs develop with aging. In some cases, the walls of the arteries harden as a result of the deposit of calcium. In other cases, a fatty deposit, called *cholesterol*, accumulates on the inner surface of the arteries. Both of these conditions can lead to high blood pressure and heart damage.

There are no special preventive measures for many circulatory diseases. However, there are some recommended general practices. Among these are relaxation and rest; moderation in all activities; regular exercise; eating an adequate, varied diet; avoiding the use of tobacco and addicting drugs; and having regular medical examinations.

Lung Diseases

Certain types of lung diseases appear to be associated more with nonliving agents than with other factors. In *bronchitis*, the major symptom is a cough that lasts at least two months and comes back again from time to time. The cough results from accumulations of mucus in the bronchial tubes, the tubes that lead air into and out of the tiny air sacs of the lungs.

In *emphysema*, the major symptom is shortness of breath. This occurs because the air sacs do not operate properly. The walls of the air sacs break down, and their ability to exchange oxygen for carbon dioxide in the blood is lost. Emphysema is a particularly important disease in modern times because the death rate from emphysema is increasing. For every person who died from emphysema in 1950, seventeen died in 1966.

Both bronchitis and emphysema are associated with air pollution and excessive cigarette smoking. Although both diseases can be treated to relieve the symptoms, they cannot actually be cured. For those people not afflicted by bronchitis and emphysema, the best hope lies in prevention—reducing air pollution and avoiding cigarette smoking.

Deficiency Diseases

The lack, or deficiency, of particular nutrients or hormones can lead to some diseases. For example, a lack of iron can result in *anemia;* lack of vitamin C can result in *scurvy*. Supplying the body with the substances it lacks usually prevents the condition or cures it. A lack of the hormone insulin causes *diabetes*. Injections of insulin are used to control diabetes.

Hereditary Diseases

Some diseases that "run in the family" are called hereditary diseases. *Hemophilia*, the "bleeder's disease," and *sickle-cell anemia* are examples. It is possible for normal people to carry genes (the controllers of heredity) for such conditions without being aware of them. Because these genes cannot be changed, it is possible for future generations to inherit them.

Looking Back

In this book, we have become familiar with the atoms of our world, the atmosphere, the solar system, and the energy that is responsible for the movement of all matter in the universe. Our uses of the matter and energy available to us have made us one of the most advanced and comfortable nations in the world. Could we do without artificial light, without heat in our buildings, without electricity, without automobiles, and without large cities? Obviously not. But what should we do with all the harmful waste products our nation produces?

Regardless of the type of fuel we use to supply the energy we need, every fuel contributes to some kind of air pollution which, in turn, often causes some type of noninfectious disease. Regardless of how we dispose of our increasing amount of sewage and garbage, we usually run the risk of polluting the environment with the germs of many infectious diseases.

Looking Ahead

What can we do to provide a satisfactory environment for ourselves and for those who will come after us? We must try to control the pollution of our environment by factories, power plants, automobiles, sewage, and garbage. We must find methods that will not permit pollutants to spoil the environment. In other words, everyone who depends on energy (all of us) must face the responsibility of cleaning up our environment and keeping it clean.

Multiple-Choice Questions

1. The effectiveness of antiseptics can be measured by
   a. the rate at which they are oxidized
   b. the clear zones that occur in agar plates containing bacteria
   c. the strength of their odors
   d. the burning sensation they produce in a wound
2. A child born today can expect to live about 72 years; one born in 1900 had a life expectancy of 50 years. The most important reason for this increase in life expectancy is the
   a. improvement in food production
   b. conquest of many diseases
   c. conquest of heart disease
   d. improvement in housing
3. Who introduced the use of antiseptics in surgery?
   a. Lister b. Jenner c. Pasteur d. Salk
4. Louis Pasteur proved that
   a. polio was caused by a germ
   b. tuberculosis could be fatal
   c. penicillin came from a mold
   d. germs were often responsible for disease
5. The bacterium that causes tuberculosis was discovered by
   a. Joseph Lister
   b. Edward Jenner
   c. Louis Pasteur
   d. Robert Koch
6. Wearing the socks or stockings of a friend could be a means of getting
   a. a cold b. athlete's foot c. housemaid's knee d. malaria
7. The germ of African sleeping sickness is spread by
   a. droplets b. direct contact c. an insect d. a dog
8. Poisons produced by bacteria are called
   a. toxins b. toxoids c. vaccines d. spores
9. The body tissue upon which the malaria germ feeds is
   a. muscle b. blood c. bone d. nerve
10. Body cells that can destroy bacteria are the
    a. red blood cells
    b. bone cells
    c. nerve cells
    d. white blood cells

11. A secretion of the stomach that can kill some bacteria is
    a. rennin b. thyroxin c. hydrochloric acid d. adrenin
12. Antibodies are produced in the body when
    a. germs enter the body
    b. germs leave the body
    c. antiseptics enter the body
    d. antibiotics enter the body
13. Natural immunity depends on
    a. vaccines b. toxoids c. heredity d. antibiotics
14. The live, but weakened, smallpox virus vaccine was developed by
    a. Albert Sabin
    b. Jonas Salk
    c. Edward Jenner
    d. Joseph Lister
15. A toxoid injection stimulates the body to make its own
    a. antitoxin b. toxin c. red blood cells d. lysins
16. The Salk vaccine is useful in preventing
    a. smallpox b. anthrax c. rabies d. polio
17. The type of immunity that is most rapidly developed in the body of a patient is
    a. passive immunity
    b. active immunity
    c. toxoid immunity
    d. natural immunity
18. Because of the development of an effective vaccine, no child need suffer from
    a. colds b. malaria c. athlete's foot d. measles
19. Sulfa drugs are effective against diseases caused by
    a. bacteria b. worms c. deficiencies d. heredity
20. Who discovered the antibiotic penicillin?
    a. Selman Waksman
    b. Jonas Salk
    c. Edward Jenner
    d. Alexander Fleming
21. The organisms that are disease agents are
    a. green algae
    b. viruses
    c. bread mold
    d. bacteria normally present in milk
22. African sleeping sickness can be prevented by destroying
    a. tsetse flies b. houseflies c. mosquitoes d. rabid dogs
23. Rickettsias are disease agents that are
    a. viruses
    b. smaller than bacteria but larger than viruses
    c. larger than bacteria
    d. larger than an ameba
24. Athlete's foot is caused by a
    a. worm b. lack of hormones c. fungus d. vitamin deficiency
25. The best method for preventing the spread of the common cold in a school is
    a. giving pupils antitoxin
    b. vaccinating all children
    c. having all pupils take aspirin
    d. keeping pupils with colds at home

26. Why is an insecticide spray helpful in preventing malaria?
    a. It kills the tsetse fly.
    b. It aids in producing antibody.
    c. It kills mosquitoes.
    d. It kills the protozoan that causes malaria.
27. Measles is caused by a
    a. yeast b. virus c. mold d. coccus
28. When discovered early, pneumonia is readily cured with
    a. penicillin b. peroxide c. toxoids d. antitoxins
29. The Sabin vaccine for polio consists of
    a. dead virus c. weakened bacteria
    b. dead rickettsia d. weakened virus
30. Smallpox is rare in the United States because most people have received
    a. antibiotics c. smallpox vaccine
    b. smallpox antitoxin d. sulfa drugs
31. Lung damage by the bacillus of tuberculosis can be detected by means of
    a. X rays c. tuberculosis toxoid
    b. ultraviolet rays d. streptomycin
32. Oysters that are taken from polluted water and eaten by humans may spread the germ of
    a. measles b. malaria c. trichinosis d. typhoid fever
33. Typhus fever is spread by
    a. spraying droplets c. sparrows
    b. rat fleas d. victims of typhoid fever
34. A certain kind of mosquito can spread
    a. yellow fever b. trichinosis c. tapeworm d. colds
35. Hereditary diseases are
    a. contagious c. spread by insects
    b. not contagious d. spread by birds

Modified True-False Questions

1. A disease that affects both dogs and humans is *yellow fever.*
2. *Infectious* diseases are those that can be caught.
3. A disease that can be spread by direct contact is *influenza.*
4. Droplets of *mucus* that have been discharged from the nose of a person with a cold can spread the disease to others.
5. Dysentery can be spread by polluted *air.*
6. A clean, unbroken *skin* is a good protection against bacteria.
7. Cilia in the *digestive* system protect us against bacteria that enter the body.
8. *Immunity* is the ability of the body to resist disease.
9. A person who has acquired *a passive* immunity to a disease probably had the disease and recovered from it.
10. *Cancer* is a disease in which cells divide abnormally.
11. Chemicals produced by certain molds and used in treating disease are called *antitoxins.*

12. The scientist who discovered streptomycin is *Waksman.*
13. Itching and running eyes can be caused by *pollen* in the air.
14. Recovery from smallpox usually makes a person immune to this disease for *4 weeks.*
15. A biopsy can be used to detect *heart disease.*

Thought Questions

1. Make up a story about a healthy boy who visited a sick friend suffering from diphtheria. In this story, use the following words in such a way that the reader will know that you understand them. These words are: toxin, antitoxin, toxoid, immunity, susceptibility (ability to catch a disease), droplets.
2. Describe how each of the following structures helps keep us healthy:
   a. cilia
   b. white blood cells
   c. skin
   d. tear glands
   e. gastric glands
3. Match the doctor's action with each of the conditions that a patient might have.

a. malaria	1. prescribes spinach in diet
b. lump on the leg	2. starts Pasteur treatment
c. dog bite	3. prescribes atabrine
d. gunshot wound	4. orders a biopsy
e. anemia	5. injects an antitoxin
	6. removes the appendix

APPENDIX

The following tables show you simple ways to convert (change) units from the customary system of measurement to the metric system, and the reverse.

Table A–1. Weight Conversions

When You Know	*Multiply By*	*To Find*
Ounces (oz)	28.3	Grams (g)
Pounds (lb)	0.45	Kilograms (kg)
Tons (T)	0.91	Metric tons (MT)
Grams (g)	0.035	Ounces (oz)
Kilograms (kg)	2.2	Pounds (lb)
Metric tons (MT)	1.1	Tons (T)

Table A–2. Length Conversions

When You Know	*Multiply By*	*To Find*
Inches (in)	2.54	Centimeters (cm)
Feet (ft)	30.5	Centimeters (cm)
Feet (ft)	0.3	Meters (m)
Yards (yd)	0.91	Meters (m)
Miles (mi)	1.6	Kilometers (km)
Centimeters (cm)	0.4	Inches (in)
Centimeters (cm)	0.033	Feet (ft)
Meters (m)	3.3	Feet (ft)
Meters (m)	1.1	Yards (yd)
Kilometers (km)	0.62	Miles (mi)

Table A–3. Volume Conversions

When You Know	*Multiply By*	*To Find*
Ounces, fluid (fl oz)	29.6	*Cubic centimeters (cc)
Pints (pt)	0.47	Liters (l)
Quarts (qt)	0.95	Liters (l)
*Milliliters (ml)	0.034	Ounces, fluid (fl oz)
Liters (l)	2.1	Pints (pt)
Liters (l)	1.06	Quarts (qt)

* *Note:* A milliliter (ml) and a cubic centimeter (cc) are approximately equal in volume. They are often used interchangeably.

Table A–4. Temperature Conversions

When You Know	*Do This*	*To Find*
Degrees Fahrenheit (F)	1. Subtract 32 2. Multiply by 5 3. Divide by 9	Degrees Celsius (C)
Degrees Celsius (C)	1. Multiply by 9 2. Divide by 5 3. Add 32	Degrees Fahrenheit (F)

PERIODIC TABLE

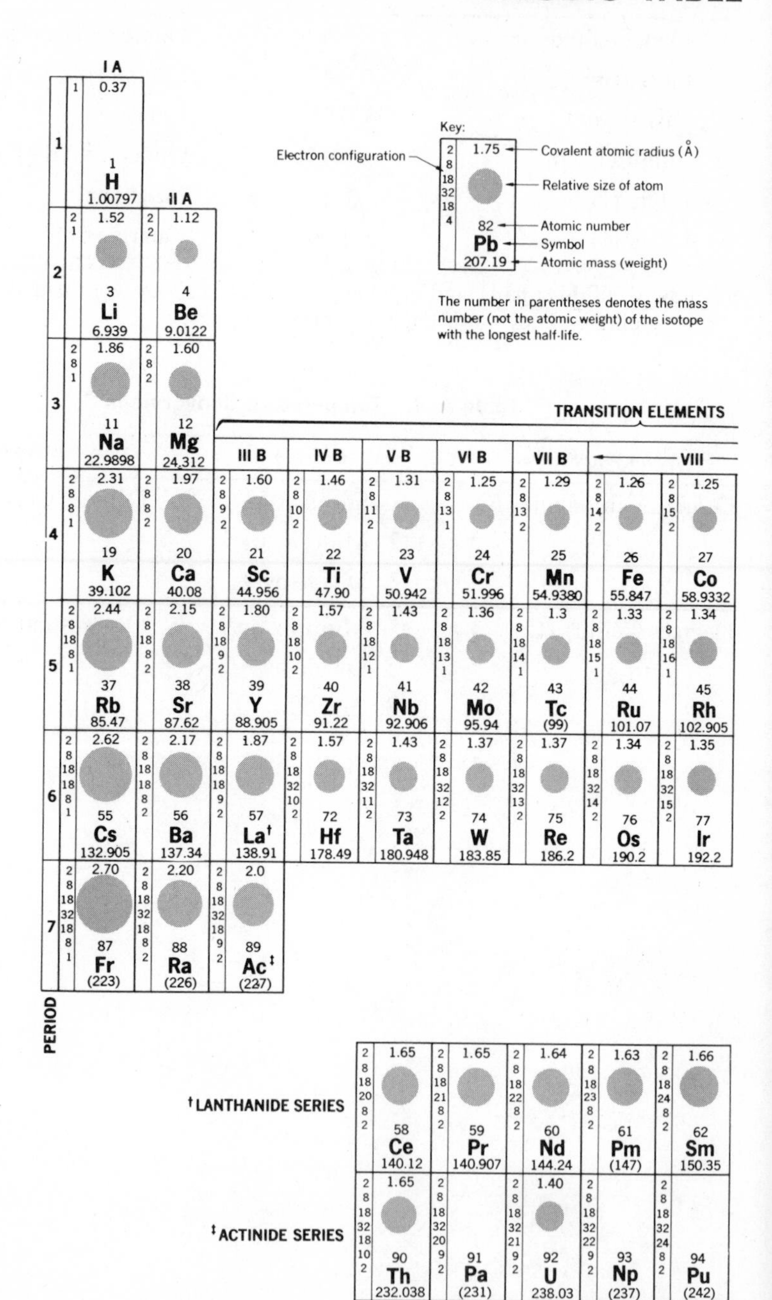

OF THE ELEMENTS

	I B	II B	III A	IV A	V A	VI A	VII A	0
								2 0.93 2 **He** 4.0026
			2, 3 0.88 5 **B** 10.811	2, 4 0.77 6 **C** 12.01115	2, 5 0.70 7 **N** 14.0067	2, 6 0.66 8 **O** 15.9994	2, 7 0.64 9 **F** 18.9984	2, 8 1.12 10 **Ne** 20.183
			2, 8, 3 1.43 13 **Al** 26.9815	2, 8, 4 1.17 14 **Si** 28.086	2, 8, 5 1.10 15 **P** 30.9738	2, 8, 6 1.04 16 **S** 32.064	2, 8, 7 0.99 17 **Cl** 35.453	2, 8, 8 1.54 18 **Ar** 39.948
2, 8, 16, 2 1.24 28 **Ni** 58.71	2, 8, 18, 1 1.28 29 **Cu** 63.54	2, 8, 18, 2 1.33 30 **Zn** 65.37	2, 8, 18, 3 1.22 31 **Ga** 69.72	2, 8, 18, 4 1.22 32 **Ge** 72.59	2, 8, 18, 5 1.21 33 **As** 74.9216	2, 8, 18, 6 1.17 34 **Se** 78.96	2, 8, 18, 7 1.14 35 **Br** 79.909	2, 8, 18, 8 1.69 36 **Kr** 83.80
2, 8, 18, 18 1.38 46 **Pd** 106.4	2, 8, 18, 18, 1 1.44 47 **Ag** 107.870	2, 8, 18, 18, 2 1.49 48 **Cd** 112.40	2, 8, 18, 18, 3 1.62 49 **In** 114.82	2, 8, 18, 18, 4 1.40 50 **Sn** 118.69	2, 8, 18, 18, 5 1.41 51 **Sb** 121.75	2, 8, 18, 18, 6 1.37 52 **Te** 127.60	2, 8, 18, 18, 7 1.33 53 **I** 126.9044	2, 8, 18, 18, 8 1.90 54 **Xe** 131.30
2, 8, 18, 32, 17, 1 1.38 78 **Pt** 195.09	2, 8, 18, 32, 18, 1 1.44 79 **Au** 196.967	2, 8, 18, 32, 18, 2 1.55 80 **Hg** 200.59	2, 8, 18, 32, 18, 3 1.71 81 **Tl** 204.37	2, 8, 18, 32, 18, 4 1.75 82 **Pb** 207.19	2, 8, 18, 32, 18, 5 1.46 83 **Bi** 208.980	2, 8, 18, 32, 18, 6 1.4 84 **Po** (210)	2, 8, 18, 32, 18, 7 1.40 85 **At** (210)	2, 8, 18, 32, 18, 8 2.2 86 **Rn** (222)

2, 8, 18, 25, 8, 2 1.65 63 **Eu** 151.96	2, 8, 18, 25, 9, 2 1.61 64 **Gd** 157.25	2, 8, 18, 27, 8, 2 1.59 65 **Tb** 158.924	2, 8, 18, 28, 8, 2 1.59 66 **Dy** 162.50	2, 8, 18, 29, 8, 2 1.58 67 **Ho** 164.930	2, 8, 18, 30, 8, 2 1.57 68 **Er** 167.26	2, 8, 18, 31, 8, 2 1.56 69 **Tm** 168.934	2, 8, 18, 32, 8, 2 1.70 70 **Yb** 173.04	2, 8, 18, 32, 9, 2 1.56 71 **Lu** 174.97
2, 8, 18, 32, 25, 8, 2 95 **Am** (243)	2, 8, 18, 32, 25, 9, 2 96 **Cm** (247)	2, 8, 18, 32, 26, 9, 2 97 **Bk** (247)	2, 8, 18, 32, 28, 8, 2 98 **Cf** (251)	2, 8, 18, 32, 29, 8, 2 99 **Es** (254)	2, 8, 18, 32, 30, 8, 2 100 **Fm** (253)	2, 8, 18, 32, 31, 8, 2 101 **Md** (256)	2, 8, 18, 32, 32, 8, 2 102 **No** (253)	2, 8, 18, 32, 32, 9, 2 103 **Lw** (257)

USING SIGNIFICANT FIGURES

Uncertainty in Measurement

A student weighs a block of metal on three different balances and obtains the following weights: 14.61 grams, 14.62 grams, and 14.63 grams. What is the weight of the block? In each of the weighings, only the first three digits have been reproduced. This is the same as saying that in each weighing the last digit is doubtful. The weight of the block can therefore be described as lying between 14.61 grams and 14.63 grams. The block could be weighed on any number of balances and the weights would agree only in the first three digits. This experiment and many similar ones that could be performed suggest that it is impossible to reproduce a series of measurements without error.

The limitation of measurement caused by errors is called *uncertainty*. It results from shortcomings of the experimenter or of the equipment used. Consequently, our experimental observations, which we call facts, are uncertain to some degree. The experimenter, by developing his powers of observation and by refining his equipment, cannot eliminate uncertainty but can only reduce it. Thus scientists continue to refine the values of such important quantities as the velocity of light.

Expressing Uncertainty With Significant Figures

The weight of the metal block in the above example was described as lying between 14.61 grams and 14.63 grams. To express the proper uncertainty, we can describe the weight as 14.62 grams ± 0.01 gram. The symbol ± (plus or minus) expresses the uncertainty range.

The measurement 14.62 grams contains three certain digits (1, 4, and 6) and one doubtful digit (2). We can summarize this information by stating that 14.62 grams contains four significant figures. The numbers that express a measurement (including the last digit, which is doubtful) are called *significant figures*.

The number of significant figures obtained in a measurement is determined by the calibration (scale marking) of the measuring instrument. Some balances are calibrated to the nearest 0.01 gram. Hence, measurements obtained from such balances are expressed to at least two decimal places—indicating that the doubtful digit is in the hundredths place, the second figure to the right of the decimal point. In expressing the result of a measurement, use the proper number of significant figures. Where possible, also indicate the ± range.

Rules for Working With Significant Figures

The interpretation and use of significant figures require the understanding of some fundamental rules:

1. Zeros that appear before other digits or zeros that show only the position of a decimal point are not considered significant figures. The measurement 0.0043 gram has two significant figures, 4 and 3.

2. Zeros that appear between other digits are significant figures. The measurement 4.003 grams has four significant figures, 4, 0, 0, and 3.

3. Zeros that appear after other digits may or may not be significant, depending on the precision of the measuring instrument. Consider the measurement 14.2 grams. Can it also be expressed as 14.20 grams? If a balance that measures weight to the nearest centigram is used, the measurement must be expressed as 14.20 grams. If a decigram balance is used, the measurement must be expressed as 14.2 grams.

4. In an arithmetic operation involving addition or subtraction, the result of the operation should contain only the number of decimal places of the quantity with the fewest decimal places. Suppose we are required to add 1.46 centimeters and 2.1 centimeters. If we write the sum as 3.56 centimeters, we are assuming that 2.1 centimeters has three significant figures, that it is really 2.10 centimeters. However, 2.1 centimeters has only two significant figures. The correct sum is 3.6 centimeters, obtained by rounding off 3.56 centimeters to two significant figures. Subtraction is performed in a similar manner.

Rounding off a number means decreasing the number of significant figures. If the new number is to have one less significant figure, follow these rules for rounding off:

a. If the digit to be discarded is greater than 5, increase the last certain digit by 1. Thus 15.66 becomes 15.7.

b. If the digit to be discarded is less than 5, retain all the certain digits. Thus 15.63 becomes 15.6.

c. If the digit to be discarded is 5, the number preceding this digit becomes the nearest *even* number. Thus 15.25 becomes 15.2, and 15.35 becomes 15.4.

5. Multiplying or dividing a measurement by a *number* does not alter the number of significant figures. For example, 2 times the weight of an object weighing 4.131 grams is 8.262 grams.

If 4.130 grams (four significant figures) is multiplied by 200,000, the answer (826,000) appears to have six significant figures but actually has four. This is the same as saying 8.260 × 100,000.

6. In multiplication and division of *measurements*, the result can contain no more significant figures than are contained in the least certain measurement.

The product obtained from multiplying 4.12 inches by 2.1 inches can contain only two significant figures. The product (8.652) must be rounded off to contain the proper number of significant figures. Thus 4.12 inches × 2.1 inches equals 8.7 square inches.

INDEX